THE NAUTICAL INSTITUTE

WATCHKEEPING SAFETY AND CARGO MANAGEMENT IN PORT

A PRACTICAL GUIDE

Captain Peter Roberts, BSc, FNI

First published 1995 by The Nautical Institute,
202 Lambeth Road, London SE1 7LQ, UK.

ISBN 1 870077 29 6

Although great care has been taken with the writing and production of this volume, neither The Nautical Institute nor the author can accept any responsibility for errors, omissions or their consequences.

This book has been prepared to address the subject of watchkeeping in port. This should not, however, be taken to mean that this document deals comprehensively with all of the concerns which will need to be addressed or even, where a particular matter is addressed, that this document sets out the only definitive view for all situations.

The opinions expressed are those of the author only and are not necessarily to be taken as the policies or views of any organisation with which he has any connection.

Readers and students should make themselves aware of any local, national or international changes to bylaws, legislation, statutory and administrative requirements that have been introduced which might affect any decisions taken on board.

Cover photograph supplied by courtesy of the UK Chamber of Shipping.
Text set in Baskerville and printed in England by the Silverdale Press, Southall, Middlesex, UB2 5LF.

A message from the Secretary-General of IMO

IMO's most important responsibility is the safety of international shipping. All our experience has shown that the best way of ensuring safety is by raising personnel standards to the highest level possible. By personnel I mean everybody involved in shipping, including Government administrators, classification societies, shipping company managers, port operators and of course the seafarers who operate the world's ships.

Seafarers have a particular importance because they are in the best position to implement safety measures and detect any faults—and they are the first to suffer the consequences when anything goes wrong.

IMO is very aware of the importance of what is sometimes referred to as the human element. Major changes have been made to the convention dealing with standards of training, certification and watchkeeping and other measures have been adopted. But IMO believes that major improvements in safety can only be made by ensuring that standards are implemented more effectively.

When an accident happens it is usually shown that human error was involved at some stage—an error that could and should have been avoided. Accidents usually happen not because regulations are lacking but because they are ignored, either out of ignorance or carelessness. IMO is trying to ensure that *attitudes* in the shipping industry are changed, not just the regulations. We are trying to make safety part of the culture of shipping, not some sort of optional extra.

This book will contribute to that process. It is written by a serving master assisted by fellow seafarers working in various trades and therefore is based upon a great deal of practical experience and knowledge.

It is intended to give guidance to port duty officers in carrying out watchkeeping and explains the meaning and significance of IMO conventions, codes and resolutions in a clear and practical way.

The officer of the watch is the first point of contact should anything go wrong on board ship and must be in a position to know how to seek assistance and how to take appropriate action. To carry out his duties he must be well trained and must understand his responsibilities fully. This book will help him to do so and that is why I welcome its publication.

William A. O'Neil
Secretary-General
International Maritime Organization

PREFACE FROM THE CHAIRMAN
OF THE UK P&I CLUB

A SHIP IN PORT costs money, runs the old saying; but a ship can only earn freight if it has cargo on board.

There is undoubtedly some human tension when a ship is alongside to load or discharge cargo. The aim is to complete the operation safely, efficiently, with the minimum downtime, whilst avoiding loss or damage.

There are five essential elements to ship work. First, there has to be good planning, so that the resources available for loading and discharging the cargo can be optimised.

Secondly, the ship must, in all respects, be able to meet its operational specification with hatches and deck machinery fully operational or, in the case of tankers, their pumps, pipelines and control systems fully operational. The ballast system must be working; moorings and access must be tended.

Thirdly, the operations which have been so carefully planned in advance must be monitored and supervised to ensure that the whole operation can be managed and the ship sails on time.

Fourthly, simple but accurate records must be kept to ensure that any disputes are based upon facts which the owner can substantiate with written evidence. Attention to detail with draught readings, samples, times, tallies, notification of damage and other relevant observations ensure that there is a record not only for the present activity but for analysing performance and providing a basis for improving management systems in future.

Fifthly, those involved must have the training and experience to understand fully what they are doing.

Shipping, unlike other industries, trains all its 'managers' from cadets. It is therefore vital that junior officers receive a thorough training in port work, for which a good reference book is invaluable.

The UK Club's work in analysing major liability claims has confirmed beyond doubt the importance, for any loss prevention programme, of reducing human error. Sound knowledge is a prerequisite for this, and the UK Club is therefore pleased to sponsor *Watchkeeping Safety and Cargo Management in Port*, by Captain Peter Roberts, a book which is designed to increase commercial awareness and make available the best advice to trainees and junior officers.

As with other practical guides published by The Nautical Institute, great care has been taken to consult widely and prepare a text which is concise, informative and accompanied by checklists and handy references. I hope this book will be used in cadet training programmes to instil correct, practical, and well documented knowledge in a way which encourages a positive attitude to the duties of an officer on watch in port.

N.-G. Palmgren
Chairman
UK P&I Club

CONTENTS.

INDEX OF CHAPTER AND SECTION HEADINGS

List of appendices.

INTRODUCTION

Welcome to this practical guide on Watchkeeping in Port.

THE TEXT of this guide provides a sound basis for developing effective watchkeeping in port by demonstrating good operational practices.

The junior watchkeeping officer is an important member of the shipboard management team. His proper supervision of the operations can have a major impact on the profitability of his ship. This guide is designed to improve his commercial awareness with respect to his duties in port.

Any operation which delays the ship costs the shipowner valuable time. At a charter rate of $10,000 per day, every hour which is lost costs over $400. Chapter 2 outlines the preparations made on board ship before arrival in port to make sure there are no unnecessary delays to the start of cargo operations.

Inadequate supervision of mooring operations can result in personal injury and damage to the ship or quayside and shore equipment. Damage to shore installations costs the industry $120 million a year. Chapter 3 contains guidance on safe mooring operations.

Unsafe access to and around the ship can result in personal injury, which costs the industry over $216 million a year. Fires can lead to the complete loss of the ship. All aspects of shipboard safety in port are discussed in chapter 4.

Damage to cargo costs the industry $140 million a year. The duty officer can considerably reduce this figure by appropriate supervision of cargo handling and stowage, as outlined in chapters 7 to 9.

Improper ballasting not only causes delays, but also can cause structural damage, which could result in structural failure and even the sinking of the ship. Ballasting is discussed in chapter 10.

If the condition and the quantity of the cargo are not properly ascertained, then the receiver may make huge claims against the shipowner. Guidance on these topics is provided in chapters 12 and 13.

Pollution is an emotive subject, which brings the industry to the attention of the world's Press, and costs the industry $168 million a year. The prevention of pollution from various sources is discussed in chapter 15.

Lack of security precautions can lead to stowaways, thefts, piracy and drug trafficking. Ship's security is discussed in chapter 16.

If the cargo is not properly secured it can break adrift, causing damage to itself, other cargo and maybe the ship. The cargo could be lost overside, and damage to the ship could be so severe that the ship itself is lost. Securing the cargo is discussed in chapter 17.

It is vital that everything that happens on board the ship in port is recorded, so that the shipowner has evidence he can produce in his defence of any claim. The importance of keeping records is discussed in chapter 18.

PURPOSE OF THIS GUIDE

As part of The Nautical Institute's *Commercial Awareness* programme, this guide has been prepared in response to a demand for practical guidance for the officer of the watch in port. It is designed to assist the junior watchkeeping officer to identify his duties in port, and understand their significance, so enabling him to make a positive contribution to the success of the entire commercial venture. He is part of the team who assist the Master to prevent loss, minimise expenses and so maximise the ship operator's profit.

> **The main responsibility of the officer of the watch is to ensure that all activities undertaken on board are carried out safely and efficiently.**

AIM OF THIS GUIDE

The aim of this guide is to enhance the standards of watchkeeping and cargo work in port, and promote the commercial awareness of the watchkeeping deck officer.

THE OBJECTIVES OF THIS GUIDE

Having studied this guide, the reader should be able to carry out the duties of a watchkeeping officer in port, and to list and describe the practices necessary in order to:

- Conduct a safe and efficient deck watch.
- Handover and accept a deck watch.
- Prevent damage, reduce loss and minimise expenses.
- Support the Master and Chief Officer.
- Call for assistance when required.
- Work as a member of the deck team.
- Appreciate the commercial implications of carrying cargo.
- Carry out the tasks required for each in-port activity:
  - Ensure that the ship is safely moored.
  - Maintain safe access, and a safe working environment.
  - Test deck equipment.
  - Assist with surveys.
  - Supervise loading, stowing, securing and discharging of cargo.
  - Monitor cargo condition and quantity.
  - Inspect cargo holds, and record all damage to the ship.
  - Liaise effectively with personnel from ashore.
  - Control ballast operations.
  - Understand stability and stress aspects of cargo operations.
  - Prevent pollution from oil, cargo, ballast and garbage.
  - Maintain security against drugs, theft and stowaways.
  - Record essential details in the deck log book.
  - Understand specialist ship operations.
  - Prepare the ship for the forthcoming sea passage.

REASONS FOR PRODUCING THIS GUIDE

In 1993, The Nautical Institute held a series of conferences and workshops around the world on accident and loss prevention in shipping. As a result of the recommendations from these international workshops, it was decided to address *Commercial Awareness* as a major project.

The Institute's Council recognised the need to establish guidelines on training requirements, and to demonstrate the value of commercial training. They noted that the STCW convention and its revision (1995) hardly mentions this subject. There is little commercial training in the syllabus of the deck officer's certificates in most countries, and it was perceived that an increasing number of junior officers have never received any commercial training at all.

This has been exacerbated by the lack of company led commercial management supervision and the demise of marine superintendents with a deck background. There is more discontinuity in manning, with fewer company visits by sea staff, and fewer visits to the ships by commercial managers. Another factor is the growth of manning agencies and ship management companies, which has brought about the breakdown of the formerly close relationship between the shipowner as employer and the seafarer as employee. Traditional shipboard practices, formerly considered to be customary, have suffered during this era of change.[23]

Council is aware of the wide range of commercial material available within the industry; there is no intention to duplicate the detailed texts of other publications dealing with cargo work. However, there is a need to provide a comprehensive practical programme of material addressing *Commercial Awareness* which can be obtained by individuals, used by companies for in-house training, and encouraged by P&I Clubs as a contribution to loss prevention. In this respect, The Nautical Institute gratefully acknowledges the sponsorship given by the UK P&I Club, whose contribution and support has made this publication possible.

SCOPE OF THIS GUIDE

As this guide is designed for the junior watchkeeping officer, it is presumed that he has completed his studies up to and including IMO Model Course 7.03 for an officer in charge of a navigational watch. Those readers who have not yet attained this level should be aware that the treatment of some subjects may be incomplete, and they may not be able to follow completely some of the text as they lack the assumed level of knowledge. The text is aimed at trainees or junior officers who have a proficient knowledge of basic seamanship and ship operations.

Many topics are covered in a 'reminder' form, as it is felt that these subjects will have been fully covered by the above course. More detail is provided on those topics which we feel the course does not cover to a sufficient depth to enable the OOW to supervise correctly the operation in an informed, safe and efficient manner. Where members of the advisory panel have identified a particular weakness common to many junior watchkeepers, then more background information has been provided to emphasise that topic.

Other topics will have received a technical treatment on the above course, where in this manual their commercial impact is highlighted. **It is emphasised that the text provides only an introduction to the subjects covered, it is not intended to be a complete and comprehensive treatment.** The reader is advised to continue his professional education, perhaps by consulting some of the books listed in the bibliography in Appendix I, or by enrolling on one of The Nautical Institute's courses listed below.

> **A good watchkeeper is someone who:**
> - **Has a sound knowledge of the principles involved.**
> - **Is guided by the appropriate rules and regulations.**
> - **Looks out for, and recognises when operations go wrong.**
> - **Is capable of acting on his own initiative.**
> - **Knows when to call for assistance.**

Experience helps; the people who have contributed to this guide hope that the reader will learn from their experiences.

STYLE OF THIS GUIDE

The text is based around a dry-cargo ship, as these form the majority of the world's fleet. Many of the principles involved can be applied to other types of ships, too. Reference to particular practices and methods employed on other types of ships has been made where appropriate. An outline of tanker operations has been included in a separate chapter. However, there has been no attempt to provide in-depth guidance for highly specialised operations, such as gas carriers, chemical tankers, Ro-Ros, etc. Such material is beyond the scope of this guide. The junior officer serving in such ships is advised to consult the relevant specialised publications, some of which are listed in the bibliography in Appendix I.

Throughout the text, it is assumed that all operations concerning the deck department in port are under the direct supervision of the Chief Officer. It is realised that some vessels may have a separate cargo officer who is responsible for certain operations. The junior officer must make sure that he knows who he has to consult over specific issues on each ship.

Recommendations as to action to take, and who to call, in particular circumstances are given in broad terms throughout the text, which generally reflect the usual practice at sea. However, each Master, each ship, each owner, each charterer and each operator has a different style of management, with different operational practices and requirements. Also, shipboard responsibilities may be allocated in different ways. The junior officer must always follow the system of his employer, and must never allow the advice contained in this guide to over-rule that system.

We have used the word *shipowner* as a generalisation in most cases throughout the text. It is appreciated that the true identity of the actual owner of the ship may be unknown to those on board the ship, and that this owner may be well removed from the process of operating the ship. Some readers may identify more closely with the *ship operator*—or perhaps with the *ship manager* or *manning agent*. However, it is considered that the generalisation *shipowner* is sufficient for the designed readership. In these days of common use of the expression *'as agents only'*, there is no intention to delve into the depths of legal wrangles over true ownership.

Reference to the OOW as *'he'* is made purely for editorial convenience. The Nautical Institute recognises that some of the junior officers or trainees reading this guide should be properly addressed as *'she'*.

To reflect current trends worldwide, the author has chosen to use the popular spelling of **draft** in preference to the traditional and more correct English spelling of **draught.** We trust this will not upset the purists!

Numerous checklists, reminders and lists of important considerations are provided throughout this guide.

STUDY NOTES FOR THE TRAINEE OR JUNIOR OFFICER[99]

- You should make the most of the training opportunities on board your ship.
- One of the most important resources available on board is the experience and expertise of the senior officers. Do not be afraid to consult them at appropriate times by asking questions.
- Take an interest at all times, use any opportunity to observe or participate in both routine and unusual operations, maintenance and repairs as well as any special demonstrations.
- Find out the location of and how to use all the ship's manuals, plans and publications.

ACKNOWLEDGEMENTS

I was very keen to involve as many experienced professionals as possible, in order that this manual would reflect the opinions of a wide cross-section of the industry on current operational practice. I am most grateful to the members of The Nautical Institute listed below for the valuable contributions they have made to the text of this guide, and the extensive time they freely gave to this project.

Shore Based	Seagoing
Mrs U. Dockerty MNI Claims Analyst	Mr G. Dockerty AMNI Second Officer
Ms. Sonja Fink P&I Director	Captain T. Gatt MNI Shipmaster
Captain J. Isbester Ex.C FNI Consultant	Mr. S. Gyi MNI Shipmaster
Mr. D.K. Macleod LLB MNI Solicitor	Captain L. Hesketh FNI Shipmaster
Captain L.A. Maung BSc MNI DoT Surveyor/Examiner	Captain F. Hugo FNI Shipmaster
Mr. W. Nute MNI Operations Manager	Mr. R.C. Moss MNI Chief Officer
Mr. R.I. Wallace MSc MNI Independent surveyor	Mr. N. Rainsford MNI Chief Officer
Mr. S.K. Watson BSc (Hons) FNI University Lecturer	Captain A. Tinsley MNI Shipmaster

I am grateful for the free access which I was given to the library of the **Marine Society**, especially the assistance of their Librarian **Anne McGill** and also to **David Anderson** and the staff of **Brookes Bell** in Liverpool for supplying some suitable photographs from their archives to illustrate the text.

I appreciate the assistance given to me by all the staff of **The Nautical Institute**, especially the advice and regular guidance of **Julian Parker**, Secretary.

I would like to thank the **UK P&I Club** for their sponsorship of the project, which enabled me to spend so much time researching for this guide, and particularly the encouragement given by **Peter Donnellan, Karl Lumbers** and **Nigel Carden**. Also, my thanks to the other P&I Clubs who supplied me with in-house publications as listed in the bibliography in Appendix I.

Finally, this section would not be complete without acknowledging the support of a dedicated partner. My deepest thanks to my wife Barbara for bearing with me for the past year, when writing the text of this guide has taken priority over the innumerable jobs normally assigned to the work-list of a seafarer on leave.

THE NAUTICAL INSTITUTE'S SELF-STUDY PROGRAMME

This guide on *Watchkeeping in Port* is designed to complement the companion volume *Bridge Watchkeeping - a practical guide.*[15]

It is supplemented in The Nautical Institute's *'Commercial Awareness'* programme by *Commercial Management for Shipmasters.*[19]

Having read this guide, the reader may wish to continue to expand his professional education by undertaking one of The Nautical Institute's self-study certificate schemes :

1. *Command.* (Recommended for Chief Officers aspiring to command)
2. *Pilotage and Ship Handling.*
3. *The Work of the Nautical Surveyor.*
4. *The Work of the Harbour Master.*
5. The Management Self-Development Programme.

THE NAUTICAL INSTITUTE

THE NAUTICAL INSTITUTE is an international professional body for qualified mariners whose principal aim is to promote a high standard of knowledge, competence and qualifications amongst those in charge of seagoing craft.

The Institute publishes a monthly journal, SEAWAYS, and is actively involved in promoting good operational practices, as demonstrated by this book on Watchkeeping in Port.

This book is a companion volume to *Bridge Watchkeeping*, which is widely used as a training manual for those seeking to become qualified deck officers.

Other projects and certificate schemes include The Nautical Institute on Command, The Work of the Nautical Surveyor, The Work of the Harbour Master and the confidential Marine Accident Reporting Scheme (MARS).

There are now over 6000 members in 80 different countries with 34 Branches world-wide.

The requirements for Associate Membership are an ocean going watchkeeping certificate from a recognised administration or naval watchkeeping qualifications. Later, Full Membership can be obtained by officers who achieve a recognised foreign going master's certificate of competency; naval command qualifications; a first-class pilotage certificate; or five years in command of coastal vessels..

Feedback

The Nautical Institute is always seeking to improve the quality of its publications by ensuring that they contain practical, relevant, seamanlike advice which is up to date and can be applied at sea.

If you have any suggestions which you think would improve the contents of this book please send your suggestions to:–

The Secretary
The Nautical Institute
202 Lambeth Road
LONDON SE1 7LQ
UK

or
telephone 0171-928 1351
fax 0171-401 2817

Chapter 1

WATCHKEEPING DUTIES IN PORT

PURPOSE

On completion of this chapter you will be able to explain the principles behind your watchkeeping duties in port, the reasons why watches are maintained, and the authority under which they are organised.

1.1 Officer of the Watch (OOW)

The safety and efficiency of the ship's operations in port rests in the first instance on the shoulders of the OOW. He has a most important function as the first point of contact between the ship and personnel from ashore. His initiative, dedication and professionalism can have a major impact on the safety, efficiency and commercial success of the operations.

1.2 Importance of keeping a watch in port

The role of the OOW in port is to supervise and monitor all the various activities taking place on board his ship. Without his vigilance, the ship could be exposed to the influence of shore personnel who have no responsibilities on board the ship, and limited interest in its safety or commercial viability.

There would be no-one to maintain safety, so increasing the risks of accidents and pollution.

There would be no-one to maintain security, so increasing the risks of theft, drug trafficking, stowaways and other criminal activities.

There would be no-one to supervise cargo operations, so increasing the risks of chaotic stowage and damage to both the cargo and the ship. Also, the time taken to complete the operations may be increased, such delays will result in financial loss to the ship's operator.

There would be no-one to monitor the quantity and condition of the cargo, so increasing the likelihood of claims being made against the ship.

There would be no-one to monitor the ballast and the ship's strength and stability, so increasing the risks of structural damage.

There would be no-one to maintain records, so all documentation would be biased towards the shore version of events, with little defence available to the shipowner.

The Nautical Institute hopes that by studying this publication, the OOW will understand the significance of a methodical approach to his watchkeeping duties in port, and will know when, where and how to obtain any assistance he requires, to ensure that all operations are conducted in both a safe and efficient manner.

1.3 Business of shipping

The shipowner and operator are in business to earn a profit from the safe transportation of cargo. One of the main tasks of the ship's staff is to ensure that the cargo is delivered to the consignee (or receiver) in the same condition and quantity as it was received by the vessel from the shipper. The cargo owner has entrusted his goods to the carrier, and expects them to arrive at their destination undamaged with no part missing. Should this not be the case, then the shipowner must explain how the loss or damage occurred. If he is unable to offer a satisfactory explanation, perhaps relying on exceptions permitted in the contract of carriage, then he must compensate the cargo owner for the loss or damage.

The shipowner earns revenue in the form of either freight or hire; *freight* if he carries the cargo for his own account (e.g., liners or voyage charters), or *hire* if he charters the ship to another operator for a period of time—this is discussed in more detail in chapter 6.

From this revenue, he must deduct his operating expenses. These will depend upon the commercial system adopted by the shipowner and the terms of the transportation contracts he uses in his business. Such expenses may include some or all of the following:

- Administration (including all office overheads),
- Insurance (including hull & machinery and P&I),
- Crewing (including victualling and travel),
- Vessel maintenance,
- Consumable stores, spare parts and lubricants,
- Fuel,
- Port dues (including pilotage, light dues and other charges),
- Cargo-handling costs (including stevedoring).

The exact division as to who is liable for these expenses for vessels operating on charter depends upon the terms of the charterparty; this is discussed in chapter 6.3.

The balance remaining after deducting these expenses from the revenue is the shipowner's operating profit. In order to stay in business in the long term, this operating profit must cover the capital costs of the ship (sometimes referred to as depreciation), and still leave a reasonable overall profit.

Depreciation is the annual, or voyage, charge for the capital (cash) invested in the ship. This may be calculated to equal either the actual cost or the replacement cost of the vessel, spread over its anticipated life span, depending on the system of accountancy used by the shipowner. For example, a ship which costs $35 million to build, has an estimated useful life of 15 years, after which it is expected to be sold for scrap for $5 million, could be considered to cost the owner $2 million per annum. The actual figure may be adjusted to take into account the costs of borrowing the money; such interest rates may be fixed or variable.

1.4 Loss prevention

This operating profit can be much reduced if the ship incurs any financial loss, or unforseen extra expenditure whilst she is in port. Loss prevention is the duty of the OOW in port to try to minimise such extra costs, which can be grouped under the following categories:

1. SAFETY —Personnel, fire, access, moorings.
2. DAMAGE —Ship, cargo, berth, shore equipment, personnel.
3. POLLUTION —Oil, smoke, gas, dust, garbage, ballast, hazardous cargo.
4. SECURITY —Stowaways, thieves, pirates, smuggling, corruption.
5. SERVICES —Stores, bunkers, repairs.
6. COMMERCIAL —Contracts of carriage of cargo, Labour contracts.
7. EXTERNAL —Strikes, political/war risks, *force majeure*, bad debts, currency fluctuations, fraud.

This guide shows how the OOW can help prevent loss under all the above categories, except for the seventh, which is beyond the scope of this publication.

Financial loss can arise under these categories from:

1. The actual costs of making good damage, injury or missing goods.
2. Compensation payments.
3. Fines and penalties.
4. The cost of delays to the ship, including loss of hire.
5. Loss due to lower quality or quantity of goods or services.
6. The costs of employing extra services.
7. The expenses of time and staff in dealing with the above, including legal fees and expenses.
8. Future increased insurance premiums which may result from claims.
9. Loss of goodwill and reputation.

1.5 A seaworthy ship

Article III, clause 1 of The Hague Rules (see chapter 7.1) imposes a legal obligation on the carrier *'before and at the beginning of the voyage to exercise due diligence to:*
(a) Make the ship seaworthy;
(b) Properly man, equip and supply the ship;
(c) Make the holds, refrigerating and cool chambers, and all other parts of the ship in which goods are carried, fit and safe for their reception, carriage and preservation.'
This is known as 'cargoworthiness'.

'Exercising due diligence' means **taking good care**.[1]

A seaworthy ship is one which can take its cargo to sea without risk of danger and damage to either the ship or the cargo arising out of the ordinary marine environment or the failure of the ship itself. A seaworthy ship must be fit in relation to its hull structure and machinery, its holds and equipment, and its manning and shipboard procedures. The ship must be in good condition and must have everything it needs in order to perform its task properly.[1]

If problems arise on board during a voyage, the test for determining if the carrier has exercised due diligence to make the ship seaworthy is to ask:

Should the defect have come to light by the careful checking of the ship before the voyage began? If so, would a careful owner have mended that defect before sending the ship, with her cargo on board, to sea?[1]

1.6 Watch in port

The Master usually delegates the control of cargo operations to the Chief Officer. At all times when cargo is being worked in port, there will be a junior deck officer available to assist him. It is normal for these OOWs to work a duty rota system; the exact details will depend on the work load, the number of officers available and the hours of work of the stevedores. Also different companies have different procedures.

Even when cargo is not being worked, sufficient officers and crew should be available to deal with any emergency which may arise. In some ports, for example Hong Kong, the local regulations specify the minimum numbers of officers and crew who must remain on board. There should always be a nominated duty officer, known to the ship's watchman, who can be called if required. This officer should be aware of any conditions that could affect the safety of the vessel, including weather, tides, moorings, security, etc. He should make a final round of inspection of all parts of the vessel to satisfy himself that all is well before retiring for the night.

The OOW may need to keep a full 'live' watch for duties other than cargo operations, such as supervising bunkering, receiving ship's stores, assisting with surveys or repairs, maintaining security, etc. 'Live' means awake, alert, suitably dressed and equipped, and taking an active interest in the relevant operations.

1.6.1 Mitigation[2]

The concept of mitigation is to minimise or reduce the consequences of an incident after it has arisen. In most cases, if the OOW takes the correct action immediately after an incident occurs, then considerable extra damage, losses and expenses can be avoided. A vigilant deck watch must be maintained at all times, so that if a problem arises, the OOW will detect it immediately, and be able to deal with it promptly in order to mitigate its effects.

The OOW should never be tempted to ignore a problem, hoping that no-one will notice, or that it will go away, or that someone else will deal with it. **As with keeping a bridge watch at sea, the OOW is in charge of the ship whilst he is on duty in port, and he must never try to avoid this responsibility.** The senior officers will be able to offer advice and support, and should be consulted whenever the OOW is in any doubt.

1.6.2 Human error

Two thirds of the major claims of the UK P&I Club are directly caused by human error[21]—see the pie-charts on page 24. There is no single reason for human error, rather it is a general category used to cover:

- A lapse in concentration.
  Fatigue, discomfort, boredom, anger and stress make people more prone to make mistakes.[21]
- An error of judgement.
- Inexperience.
  (Sometimes *pride* can lead to a failure to seek assistance.)
- Inadequate training and qualifications.
- A lack of knowledge and/or skill.
- Inappropriate guidance.
- Incompetence.
- Carelessness or negligence (sometimes due to over-confidence or familiarity).
- Recklessness.
- Wilful misconduct.
- Confusion, including misapplication of rules and procedures
- Misinterpretation, including language difficulties and multi-cross-cultural incompatibilities.
- Lack of motivation, often resulting from employment conditions, or poor standards of leadership.

The Nautical Institute hopes that this guide will provide the OOW with the skills and attitudes necessary to reduce claims of this category.

1.7 Watchkeeping duties

MAINTENANCE OF SAFETY IS PARAMOUNT

As with keeping a watch at sea, the main duty of the watchkeeper in port is to maintain a proper aural and visual lookout. This means that he must always be watching what is happening around the ship. Only in this way can he be sure that he is fulfilling his primary role of maintaining the safety of the ship, her cargo and all persons on board.

The OOW must always spend as much time as possible actually on deck.

By continuously observing all operations, he will be immediately aware when things do not go according to plan, or if accidents occur. He will then be in the best position to influence the course of events. This may involve altering the procedures or methods of work, providing additional labour to assist, or arranging for the supply of extra or more suitable equipment. His very presence may encourage others to work and/or behave in a more correct and efficient manner, and may discourage poor stowage, unsafe practices and criminal activities such as thieves and stowaways.

The importance of OBSERVING and NOTING *all* events that occur around the deck cannot be overemphasised. If there are any disputes, the Master will rely on the logbook entries of the OOW as the basis for the ship's version of the story. This subject is expanded upon in chapter 18.

Although the shipowner may be insured against many of the losses discussed in this manual, this fact should not affect the vigilance of the OOW. The insurance policy will contain some deductible, which is an amount which the shipowner has to pay in all cases. The insurance company pays out only for claims in excess of this deductible, so in effect the shipowner is uninsured for this amount. Even when the costs can be fully recovered, the shipowner will have to bear the expenses of handling the claim. Ultimately, increasing claims will result in increasing insurance costs, so reducing the shipowner's operating profit. It should be remembered that the shipowner's insurance premium and his deductible is directly related to the claims record of each each ship. The premium for a ship with a poor claims record can be more than double that of an identical ship with a good claims record.

Whenever another person suffers a financial loss which he believes has been caused by the ship, he will make a claim for compensation. The UK P&I Club has analysed these claims, and the results are illustrated in the pie-charts on page 24. As the UK P&I Club provides insurance cover for around a quarter of the world's fleet, one can safely assume that these figures represent the pattern of the entire industry. The reader should note that in the types of major claim, cargo and personal injury are dominant. We shall be returning to these subjects throughout this manual. The second diagram on reasons for major claims speaks for itself! (See also section 1.6.2.)

Eventually, the very livelihood of the OOW depends upon the success of the commercial venture. So it is also in his own interest to reduce potential claims and unnecessary expenses as much as possible. In many respects, watchkeeping in port is an organisational and administrative function, in addition to providing operational control.

> **To summarise, the OOW is responsible for ensuring that all activities onboard the vessel are carried out in a SAFE and EFFICIENT manner.**

1.8 STCW Convention[37]

Whilst this manual covers all the duties of the OOW in port, we have highlighted the commercial implications of the performance of these duties. The noncommercial duties of the OOW are embodied in the IMO *International Convention on the Standards of Training, Certification and Watch-keeping for Seafarers*[37] *of 1978, revised in 1995.*

Regulation 4.90 of the consolidated text of this convention states that *on any ship safely moored or safely at anchor under normal circumstances in port, the Master shall arrange for an appropriate and effective watch to be maintained for the purpose of safety.*

1.8.1 Hazardous cargo

Regulation 4–5 105/106 of the 1995 consolidated text covers the minimum requirements for a watch in port on ships carrying hazardous cargo.

105 The Master of every ship carrying cargo that is hazardous, whether explosive, flammable, toxic, health-threatening or environment-polluting, shall ensure that safe watchkeeping arrangements are maintained. On ships carrying hazardous cargo in bulk, this will be achieved by the ready availability on board of a duly qualified officer or officers, and ratings where appropriate, even when the ship is safely moored or

Types of Major Claims

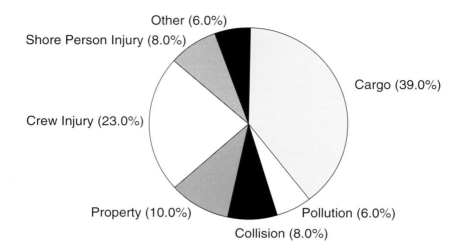

Reasons for Major Claims

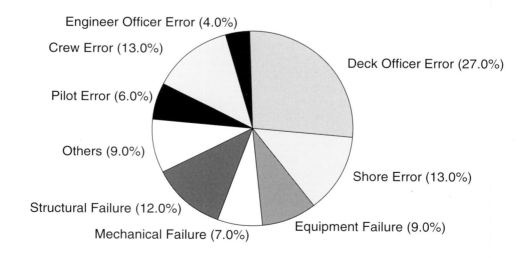

Reproduced from the UK P&I Club *Analaysis of Major Claims, 1993*

safely at anchor in port.

106 On ships carrying hazardous cargo other than in bulk, the master shall take full account of the nature, quantity, packing and stowage of the hazardous cargo and of any special conditions on board, afloat and ashore.

1.8.2 Watch arrangements

The STCW has adopted the *Recommendations on principles and operational guidance for deck officers in charge of a watch in port.* These provide a set of international standards to which the OOW must adhere. The consolidated text 1995 provides:

91 Arrangements for keeping a watch when the ship is in port shall at all times be adequate to:
1 ensure the safety of life, of the ship, cargo, port and the environment, and the safe operation of all machinery related to cargo operation;
2 observe international, national and local rules;
3 maintain order and the normal routine of the ship.

92 The Master shall decide the composition and duration of the watch depending on the conditions of mooring, type of ship and character of duties.

93 If the Master considers it necessary, a qualified officer should be in charge of the watch.

94 The necessary equipment should be so arranged as to provide for efficient watchkeeping.

1.8.3 Keeping a watch

Part 4-3 states: *102 The officer in charge of the deck watch shall:*
.1 make rounds to inspect the ship at appropriate intervals;
.2 pay particular attention to :
.2.1 the condition and fastening of the gangway, anchor chain or moorings, especially at the turn of tide or in basins with a large rise and fall and, if necessary, take measures to ensure that they are in normal working condition.
.2.2 the draught, underkeel clearance and the general state of the ship to avoid dangerous listing or trim during cargo handling or ballasting;
.2.3 the weather and sea state;
.2.4 observance of all regulations concerning safety and fire protection;
.2.5 water level in bilges and tanks;
.2.6 all persons on board and their location, especially those in remote or enclosed spaces;
.2.7 the exhibition and sounding where appropriate of lights or signals;
.3 in bad weather, or on receiving a storm warning, take the necessary measures to protect the ship, persons on board and cargo;
.4 take every precaution to prevent pollution of the environment by the ship;
.5 in an emergency threatening the safety of the ship, raise the alarm, inform the Master, take all possible measures to prevent any damage to the ship its cargo and persons on board and, if necessary, request assistance from the shore authorities or neighbouring ships;
.6 be aware of the ship's stability condition so that, in the event of fire, the shore fire-fighting authority may be advised of the approximate quantity of water that can be pumped on board without endangering the ship;
.7 offer assistance to ships or persons in distress;

.8 take necessary precautions to prevent accidents or damage when propellers are to be turned;
.9 enter in the appropriate log book all important events affecting the ship.

Clauses 96 to 99 on 'Taking over the watch' are reproduced in chapter 5.

1.9 Company's instructions

A properly managed ship operating company will issue its own set of instructions on what standards of performance are expected from each officer. They will list the responsibilities of the OOW, and any special duties allocated to individual officers.

Specific guidance will be found in the company's handbooks, whose composition and titles vary from company to company, but may include some or all of the following titles:
- *General Handbook,*
- *Deck Handbook,*
- *Operations Manual,*
- *Cargo Manual,*
- *Bridge Procedures Manual,*
- *Safety Manual,*
- *Training Manual and*
- *Planned Maintenance Manual.*

> The OOW should read these publications when he first joins the ship; if he is required to sign any of them, he should only do so when he fully understands their meaning.

He must seek clarification from the Master or other officers of any points on which he is not clear. Company instructions supplement the STCW regulations.

In the past, some shipowners provided little documentary guidance for the ship's staff, but in the future the ISM Code[39] will ensure that all ships will have to be provided with suitable operational manuals.

1.9.1 The International Safety Management (ISM) Code[39]

The purpose of the new ISM Code is to establish an international standard for the safe management and operation of ships and for pollution prevention.[39]

Every ship operator has to develop a Safety Management System (SMS), which documents its management procedures to ensure that all activities both ashore and onboard are planned, organised, executed and checked in accordance with company, national and international requirements. Each ship will be issued with its own Safety Management Certificate when it is verified that the company and its shipboard management operate in accordance with the approved Safety Management System.

The requirements for the SMS are incorporated into a *Safety Management Manual* which should include:
1. A safety and environmental protection policy;
2. Instructions to ensure safe operation of ships;
3. Defined levels of authority and lines of communication between, and amongst, shore and shipboard personnel;
4. Procedures for reporting accidents and non-

conformity with this code;

5. Procedures to prepare for and respond to emergency situations;

6. Procedures for internal audits and management reviews.

1.9.2 Shipboard operational documents

Regulation 7 of the ISM Code specifies that *the company should establish procedures for the preparation of plans and instructions for key shipboard operations... The various tasks involved should be defined and assigned to qualified personnel.*

Suggested subject-matter for operations documentation was appended to an earlier IMO resolution, and included the following topics dealing with the ship in port:

1. Accepting the cargo.
2. Loading and discharging procedures.
3. Harbour watches and patrols.
4. Liaison with shore authorities.
5. Monitoring trim and stability.
6. Procedures when the ship is temporarily immobilised.
7. Accidental spillage of liquid cargoes and ship's bunkers.
8. Use of reception facilities for oil, noxious liquids and garbage.
9. Response to oil pollution incidents.

Other sections provided suggestions on topics dealing with:

General organisation,
Preparing for sea,
The ship at sea and
Preparing for arrival in port.[89]

Regulation 10 of the ISM Code requires the establishment of a planned maintenance system, with appropriate records and inspections.

1.10 Master's standing orders

Some companies fail to issue comprehensive instructions. If the Master thinks there is a need to clarify what standards of performance he expects from the junior watchkeeping officers, he may choose to issue his own standing orders in port. An example of such standing orders is given below.

The Master may issue supplementary orders for a particular voyage, to augment the company instructions, or in a particular port, to offer guidance on local rules, regulations or practices, or extra precautions that may be required.

1.11 Chief Officer's instructions

Most Masters delegate the detailed organisation of the ship's operation in port to the Chief Officer, who may issue his own standing orders, perhaps supplementing the Master's orders. The Chief Officer's standing orders will lay out the framework in which the OOW is to perform his duties. At each port he will issue instructions to the OOW detailing the activities expected at that port, bringing any local rules and regulations to his attention, and giving guidance on the performance of specific tasks.

Whilst the OOW will be expected to act on his own initiative, his actions must always comply with the Master's and Chief Officer's orders, and the OOW must always call these officers if he is in any doubt whatsoever.

1.10.1 Example of a Master's standing orders in port

1. All deck officers must ensure that the deck watch is maintained strictly in accordance with:
   (a) All company instructions and regulations,
   (b) All international and local rules and regulations,
   (c) The STCW guidelines : 'Principles and operational guidance for deck officers in charge of a watch in port".

2. **The safety of the ship and ALL personnel on board is paramount.**
   This takes precedence over all your other responsibilities.
   You should be aware of the on board location of all shore personnel.

3. When cargo is being worked, your prime place of duty is on deck, where you can best supervise the cargo operations. I expect the duty officer to be available to the stevedore on duty at all times. Identify and introduce yourself to the foreman stevedore at each change of shift. Ensure that the foreman stevedore and the duty sailor know of your location at all times, particularly should you be temporarily absent from the deck, for example whilst engaged in ballast operations in the engineroom.

4. Ensure that the cargo is handled, stowed and secured properly.
   The detailed instructions of the Chief Officer concerning cargo operations must be followed at all times, and you <u>must</u> call him if you are ever in any doubt.
   It is our job to deliver the cargo in the same condition as it was received, and remember that it is the freight on the cargo which pays all our wages.

5. Ensure that all cargo and ballast operations are carried out in the sequence advised by the Chief Officer, and that he is informed of any unscheduled occurrences immediately.

6. Ensure that the duty sailor remains alert, and is stationed at the gangway unless he is required elsewhere. You should remain in radio contact with the duty sailor at all times with walkie-talkies. You and he must ensure that <u>NO UNAUTHORISED VISITORS ARE ALLOWED ON BOARD</u>.

7. Ensure that moorings, gangway and safety nets are adjusted as required. Ensure that ALL parts of the vessel are adequately illuminated at night, both for safety and security. Ensure that all necessary flags and other signals are flown as required.

8. Watch the movements of other ships which may cause damage to our ship. Keep a close watch on the moorings when other vessels are sailing or berthing ahead or astern.

9. Pay special attention to any damage done to the vessel, fittings or cargo. Keep a constant watch for new damage, and report it to the Chief Officer immediately, even if you don't actually see it happen. Investigate every loud bang!

10. Take all necessary precautions to prevent pollution, from bunkers, cargo spills, ballast and garbage. Call me immediately if any incident occurs which may lead to pollution. If pollution is seen coming from other ships or ashore, this sighting should be logged.

11. Ensure that all personnel on duty (including those from ashore) observe the requirements of the company's drug and alcohol policy. Report any suspicions of violations to me immediately.

12. You must personally supervise the opening and closing of all hatch-covers; check the coamings and drains are clean before closing.

13. Do <u>NOT</u> sign <u>any</u> documents from ashore without my permission.

14. Write up the logbook after each deck watch, ensuring that all relevant events are recorded. It is always better to write too much than too little. Remember that the logbook can be used in Court as evidence.
    Entries should include times, and full details of:
    (a) Arrival on board and departure ashore of all officials, surveyors, contractors, stevedores, lashers, etc., including number of gangs.
    (b) Commence, cease, resume and complete work at each hatch.
    (c) All delays to cargo work, for example due to weather, breakdowns, no cargo available, transportation problems, disputes, etc.
    (d) Durations of surveys, inspections, etc. Log the names of surveyors.
    (e) Forward, midships and aft drafts, at each change of OOW.
    (f) Weather details every four hours, as with normal sea watches, plus the times when precipitation starts and stops.
    (g) Taking bunkers, fresh water, etc. (also note quantities)
    (h) Other craft or vessels alongside, and away. Log their names.
    (i) Any accidents to ship and personnel onboard.

15. All officers and crew should advise the OOW or gangway watchman when they are going ashore, and when they return on board. A tally should be kept so that it is always known who is on board—this is a safety requirement.

16. Make sure that you provide a thorough and clear handover to your relief ; sign the C/O's Port Orders Book.

17. Whenever there is no cargo being worked, there must be a nominated duty deck officer, who should make himself known to the duty sailor, so he knows who to call if required. This OOW should make frequent safety rounds of the vessel to ensure that all is well, and make a thorough inspection before turning in for the night.

18. You are fully responsible for all aspects of the watch at all times, and passing an order on to someone else does not relieve you of this. You should check that all actions and orders have the desired effect.

19. I require a system of POSITIVE REPORTING. This means that if you are requested by me, either directly or in these orders, to perform a certain task, you must report back directly to me as soon as that task has been completed.

20. <u>You must call for assistance immediately if you are in any doubt whatsoever, at any time, or you feel unable to cope alone, or you become fatigued.</u> In general you are to call the Chief Officer first, but if he is not available, then you must call me.

Signed: Captain Hopeful.

I HAVE READ AND UNDERSTOOD THE ABOVE MASTER'S STANDING ORDERS,

Signed: 1/O: _____ 2/O: _____ 3/O: _____ Trainees: _____

Date: _____   _____   _____   _____

Chapter 2
ARRIVAL IN PORT
PURPOSE

On completion of this chapter you will be able to describe the tasks which need to be completed before, and upon arrival to ensure that there is an efficient start to cargo operations.

2.1 Minimise time in port

The ship earns revenue by transporting goods from the port of loading to the port of discharge, so it could be considered that she is not earning anything whilst berthed in port. Hence the commercial success of the vessel requires that the time in port is kept to the minimum. **It is a prime duty of the OOW to ensure that the various activities outlined in this guide are completed to an acceptable standard in the shortest possible time.**

The navigational aspects of arrival preparations, port approaches and berthing operations have been covered in the companion publication *Bridge Watchkeeping*.[15] However, the ship must also make commercial preparations to ensure there is no delay to the commencement of cargo operations after berthing. This chapter covers these issues.

2.2 Prearrival meeting

On a well-managed ship, the Master will hold a prearrival discussion between the members of the deck department. This will involve the Chief Officer and all the deck OOWs, plus any other officers as appropriate—perhaps the Chief Engineer, Petty Officers and other specialists who will be involved in the port operations. The purpose is to communicate information, so that everybody concerned will know what is expected to be done, and what will be their own involvement and responsibilities. This will enable adequate preparations to be made in sufficient time.

This meeting should cover items such as likely loading or discharging problems, anticipated methods and equipment including any ship's equipment required, local regulations likely to affect the operations, surveys expected, extra meals and accommodation required to be provided by the ship, expected timings, manning levels, and anticipated security arrangements.

The Master will have studied any charterparty, and he will explain any special requirements for dealing with:

● Stevedore damage,
● Cargo damage (including arrangements for clausing mate's receipts),
● Defective cargo-handling equipment,
● The provision of extra ship's personnel to assist, (e.g., winch drivers, security watchmen, etc.)
● Any extra entries required in the deck logbook,
● Other records to be kept.

The Chief Officer will explain the cargo pre-plan, any unusual characteristics of the cargo, and any special handling and stowage requirements. The OOWs should seek guidance if they are unfamiliar with any of the commodities to be handled. The Chief Officer will also explain any ballast procedures, and any required co-ordination with the cargo operation.

2.3 Prearrival preparations

The junior deck officer should be aware of the various prearrival preparations required; he may be called upon to assist with their organisation or supervision during the previous sea passage. The degree of his involvement will depend upon the regime of the particular ship. However, a good officer will always take an active interest in all the operations on board ship, and not limit his involvement to those activities which are strictly contained within his job description or areas of responsibility.

Always remember that successful ship operation is a team effort.

2.3.1 Hold cleaning

Before the ship can load her next cargo, the cargo hold must be adequately cleaned. The degree of cleanliness will depend on the nature of both the previous cargo and the next cargo. In consultation with the Master, the Chief Officer will decide what sort of cleaning needs to be done, when it is done, and by whom. It is good practice always to keep all cargo compartments as clean as possible, even if this not required for the next cargo, though often the time available limits the thoroughness of the cleaning.

● For break-bulk cargoes, and some 'dirty' dry-bulk cargoes, it may be sufficient for the holds to be swept by the crew.
● For cleaner dry-bulk cargoes, the holds may be washed out with high pressure hoses to remove all trace of the previous cargo. It is good practice to rinse the holds with fresh water after washing with salt water in order to minimise any future corrosion; also, this may be essential if the next cargo can be damaged by salt—e.g., steel. The highest standards of cleanliness are usually referred to as 'grain clean', which may be required for sensitive cargoes other than grain—See also chapter 8.1.4.
● For foodstuffs, the holds must be free of infestation, and will need to be sprayed with an insecticide if any infestation is found. This may be a job for a specialised contractor.
● For most cargoes, the holds must be dry, and free from odours which may taint the next cargo. On reefers (refrigerated cargo vessels), it is

particularly important that all traces of odours from previous cargoes are removed using an 'Ozonator'.

- The holds should be free of all loose rust, which may contaminate certain sensitive cargoes. Some cargoes may require the hold to be specially coated—e.g., with lime for some salt or sulphur cargoes.
- On some trades, where the same cargo is carried on successive voyages, no hold cleaning may be required. On some bulk trades, 'shovel clean' by the discharging stevedores may be sufficient. The ship's staff must always be sure if this is the case, preferably by seeking confirmation in writing.

When on a time charter, it is usual to ask the charterer what cleaning they require. *Charterers understandably object to paying the owners for a wash costing $1,000+ per hold, when all they require is a sweep, which is often free.*[3]

Detailed guidance on the cleaning of holds is given in the Nautical Institute publication *Bulk Carrier Practice.*[3]

Tank cleaning on tankers is discussed in chapter 9.19.

2.3.2 Testing systems

Before arrival at the loading port, the following items must be tested. Some of these tests may be performed on a regular routine basis, and so may not need repeating before each loadport.

1. HOLD BILGES OR WELLS.
- Any tween-deck scuppers must be proved clear.
- The bilge space must be clean, including the strum box. It is good practice to leave the bilge dry, this is an essential requirement for Reefers and with sensitive bulk cargoes such as grain.
- The sounding pipes must be proved clear, and watertight caps checked.
- The non-return valve must be working.
- Any high-level alarm must be working.
- The bilge pump must be proved to pump water from the space.
- The bilge space cover should be covered with burlap if required.

2. VENTILATORS.
- Fire flaps must be proved free.
- Closing devices must be proved free, and the rubber seals intact.
- Fans must be working—test in forward and reverse if applicable.
- Spark arrestors and insect grills must be intact.
- Non-return floats in tank airpipes must be proved to be free and functioning correctly.

3. SENSORS.
- Fire detecting heads must be working. (Heat and/or smoke tested).
- The outlet pipe of the smothering system must be clear. Often this can be checked by blowing through pipes with compressed air, after blanking of the pipe to the fire detection system.
- Thermometer or sampling pipes must be clear, and their watertight caps checked.
- All portable thermometers and their rope lines

should be checked.
- Any temperature probes must be working—check for broken leads and damaged sensing heads.

4. ACCESS.
- All ladders and handrails must be undamaged.
- All doors and lids to accesses must be free and their watertight seals in good condition. The pins or other means of keeping these doors and lids open should be operating correctly.

5. LIGHTING.
- Fixed system tested, bulbs or tubes renewed as necessary.
- Conduits and cables examined for damage.
- System isolated by removing the fuses, if required by next cargo.
- Sufficient portable lights (clusters) available, and tested, with their rope lanyards and cables examined for wear and/or cuts.

6. HOLD DAMAGE.
- All pipelines examined for leakage. (includes air and sounding pipes)
- Manhole lids checked for leakage.
- Steelwork and welds examined for fractures and excessive corrosion—see also chapter 19.2 and appendix V.

7. HATCH COVERS.
- Operating satisfactorily.
- Water-tight integrity tested.
- Drains cleared and proved free and nonreturn valves proved to be functioning correctly.
- Securing devices proved functional—see also chapter 19.5.

8. CARGO-HANDLING SYSTEMS.
   —see chapters 4.5 (dry cargo), 8.3.4 (reefers) and 9.7 (tankers).

These tests are made to verify that systems are in good order. Any faults discovered must be rectified as soon as possible. This may involve the assistance of the engineering staff on board, or require specialists to attend on arrival at the next port to effect repairs. All faults which effect safety must be clearly marked and the part isolated or else the system withdrawn from use. Pre-arrival preparations on tankers are discussed in chapter 9.

2.3.3 Dunnage and lashing materials

Any dunnage remaining in the hold must be stacked clear of the working area, ready for use with the next loading. Dirty and broken dunnage materials should be discarded, stained or damp dunnage must never be reused with sensitive cargoes. Sometimes it will be possible for the crew to lay out any dunnage required for the next cargo loading in advance. The stevedores in the discharge port must be provided with direct access to the cargo they have to handle, and not waste time and money clearing up dunnage and lashing materials. This also applies to such items as twistlocks and other container securing devices. Dunnage is discussed in chapter 7.9.

If it is safe to do so, cargo lashings can be released before berthing, to allow the stevedores to commence discharge with the minimum of delay.

Once released, these lashings should be stored well clear of the cargo stow, so as not to interfere with safe access. The Master must judge when this can be done in complete safety, which will depend on the weather, the duration of any anchorage or river passage, the type of lashings involved, the physical nature of the cargo stow and the provision of a safe access to the lashings.

2.4 Pre-berthing preparations

1. Holds opened, including tween-decks where appropriate, if it is safe to do so, and weather and local rules permit. This is a large cost saving in ports where labour is expensive, and local rules give stevedores a fixed time allowance for this job. Also, it is a requirement of many charterparties. Ensure all open hatches are secured, or lashed as appropriate.
2. Gangway rigged on correct side, if the pilot verifies there are no obstructions on the quayside, and it will not interfere with tugs.
3. Cargo gear set up, and ready to operate, provided this does not obscure vision during berthing operations. Before switching on such equipment, the engineers must be advised, so that there will be sufficient electrical power available.
4. Mooring ropes or wires prepared, as discussed in chapter 3.
5. Mooring winches powered up and tested.
   ● Check breakers are in, or steam valves open, as appropriate.
   ● Pump up hydraulic oil to header tank, if appropriate.
6. Officers and crew called to their berthing stations.
7. Communications between the bridge and mooring stations tested, including the back up.

Many of the above preparations require good lighting, and can only be made at night where the provision of such lighting does not effect the navigation of the vessel. Some can only be made once the vessel has entered sheltered waters, and is approaching the berth. The Master will decide when it is safe to undertake these preparations.

2.5 Time factor

When a ship first berths, junior officers may think that there seems to be insufficient time available to perform all the necessary tasks. Along with the short time between completion of cargo operations and sailing, the time between berthing and commencing cargo operations is one of the most busy periods of the ship's itinerary. To ensure that the required tasks are completed to a satisfactory standard within the allotted time, it is necessary for them to be well planned, with adequate preparations made well in advance. The role of the OOW will be to co-ordinate these activities in order to avoid any delays.

TIME LOST = MONEY LOST

Many times the ship remains at anchor until early in the morning. This is because berthing is timed so that overtime payments to tugs and linesmen are minimised. Berthing is often timed between the end of their overtime hours and the start of the next

stevedores shift. It cannot be delayed too long, as otherwise the stevedores may claim large compensation for idle time, particularly where they are paid on piece rates.

That means there is little time available after berthing before the start of the next stevedore shift. Before then, the OOW must check that the ship has been properly prepared so that cargo operations can start without delay. If the gangway net is not rigged correctly (see chapter 4.2.), the stevedores may refuse to come on board, and costly penalty payments may be claimed, particularly in the USA and some other ports in the developed world. Other causes which attract such penalties include the hatches not being opened or secured properly, the ship's cargo-handling gear being incorrectly rigged, and a lack of safe accesses or insufficient lighting around the vessel.

The OOW has an important function in ensuring that everything is ready, so avoiding delays, and their associated high costs.

2.6 Reading the arrival draft

On larger vessels, it is good practice to always read a six-point draft, which means both port and starboard readings forward, midships and aft. On smaller vessels, the fore and aft drafts as read from the quayside are often sufficient, but the midships port and starboard drafts <u>must</u> be read in all cases when the ship is carrying a deadweight cargo—i.e., she is floating at or near her appropriate maximum loadline. When reading the midships drafts is difficult, it may be easier to measure the freeboard—the distance from the waterline to the main deck line marked on the side of the hull. The midships draft is obtained by deducting this freeboard from the freeboard constant. The freeboard constant is the sum of the summer draft and summer freeboard as shown on the vessel's loadline certificate. The OOW may need to organise the rigging of extra ladders to gain access to some of the draft marks.

The OOW should compare these visual observations with the readings on any draft gauges, and establish an updated error, which then can be applied to the gauge readings to obtain the true draft quickly during cargo/ballast operations.

If a draft survey is being conducted, the OOW may be required to accompany the Chief Officer and the surveyor, **but he must always read and record the drafts independently**—See chapter 13.9.

2.7 Assisting with surveys

The OOW may be called upon to assist with surveys conducted on arrival such as hold condition, on/off-hire, or draft survey. Other surveys which may take place at any time during the ship's period in port are outlined in chapter 14.6.

During the period of peak work load soon after berthing, several authorities may require the assistance of a ship's officer. Although the Chief Officer would like to deal with each person separately himself, invariably they all arrive onboard at the same time, and require immediate attention. The Chief Officer may ask the OOW to assist him, for example by accompanying a surveyor around the ship. The OOW should ensure that he receives a briefing on the particular requirements of the surveyor, and that he has sufficient knowledge to assist properly with the survey.

The OOW should politely ensure that all surveyors follow safe practices, and seek assistance from the Chief Officer if he is in any doubt. It is good practice to treat all shore personnel courteously—even those who do not reciprocate!

2.7.1 Hold condition survey

Before loading many cargoes, a surveyor will inspect the hold to see that it is in a suitable condition to receive the intended cargo. He will be looking for damp, residues of previous cargoes, loose scale, taint (strong odours), infestation, etc.—in fact anything which will affect the condition of the next cargo whilst it is stowed in the hold. On a ship about to load a refrigerated cargo, he will check that the compartments have been precooled to the required temperature.

The OOW should record any criticisms which the surveyor makes about the hold condition, so that he can direct the crew to rectify the faults as quickly as possible. This may enable a resurvey to take place with the minimum of delay. All the surveyor's comments should be reported to the Chief Officer.

Tank condition surveys are discussed in chapter 9.

2.7.2 On/off-hire survey

Another type of condition survey may be undertaken if the ship is going on-hire to a new charterer. The on-hire surveyor will be looking at the physical condition of the entire ship. He will be looking for previous damage—for example, noting all dented and broken handrails, ladder rungs and protection bars. Usually he will pay particular attention to the condition of the hatchcovers and the state of the holds. His purpose is to establish the exact state of the ship at the start of the charter.

An off-hire survey is conducted to establish the exact state of the ship at the end of the charter. Any differences in the state of the ship from the on-hire survey will be deemed to have occurred during the charter, so are the responsibility of the charterer. The OOW should be able to point out recent damage to the surveyor, and liaise with the Chief Officer to identify any relevant stevedores' damage reports.

It is usual for this surveyor to establish the quantities of bunkers remaining on board at the time of on- and off-hire. The OOW should refer the surveyor to the Chief Engineer.

2.7.3 Draft survey

A draft survey may be conducted in order to calculate the ship's displacement. By comparing the displacements on arrival and departure, the quantity of cargo loaded or discharged can be determined. This procedure is discussed in chapter 13.9.

2.7.4 Cargo condition survey

A surveyor may be appointed to ascertain the condition of the cargo before it is loaded. Such preshipment surveys are discussed in chapter 12.4. Regardless of whether or not there is a preshipment survey, the OOW should always try to view the cargo before it is loaded, to establish its condition. Such preloading inspections are discussed in chapter 12.5.

When the hatches are first opened at the discharge port, the OOW should satisfy himself that all is in good order. If there are any signs of cargo damage, such as due to failed lashings, or there are any signs of water entry, such as stained or caked cargo, rust streaks, or even pools of water, these must be reported immediately to the Chief Officer. The reasons for such damage will need to be discovered, but this should not cause any delays to the cargo operation.

When the ship first arrives at the discharge port, the receiver may appoint a surveyor to verify the condition of the cargo. The OOW should not allow such surveyors access to the ship unless he has received clear authority from the Master or Chief Officer.

The subject of cargo damage is covered in chapters 7 and 12. Sampling procedures on tankers to ascertain the condition of the cargo are discussed in chapter 9.18.

2.8 Shore cargo-handling equipment

At many terminals, the cargo operations will be conducted using shorebased handling equipment. The OOW must understand how this works, and be aware of any limitations in its use, especially with respect to movement of the ship. He should familiarise himself with the method for communicating with its operator, both for routine operations and in an emergency. Similarly, it is essential that the OOW identifies each shift foreman, and knows how to contact him at any time.

The clearance under some shorebased cargo-handling equipment may be limited, and the ship may be required to maintain a certain minimum distance between such equipment and her hatch-coamings. The OOW must be aware of this figure, and he should check that it remains sufficient throughout the cargo operation. He will need to know the height of the tide at the berth throughout his watch, the distance from the dock water level to the equipment at high water, and the distance from the dock waterlevel to the hatch coaming, which is known as the air draft. Note that the air draft depends on the trim of the ship, and so may vary along its length. If the air draft approaches any limiting figure at a particular hatch, the OOW must inform the Chief Officer, who may decide to change the sequence of the cargo and/or ballast operations. The OOW will need to pay particular attention at high water, and when there is little cargo or ballast in the ship. This coaming air draft is not to be confused with the air draft for pilotage, which is the distance from the waterline to the highest point on the ship, usually the top of the mast.

Some equipment can only operate in wind speeds up to a certain value, otherwise its safe operation is compromised. The OOW should know this maximum figure, so he is aware of likely stoppages to the cargo handling operation.

Shore handling equipment must not be allowed to come into contact with any part of the vessel. Sometimes the operator of a gantry does not have an absolutely clear view of all parts of its structure. The OOW should monitor any movements of such equipment in close proximity to the gangway, derricks, cranes, masts and delicate ship's fittings such as radar scanners and aerials, and warn the operator accordingly. Grab damage is common on bulk carriers, and is discussed in 8.1.10.

To avoid any possibility of damage, ship's engine trials must not be permitted whilst any shore equipment is close to the ship's side or within the ship's holds. This also applies to ships which have ramps resting on the quay or cargo doors or ports opening over the quay.

2.9 Handling ship's equipment

Some ports, particularly in the USA and Australia, have strict rules on who should handle ship's equipment, such as opening and closing hatches, shifting cranes and derricks, or even handling ship's stores and spare gear. The OOW should always verify with the Chief Officer, or the stevedore foreman, before he permits the crew to undertake these duties, as failure to obtain authority can sometimes lead to the ship paying a large penalty, such as the local wages for a whole gang for an entire shift.

2.10 Stevedore's working hours

The OOW must know how many gangs will be working on board, the times of changes of shift, any meal breaks, and other planned stoppages. He will need to establish the timings of any special operations, for example extra-heavy lifts or valuable cargo, or any other situations which may require his particular attention, additional manpower or other extra assistance.

2.11 Ship's working hours

The OOW must know the arrangements made for the crew's watch duties, how many men are available to assist him, and when.

On some ships, the Chief Officer will organise the duty rota for each OOW. On other ships, the junior officers organise their own watch rota. They should ensure that no-one works such long hours that he becomes fatigued, and that there are sufficient people available to assist with all activities expected to take place, particularly at times of peak activities. The Chief Officer will brief them on what operations to expect during the ship's stay in port, and he must always be informed of any changes to their duty-rota which the junior officers arrange amongst themselves.

Nearer sailing time, the port work rota must be arranged to ensure that the officer taking the first bridge watch is adequately rested.

2.12 Draft limits and grounding

The OOW must know any draft limits at the berth, and if there is any doubt, he should have a set of hand soundings taken around the ship to verify this information. If the vessel is loading close to the maximum permissible draft, it is good practice always to take such hand soundings.

He must remain alert at critical states of the tide and cargo programme, to ensure that the vessel remains safely afloat at all times. Any unexpected lists, or signs of the vessel lying off the berth, must be reported to the Master or Chief Officer, as the vessel may have grounded. Many berths have much lower depths close to the quayside, caused by cargo spillage or difficulties in dredging close to the quay. It is not unknown for ships to slide away from the quay—i.e., they are aground on the inshore side.

If the berth is one where the vessel usually lies aground for part of the time, the OOW must check with the Chief Officer as to the extra precautions required. In particular, he must remain alert for undue lists as the vessel refloats.

The times and heights of tides for the duration of the vessel's stay in port should always be clearly displayed in the cargo control room or office. It is a good idea if these times are also displayed near the gangway, to alert the ship's watchman for adjusting the gangway.

2.13 Miscellaneous local regulations

The OOW should enquire from the Chief Officer if there are any local regulations which may affect his watchkeeping duties, in particular where extra vigilance may be required.

It is important to check regularly that the rat guards remain in place on the mooring lines, and that all garbage, particularly food, is kept in securely covered containers.

In many ports in Canada and the USA the crew are not permitted to fish. If they are caught engaging in this popular hobby of seafarers, they and the ship are liable to be fined. In other ports, especially where the seawater is contaminated by chemical or effluent discharges, fishing may be restricted as a health precaution.

If certain crew members are not permitted shore leave, the OOW should be aware of their identities, and ensure that the gangway watchman is alerted to prevent them leaving the ship. No-one should be permitted to go ashore in ports where there are known dangers ashore or the local population is known to be hostile. Any time limits for shore leave must be clearly displayed near the gangway, and made known to all ship's personnel. The OOW should be familiar with such times so that he can advise any crew member who is in doubt.

Some ports will only permit access to the vessel if the visitor is in possession of a pass issued by the ship. The issuing of these passes is often delegated to the OOW, who should understand under what circumstances they are to be issued, including to whom, for what purpose, and the duration of their validity.

In order to be allowed to take goods out of the port area, a pass may have to be issued to the person removing the goods. These may be items of ship's equipment being sent for repair, excess stores being returned, or personal effects of a crew member. The issuing of these passes is often delegated to the OOW, who should be sure that the person requesting the pass has the authority to remove the goods, and that this removal does not contravene local Customs regulations.

Lowering a lifeboat into the water during a drill can contravene local regulations in some ports, and written permission should always be obtained if the ship is in any doubt. One ship's boat was chased by a gunboat, its crew arrested, an alternate crew had to be sent to recover the boat, and the ship was fined for not having written permission for this activity.

In some ports, photography is prohibited both within the port area and on board one's own ship—see chapter 18.9.

Particular attention to flag etiquette is advisable in some ports, where local rules on the timing of raising and lowering flags, and care in handling the national courtesy ensign, may be strictly applied with large fines levied on offenders.

Certain activities on board ship may be subject to obtaining written permission, or completely banned. These activities include immobilisation of the main engine, chipping and scaling, painting the ship's side, making radio or satellite transmissions, etc. The Master will have advised the relevant heads of departments of such rules, but the OOW should be aware of their existence.

See also chapter 16.9.

The OOW should check the moorings regularly to ensure that the vessel is properly secured to the berth. The ship illustrated could be damaged if the wind increases, or another ship passes close by. See chapter 3.1 and 3.12. Photograph: courtesy of Brookes, Bell & Co.

Chapter 3
MOORING OPERATIONS
PURPOSE
On completion of this chapter you will be able to supervise safe mooring and anchor-handling operations.

3.1 Importance of moorings

The purpose of moorings is:

- to assist the ship in heaving on to the berth and in leaving it,
- to prevent the ship from drifting away, and to
- hold it accurately in place in relation to any fixed cargo-handling systems. The latter is particularly important on tankers and Ro-Ros.

Moorings have to maintain the ship's position against forces of wind, current, swell, and suction from passing ships. They require adjusting as the ship's freeboard changes during cargo and ballast operations, and due to changes in the level of the tide. In this respect, it is useful to display the times of high and low water adjacent to the gangway.

It should be remembered that the securing of a ship at a berth is not something which just happens—it requires knowledge of the ship's equipment, application of good principles and careful planning—and this does not finish once the vessel is securely moored.[92]

3.2 Choice of moorings

As a rule, when two or more lines lead in the same direction, they should be the same length and the same material. This is because the load on the line is proportional to its length and elasticity. It is best if all lines share the total load equally—see section 3.12.

If the vessel is provided with a mix of wire and fibre ropes, it is best to use the wires for breastlines and springs, and the fibre ropes for head or sternlines, and for the first line ashore during manoeuvring.

Wires are best for preventing the movement of the ship, so are employed when this must be limited in relation to fixed cargo-handling equipment, for example on tankers. Wires usually have fibre rope tails to provide a minimal elasticity, and to assist with handling.

3.3 Principles of mooring layout[92]

1. Breastlines provide the bulk of athwartships restraint.
2. Backsprings provide the largest proportion of fore-and-aft restraint.
3. Very short lengths of line should be avoided, because they take a large proportion of the total load if the ship moves, and their effectiveness is likely to be reduced by 'dip' (see below).
4. Whenever a line is unable to act exactly in the same direction as the force it is trying to withstand, its holding power is reduced. For example, a line which leads 45° below the horizontal ('dipped') loses around a third of its effectiveness.

3.4 Pattern of moorings

On berthing, the Master will decide the number and layout of mooring lines for that particular berth. Often there will be a normal arrangement for the ship, but he may choose to vary this if:
1. The berth is exposed to bad weather or swell.
2. There is an unusually strong tide or current.
3. The bollards ashore are not placed conveniently.
4. Mooring buoys or dolphins have to be used for some or all of the lines.
5. The berth is much shorter than the ship.
6. The ship has regularly to shift along the quay, for example, under a fixed loading spout.
7. Local regulations dictate, or pilot advises some change.

3.5 Mooring operations

The junior officer may be required to supervise the mooring operations forward or aft; he must ensure that he fully understands:
1. The meaning of all mooring terms: head/stern lines, breasts, springs, bights, tails, messengers, surge, make fast.
2. The length, size and type of all mooring lines, and their safe working load and breaking strain.
3. The correct method of applying a rope or chain stopper, (see section 3.9).
4. The operation of all mooring equipment, including the windlass and winches, and all their controls.
5. The limitations of any self-tensioning devices.
6. The brake holding power, and winch render loads.
7. Routine and emergency communications from the mooring position to the bridge.

If he is unfamiliar with any of the above, then the new-joining officer should seek explanations from an experienced seaman or officer, and/or consult a book on seamanship[78,79] or the machinery manufacturers' handbooks.

When the junior officer is given the duty of standing-by forward or aft during a berthing operation, it is his responsibility to supervise the safe handling of the lines to ensure the ship is properly moored, without being damaged, and that the crew are not exposed to any hazards which may result in personal injury.

3.6 Safe working environment[24]

1. The decks in the working area around the mooring station should be clear of obstructions, free of oil and grease and preferably treated with non-slip paint, or fitted with treads.

2. Steam pipes should be lagged to avoid accidental contact.
3. Fairleads and rollers should be well lubricated and rotate freely.
4. Winches should operate smoothly, including the brakes, with all controls and stops tested regularly.
5. Drum ends should be smooth, clean and free of rust, paint and oil.
6. The entire area must be well illuminated at night. However, the OOW should obtain permission from the bridge before switching on any lights whilst the ship is manoeuvring, as these may interfere with visibility from the bridge.

The junior officer must report any deficiency he observes in the above requirements to the Chief Officer.

3.7 Safe fibre ropes

1. Ropes should be covered when they are not being handled, and stowed away when not in use at sea, to prevent contamination by oils and chemicals, and degradation by sunlight.
2. Ropes must be kept away from heat, oil, paint and chemicals.
3. Ropes should be stowed on gratings for ventilation and drainage.
4. Ropes must be examined regularly for wear, stranding, melting and powdering, and replaced if serious defects are found. If the junior officer is unaware of how to recognise such defects, he should ask an experienced seaman or officer for guidance.

3.8 Safe wires

1. Wires should be lubricated regularly with an approved lubricant.
2. Everyone who handles wires should wear leather - palmed gloves to protect their hands from snags.
3. Wires must be examined regularly for wear, stranding, dry core, kinks, and excessively flattened areas. They must be replaced if the number of broken strands (snags) exceed 10% of the strands in any length equal to eight diameters, or if any other serious defects are found.

3.9 Safe line-handling

1. Flake out all mooring lines on the deck, clear, and ready to send. This will ensure that any fibre lines which have become buried on reels can be freed in advance, when there is less likelihood of accidents. Do not use a wire direct from a reel designed only for stowing.
2. Have all necessary heaving lines, messengers, tails and stoppers available at the mooring station, and rat guards ready for use.
3. Have sufficient crew available taking into account the number of lines being handled and the mooring equipment available.
4. All crew should wear safety helmets and safety shoes, and have no loose clothing which could become entangled in the winches or trapped by the lines. Gloves should be tight fitting, to reduce the risk of becoming trapped by lines, and should have a leather palm to protect the hand against abrasion and prevent wounds caused by snags of wires; they should provide adequate insulation in cold weather.
5. When one seaman is handling a line on a drum end, he should not stand too close to the drum to avoid being drawn in. There should be an additional seamen whose duty is to clear the loose line when heaving, and supply the loose line when slacking.
6. The person operating the winch controls should have a clear view of the entire area including any seaman handling lines with that winch.
7. Never leave winch controls unattended, particularly if running. They must NEVER be lashed 'ON' or weighted to prevent the operation of their designed safeguard to spring back to 'OFF' when released.
8. Do not allow anyone to stand on machinery to get a better view.
9. Avoid excessive surging, which may cause synthetic lines to melt, and fuse or stick to the drum, then jump back with a serious risk of injury to personnel. Also, the rope will be permanently weakened. Try to slack the line by reversing the winch whenever possible.
10. Do not use too many turns, three or four turns are recommended for fibre ropes.
11. Do not bend wires sharply, particularly around a lead, because this damages the wire and weakens its strength.
12. Do not cross wires on the drum end, as this causes them to flatten, and weaken their strength.
13. Never allow anyone to stand in a bight of a line.
14. Do not stop a line from running by grabbing or standing on it; this can result in severe injuries and loss of limbs. If a line begins to run uncontrolled, ensure that all personnel stand clear.
It is better to lose a line than lose a seaman.
It is recommended that the tail end is securely fixed onboard to prevent complete loss of the line in such circumstances.
15. Stand well clear of all lines under tension.
This means everybody, not just those handling that line.
Synthetic fibre ropes may break without warning, and the resultant whiplash may cause severe injuries or even death.
16. Synthetic fibre mooring ropes should be stoppered using two tails of fibre rope, half-hitched under the mooring rope, with the two free ends criss-crossed over and under, as shown in the diagram below:
(This is sometimes known as a Chinese stopper.)

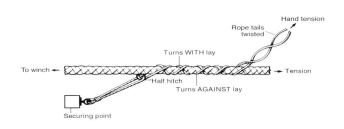

A traditional stopper using a single line may be used <u>only</u> on a mooring line made of natural materials, as shown below, but such mooring lines are no longer common on board ship.

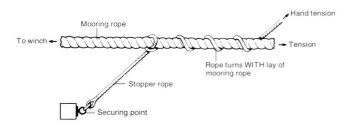

17. Mooring wires should be stoppered using a chain stopper with a well-spaced cow hitch (it is recommended that the two hitches are at least 25cm. apart) and with the remainder of the chain and its rope tail turned up several times against the lay, as shown in the diagram below. The cow hitch is used because it is easily pulled loose when no longer required, a clove hitch is likely to jam. The further turns of chain are made against the lay so as not to open up, distort and weaken the wire.

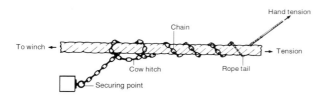

As an alternative to the chain stopper, some ships are provided with a specially designed patent device, known as a Carpenter's stopper:

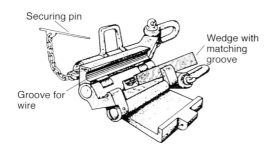

18. **Do not use a stopper on the only rope which is tight.**
    The stopper cannot hold the same weight as a mooring line.
    Always have a second line tight before making fast the first.

19. When making a synthetic fibre rope fast to bitts, DO NOT use a figure of eight alone, but FIRST use two round turns (NO MORE) around the leading post of the bitts (for large size bitts) or around both posts (for bitts with smaller circumferences).
    This system allows better control of the line, so it is safer.[92]

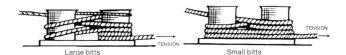

3.10 Safe mooring

1. All operations must be carried out ONLY under the direct orders of the supervising officer, unless the Master has clearly authorised a senior petty officer to supervise an operation.

2. The supervising officer must ensure that communications with the bridge are CONTINUOUSLY maintained. If using radios, all calls should start with the ship's name to avoid confusion with other ships who may be working the same channel/frequency, and then the caller should immediately identify himself and who he is calling to avoid confusion on one's own ship.
   A spare fully-charged battery should be carried whenever portable radios are used.
   A back up system must be readily available at all times.

3. Check with the bridge before sending the first lines, and before making any lines fast.

4. Keep the bridge informed of distances off the quay, any obstructions and other moored ships, lighters or other floating objects.

5. Advise the bridge if there is any possibility that a slack line may become entangled in the propeller or thrusters.

6. Warn the bridge if any lines become excessively taut.

7. Make fast and cast off tugs only on orders from the bridge.

8. When heaving lines are being thrown, ensure that all personnel ashore and on board are alerted, and stand well clear.

9. The supervising officer must make sure he can always see both the winch operators and the

particular line when giving orders for adjusting the tension in a line.

10. Secure the lines as per the Master's orders.
    i.e.   Which lines to leave on the drums,
    Which lines to make fast on bitts,
    Which lines to leave in auto/self-tension, if any, and what level to set the controls.
11. Ensure rat guards are properly fitted to all lines.
12. The supervising officer must remain at the mooring station, with his full crew, until he is dismissed by the Master.

3.11 Self-tensioning winches[92]

The heaving power of a winch is always lower than its render force. This means that if a winch is left in self-tension, and the external forces increase, the line will pay out, and it may not be possible to heave it in again until such external forces reduce. Also, the render force of the winch is much less than the holding power of the brake—see section 3.14.

Self-tensioning winches at opposite ends of the ship can work against each other, so that the ship can sometimes 'walk' along the berth, when an external force is applied at one end.

Hence it is recommended that mooring lines are NOT left in self-tension once the ship is secure alongside. With short breast lines in fair weather, these controls may be useful during rapid load/discharge operations. However, those winches which are directly counteracting any external forces must be left on the brake.

Self-tensioning winches are useful during berthing operations with reduced manning, as once the line is ashore and the controls set, they will reel in any slack, maintain the tension in the line, and prevent the line being damaged through excessive strain.

3.12 Keeping moorings taut

The OOW must ensure that the mooring lines are kept sufficiently taut at all times to keep the ship firmly alongside. At rapid loading or discharging berths, the Chief Officer may assign additional crew to assist the OOW, as the operation of adjusting the lines may have to be done frequently. The OOW must never attempt to adjust a mooring line by himself, unless it is permanently wound on its own drum.

If the lines are not in equal tension, they may part in succession if the ship is subject to unusually high forces, such as very strong winds, large swells or water surges from other ships passing too close and/or too fast. Apart from the damage to the ship if it breaks free, there can be enormous costs in repairing damaged quays and jetties, with claims of up to $10 million reported.[28]

Brake linings can lose their grip when oil and rust are present, and are susceptible to loss of holding power during periods of rain or high humidity, when it is reported that holding power can be halved.[92]

The OOW should remember to adjust any fire wires as the ship's freeboard changes, to ensure that their ends remain clear of the water.

It is essential for the OOW to check the moorings when other ships are arriving at or leaving from the berth immediately ahead or astern of their ship. It is not unknown for the linesmen to cast off one ship's moorings whilst unberthing another ship, or for them to trap one ship's moorings with the lines of a berthing ship, creating problems when the first ship comes to sail. It is good practice for the OOW to be in attendance forward or aft whenever the adjacent ship is arriving or sailing to watch out for contact damage, or other incidents, in addition to monitoring the moorings.

3.13 Chafing

The OOW must check the moorings at least hourly during his watch, not only to ensure they remain taut, but also to look out for chafing, where the rope rubs against an obstruction, and may part. This may occur when the ship is surging back and forth along the quay due to a large swell, or when there is excessive movement of a mooring buoy. Synthetic fibre ropes posses very low resistance to chafing when under load; the friction generates heat which causes them to melt and fuse, and the rope is then permanently weakened, and may part quite quickly.

Ropes may chafe by rubbing against each other, or against the ropes of another ship. The officers on stand-by fore and aft during mooring operations must be alert for this when sending ropes to different bollard ashore through different leads on board. If they notice any chafing, they should have that line removed and sent from a different lead. Short leads with substantial dips are prone to chafing on the ship's structure.

Sometimes a change in freeboard, or some external factors such as a change in the sea state, may cause lines to start chafing. If he notices any chafing, the OOW must clear the obstruction, change the lead of the mooring rope, or wrap the rope in canvas or some other material to bear the rubbing and wearing away action. The outside of the canvas may be greased to reduce the friction, but this grease must not be allowed to remain in contact with fibre ropes as it will cause them to deteriorate. The OOW must always advise the Chief Officer of his observations and actions.

3.14 Emergencies[92]

Occasionally unexpected changes of load may cause the brakes of the mooring line drums to slip, and the vessel is at risk of moving off the berth.

DO NOT RELEASE THE BRAKES AND ATTEMPT TO HEAVE THE SHIP BACK ALONGSIDE USING ONLY THE POWER OF THE WINCH.

The recommended action is:
1. If the winches are in self-tension—apply the brakes IN ADDITION.
2. If the brakes are in use—tighten them, put the winch in gear and heave on as many lines as possible.
3. Inform the senior officers, and seek extra crew assistance.
4. Summon tug assistance if necessary.
5. Consider reducing the freeboard by ballasting.

The OOW should remember that brake holding power is always greater than winch heaving power, but that the two together increase the load.

For example: Winch render force = 35 tonnes.
Brake holding power = 65 tonnes.
Total holding power = 100 tonnes.

But he should be careful this does not exceed the breaking strain of the rope, or the safe working load of the leads and rollers. However, in an emergency it will usually be preferable to endeavour to hold the ship in position and risk breaking the lines.

3.15 Anchor handling

The officer on station on the focsle must understand how to operate the windlass and handle the anchor. The windlass is often an integral part of the forward mooring winches; the anchor cable is held on a brake, and is driven by the gypsy which can be engaged in and out of gear from the main machinery. All officers should know how many shackles of cable are attached to each anchor on their ship.

REMINDER: 1 shackle of cable = 15 fathoms = 90 feet = 27 metres.

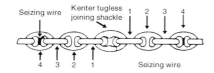

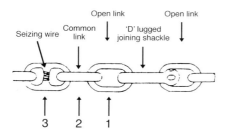

3.15.1 Letting go the anchor

1. All personnel should be appropriately dressed, wearing safety shoes, helmet and goggles, and at night they must have lamps or torches of sufficient power to see the waterline clearly from the fo'c'sle.
2. Switch on the power, check there is sufficient hydraulic oil in any header tank, and test the controls.
3. Turn the windlass to line up the gears, and put the gypsy in gear.
4. Slightly heave on the windlass to take up the slack in the gearing, then take off the brake.
5. Check there is nothing in the water close to the bows; it is not unknown for an anchor to be lowered into a tug or mooring boat!
6. Seek permission from the bridge to lower the anchor; the Master may want to delay this operation until he has reduced speed further or completed a manoeuvre.
7. Lower the anchor to the water's edge, or to the level ordered by the Master—in deep water he

may ask for the anchor to be lowered until it is just clear of the seabed, to avoid an excessive drop.
8. Put the brake on, and take the anchor out of gear.
9. Report to the bridge that all is ready for letting go.
10. Ensure all personnel wear appropriate eye protection, because when the anchor is let go, rust and mud may fly through the air.
11. The officer on the fo'c'sle must know how many shackles of cable will be used. The Master will decide this taking into account:
   (a) Depth of water, and the ship's draft.
   (b) Available sea room for swinging.
   (c) Type of holding ground on the seabed.
   (d) Expected weather, and amount of hull exposed to the wind.
   (e) Strength of current and/or tide.
   (f) Anticipated duration of anchorage.
   A rule of thumb for good weather and good holding ground is for the cable to be paid out to a minimum of four times the depth of water.
12. The Master will manoeuvre the ship to the desired position, and usually he will take all way off the ship, so that it is stopped over the ground. The ship should be head to wind or tide if possible. The ship is then given sternway either by the wind, tide or using the engines.
13. When the order to let go is received, take off the brake slowly, and try to control the chain so that it runs out evenly, by applying the brake periodically, unless the Master has ordered that the cable should be allowed to run free.

   The purpose of anchoring is to secure the ship with the weight of anchor chain, the anchor holding the end of the chain in place. Hence the chain should be laid out along the seabed, and not dropped in the one place where it will all pile up, provide little holding power, and may foul itself which makes recovery difficult.

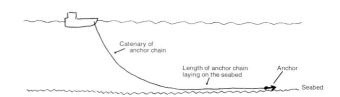

14. COMMUNICATION IS VITAL.
   The officer on the fo'c'sle must ensure that the bridge is aware of precisely what is happening at all times, as the Master is unlikely to be able to see the cable from the bridge.
15. As each shackle passes the windlass, report this to the bridge.
   It is good practice to report the direction in which the cable is leading at the same time.

16. If there is an excessive strain on the cable, or if any difficulty is experienced in stopping the cable from running, the bridge must be informed immediately. The Master may have to use the engines to reduce this strain.

17. If the cable stops running, even with the brake off, report this to the bridge. If there is no tide or wind, the Master may have to use the engines to move the ship to help the cable to run.

18. When the length of cable requested by the Master has been released, usually so many shackles on deck, or in the water, apply the brake. Watch for the cable being stretched tight as the weight of the ship comes on it, then slackens off as the ship begins to ride to the weight of the catenary formed by the anchor chain. This condition is known as 'brought up' and should be reported to the bridge.

19. Apply the anchor stopper, ensuring it lies correctly against the cable. This may be a simple bar which lies over a horizontal link, or can be a jaws arrangement which is wound shut to grip both sides of a vertical link.

20. Make sure the anchor ball is hoisted, and/or the light displayed. Switch off the power to the machinery.

3.15.2 Heaving up an anchor

1. Put the windlass in gear, remove the stopper and release the brake. On some ships, it may be necessary to double-up the windlass by engaging the power from both port and starboard units. The officer should make sure he knows how to perform this operation.

2. Ensure that there is a supply of water to the cable washers, the officer should learn the location of all valves on the system. If this equipment has an unsatisfactory record for its cleaning efficiency, extra hoses may need to be rigged, particularly if the seabed is known to be muddy.

3. When the Master orders, commence heaving away.

4. COMMUNICATION IS VITAL.
   The officer on the fo'c'sle must report to the bridge as each shackle passes the windlass, also stating the direction in which the cable is leading. Always report if there is an excessive strain on the cable, or if any difficulty is experienced in heaving the anchor cable.

5. If the cable fouls against the ship—for example, if it leads across the bulbous bow, or astern under the ship with a long lead—the bridge should be informed so that the Master can use the engines to manoeuvre the ship clear, and avoid any damage.

6. Watch for the anchor lifting clear of the seabed. The signs are the cable lying vertical (up and down) after previously leading out away from the vertical, and shaking as each link crosses the gypsy.
   Immediately inform the bridge when the anchor is aweigh—i.e., clear of the seabed—and lower the anchor ball. Remember that the ship is under way when she is not securely held by the anchor; this occurs before the anchor is sighted.

7. When the anchor is sighted clear of the water, check there are no obstructions such as wires, nets, cables or refuse attached to it, and report *anchor sighted and clear* to the bridge. If there are any attachments, the Master will decide upon the action required.

8. If the anchor is caked in mud, it may be useful to lower it back slightly into the water, until this has washed clear. Such action MUST always be first approved by the bridge.

9. To house the anchor, slowly heave it until the flukes rest against their housing on the hull. Check that the flukes have tripped the correct way, so that the anchor is lying flat against the hull in its usual housed position. Apply the brake and take the gypsy out of gear.

10. If proceeding to sea, secure the anchor with extra lashings, apply the stopper, and cover the spurling and hawse pipes. This should <u>only</u> be done when the Master has clearly instructed the officer to secure the anchors once they are no longer required, usually only after the ship has cleared the port.

3.15.3 Other anchoring techniques

1. Dredging an anchor

In order to assist with some manoeuvres, to keep a better control of the ship's bow, the anchor is just dropped on to the seabed with a short length of cable. As the ship moves ahead or astern, the anchor dredges along the seabed, limiting the athwartships (sideways) movement of the bow.

2. Use of anchor alongside

When there are insufficient tugs available, the bow may be held off the berth with an anchor. Once the lines have been run to the berth, the cable is slowly slacked off as the lines are heaved in, so as to control the speed of the bow as the ship approaches the berth. The officer on stations forward has to ensure that the cable is not too tight to hold the ship off the berth, nor too slack so that the bow collides heavily with the berth as the lines are heaved tight. Sometimes the anchor is dropped off the berth purely as an aid to leaving the berth in ports with few tugs, or strong onshore winds.

3. Use of two anchors

Two anchors are used to restrict the area through which the ship swings whilst riding at anchor. One anchor is let go, then the cable paid out to twice the desired final length. The second anchor is then let go, and as its cable is paid out, the cable on the first anchor is heaved in at the same time, until they are both the same length.

When the first anchor is let go and the engines are used to reach the next position, the manoeuvre is called a *running moor*. If the ship moves between these positions under the influence of tide or wind, it is called a *standing moor*. Frequent clear communications are vital during these manoeuvres.

4. Breaking the cable

Occasionally, the anchor cable is used to shackle on to a mooring buoy. In this case the cable must be broken at the first shackle. Some ships which perform this operation frequently have a short length of cable attached to the anchor, with an extra shackle in an easily accessible position between the hawse pipe and the windlass. This saves having to flake out the cable on deck in order to reach the first joining shackle.

The basic procedure is:-

1. Secure the anchor in the hawse pipe.
2. Flake the cable on deck to reach the first joining shackle.
3. Remove the lead plug, and tap out the securing pin using the correct size punch and a maul.
4. Carefully tap apart the two halves of the shackle, using two mauls. On board ships which do not perform this operation regularly, the shackle may need to be soaked in release/penetrating oil for a long period, or heat treatment applied, in order to free the parts. In an emergency, the ship's burning gear can be used to cut through the cable.

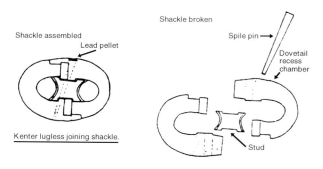

If the vessel has a specially strengthened and suitably positioned fairlead which can take the cable, then the anchor is left housed, and the broken cable is lead out through this lead. If such a lead is not available, then the anchor must be *hung off* clear of the hawse pipe, using a suitable wire. The technique for *hanging off* an anchor is described in all good seamanship books, such as *The Theory and Practice of Seamanship*[78] and the *Admiralty Manual of Seamanship*[79] This entails attaching two suitable wires to the top of the anchor. By heaving on one wire leading down the hawse pipe and back through a lead aft at the break of the fo'c'sle, and slacking on the other wire turned up on a set of bitts, the anchor is lowered gently out of the hawse pipe and brought to a position alongside the hull half way along the foscle, *hanging* between the two wires.

When approaching the buoy, the cable is lowered to the water's edge, or as advised by the pilot or mooring boat. It may be necessary to heave the first few links out of the lead, or hawse pipe, using a

messenger rope, as the cable may not lower under its own weight until several links are hanging free vertically. It is useful to have a short tail of fibre rope attached to the end of the cable to assist the mooring crew.

To reconnect the cable after departing from the mooring buoys:

1. Heave up the end of the cable on to the deck.
2. If it has been hung off, return the anchor to the hawse pipe by the reverse of the process described above.
3. Line up the two halves of the cable to be joined.
4. Link the split shackle through the links of the two free ends.
5. Tap the two halves of the shackle together, using two mauls, being very careful not to distort the mating surfaces.
6. Refit the taper pin.
7. Replug the end of the pin with fresh lead.
8. Heave up the cable and secure the anchor.

5. Anchor buoys

If an anchor buoy is to be used, one end of a length of wire greater than the depth of water is attached to the anchor shackle. The wire is led down the hawsepipe over the fo'c'sle rails and the other end is attached to the buoy on deck. When the anchor is let go, the buoy is thrown overside. It is used to mark the position of the anchor, and aid recovery if the chain parts.

3.15.4 Cargo operations at anchor

Although the primary duty of the OOW will be the supervision of cargo operations, (see chapters 7 to 9), if the ship is also at anchor, he must combine this duty with the duty of keeping an anchor watch.

1. The OOW should visit the bridge regularly to check on the ship's position. He should always be present on the bridge as the ship swings at each change of tide.
2. If available, the OOW should carry a portable VHF and monitor the appropriate port channels.
3. The OOW should seek out some transit bearings ashore. These do not have to be charted objects, but may be any features which he can readily identify from the main deck, so that he can continually monitor the transits and verify the ship's position at all times.
4. The Master or Chief Officer will be able to advise the OOW as to how he should allot his time between the deck watch and the bridge watch. Whenever cargo is not being worked, the OOW should be stationed on the bridge, except for security checks around the decks, or as ordered by the Master.
5. Guidance on keeping anchor watches is contained in the STCW convention,[37] section 51 of the Annex on *Recommendations on operational guidance for officers in charge of a navigational watch.*

Chapter 4
SAFETY IN PORT
PURPOSE

On completion of this chapter you will be able to list your responsibilities for the various aspects of safety on board ship, and describe the practices necessary to ensure that the ship is a safe place of work in port. You will know how to maintain safe access and a safe atmosphere, supervise the safety of the cargo-handling equipment, and appreciate the precautions necessary for fire safety.

4.1 Importance of shipboard safety

One of the main responsibilities of the OOW is to maintain a safe working environment in **ALL** areas of the ship at **ALL** times. This involves providing a safe place of work, a safe system of work and safe machinery and equipment as necessary. These should be provided for the safety of **ALL** personnel, including ship's staff, shore workers and visitors.

4.1.1 Safety principles

1. Unsafe acts are a failure by the individual to take care, or the result of a lack of training.
2. Unsafe conditions may be the result of bad housekeeping, but are frequently the result of unsafe acts or omissions.
3. Inadequate supervision is an unsafe omission.
   Periodic monitoring is intended to keep an operation within safe parameters, and permit correction long before an accident can occur. The better this check system is, the more successful and safe the operation.[8]
4. Accidents are caused by unexpected events, but often these could have been predicted.
5. A safe job means
   employing the *right* number of people,
   possessing the *right* skills,
   wearing the *right* protection,
   using the *right* tools,
   operated by the *right* methods,
   observing the *right* procedures,
   working in the *right* place,
   with the *right* access,
   having the *right* environment.
6. Safety does not just happen, it is the reward of thought and care.
   It is the commitment, competence, attitudes and motivation of all individuals at all levels that determine the end result.[39]
7. **Safety = prevention = forethought = good seamanship**

Seamanship has been defined as the application of common sense in the marine environment, though many authorities would add experience to this definition.

4.1.2 PLAN for safety[90]

PAUSE: Take time to review the safety aspects of the job.
Consider what could go wrong.

LOOK: Watch critically the work methods employed.
Check that equipment and machinery are being operated correctly and that safety clothing and protective equipment are being used.

ACT: Correct what is going wrong before it causes an accident.

NOTIFY: Tell people if you see them acting unsafely.
Report all equipment faults to the appropriate officer.

4.1.3 A safe ship

Gradual wear and tear may produce defects in the ship's structure or equipment over a long period. Accidents may produce defects in a very short time scale. The OOW should be on the lookout for all such defects during his regular patrols of the vessel. He should ensure that minor deficiencies are put right as soon as he notices them, and report the more serious deficiencies to the Chief Officer, or other appropriate officer, for action. Dangerous equipment must be withdrawn from service immediately. Dangerous parts of the ship's structure must be clearly marked, and access restricted to a safe distance if practicable.

4.1.4 Health and safety[91]

These two topics are inseparable. The OOW must not only look after his own health and safety, but also of all those working on board.

High standards of personal cleanliness and hygiene should be maintained, the OOW should lead by example. Those handling oil-based products should use barrier creams and wash all parts of their skin thoroughly with soap or approved cleansers after completing work. Paint remover, kerosene, soda or other chemicals must NEVER be used as skin cleansers. Cargo spills should be washed off skin and clothing.

Cuts and abrasions should be cleaned at once, and first aid treatment given to protect against infection. Water and salt intake should be increased if the temperature and humidity in port are high.

Any infestation of rats, rodents and insects should be reported to the Master, and remedial action instigated.

All ship's personnel should keep up to date with all relevant vaccinations. They should avoid going ashore into areas where there are known dangers, or where the population is known to be hostile. It is wise to avoid eating from roadside stalls, and other potentially unhygienic establishments, and avoid drinking unbottled water unless the port is known to be free of infections. All fruit and vegetables purchased ashore should be washed in treated water.

Good health depends on an even and thoughtful balance of work, rest and active play, on sensible and regular meals, on adequate sleep, and on an avoidance of excesses of rich food, alcohol, tobacco, and stress.

4.2 Safe access

IT IS OF PARAMOUNT IMPORTANCE THAT A SAFE MEANS OF ACCESS BETWEEN THE SHIP AND THE SHORE IS MAINTAINED AT ALL TIMES.

This is a legal requirement in all ports of the world.

4.2.1 Ship's gangway

1. The gangway must be clean and undamaged with no missing stanchions.
2. Safety rails, or ropes, must be taut at all times.
3. The bottom platform must be level, and fitted with stanchions, and the safety ropes continued through these.
4. The safety net must extend from one metre on board the ship from the top of the gangway to the extremity of the bottom platform on the quay, and encircle the entire gangway from the top of the outboard rail/rope to the ship's side. Do NOT make any part of the net fast to the quay.
5. There must be a lifebuoy with a heaving line, floating quoit, and self-igniting light positioned at the top of the gangway.
6. The gangway must be fully illuminated at night.
7. A ship's watchman should be in attendance at all times where possible—even if shore security are employed.
8. The MAXIMUM number of persons permitted on the gangway at one time must never be exceeded. The OOW needs to pay extra attention to this requirement at the change of shift of stevedores. This number should be prominently displayed on the gangway, as an indication of its Safe working load.
9. Special attention should be paid when large shore cargo-handling equipment, such as gantries, are moving along the quay close to the gangway, and may damage it if there is a collision.
10. Continuous supervision is necessary if the gangway cannot be landed on the quay, and has to be left suspended on its wires.
11. It is useful to display a notice at the foot of the gangway warning that it is liable to sudden movement. Other notices often displayed at the gangway include 'No Unauthorised Visitors', 'No Smoking', the times of high and low water, and the times of sailing and expiry of shore leave.
12. It is recommended that the means of access should be sited clear of the cargo working area, and that no suspended load passes over it.[91]

4.2.2 Shore gangway

In some ports, it may not be possible to use the ship's gangway because of its position or length. If a shore gangway is provided, the OOW must ensure that the safety points in 4.2.1 are fully complied with.

This includes cases when the means of access is part of the shore cargo-handling equipment. The stevedore must NOT be allowed to lower this ladder only upon demand, just because it makes his job easier when he continually moves the loader along the quay. The OOW must stress to him that a safe means of access must be CONTINUOUSLY available, although it is appreciated that this may be extremely difficult to obtain in certain ports of the world, for example Dalrymple Bay and other bulk terminals in Australia.

4.2.3 Safe access around the ship

The requirement to provide a safe means of access is not limited to the gangway. All decks, walkways, ladders, and other accesses around the decks and within the cargo compartments must be in a safe condition, which means:
- Clearly marked.
- Unobstructed (cargo, dunnage, leads from lashings, etc.).
- Undamaged.
- Clean (free from oil and grease).
- Fitted with safety rails/ropes where appropriate.
- Illuminated at night.
- Any hazards must be highlighted.

The OOW must be constantly on the lookout for unsafe accesses as he patrols the decks. Ice, dust on top of dew, and any spills of oil, grease and cargo can be very slippery and could lead to trips and slips. They must be removed as soon as they are noticed. Hardened ice may be melted with rock-salt, or its surface made safe with a coating of sand or grit. If the hazard cannot be removed, access to the area should be prevented by roping off and erecting appropriate warning signs.

The doors or lids of accesses to the holds must be either closed or secured open with toggle pins, and an adequate handrail must be located adjacent to assist people between the hold ladder and the deck.

4.2.4 Penalties for unsafe access

Some 45% of all accidents resulting in personal injuries are the result of slips or falls.[21] Apart from the fines associated with breaking statutory rules, the ship's operator may have to pay huge compensation if anyone is injured as a result of an unsafe means of access, even if this is provided by the shore. Some parts of the world are especially prone to locals making substantial claims for compensation for back injuries as a result of having tripped or slipped on deck. This *says as much about the USA legal system as (it does) about the USA backbone.*[21] The costs of employing lawyers to handle a personal injury claim can equal the amount of compensation paid to the injured party.[28] (See also the comments at the end of section 4.11.)

4.2.5 Pre-empting spurious claims

Frequently the only witnesses to alleged trips and slips are the colleagues of the stevedore involved, who will probably corroborate his story. The main problem in defending such claims is in obtaining sufficient evidence to disprove or discredit this story.

It has been suggested that a realistic and cost-effective method of claim limitation is to photograph all accesses just prior to commencing cargo operations, and repeat this process daily. If any hazards are found, they should be photographed, cleared or made safe, and the area rephotographed. Similarly any areas cordoned off should be photographed.[30]

Log entries of all inspections, clearing of hazards or cordoning off unsafe areas should be made to prove the vessel was exercising due diligence to maintain safe accesses.

4.3 A safe atmosphere

Before anyone is permitted to enter a space which has been sealed for any length of time, the OOW must ensure that the entire space has been adequately ventilated. This includes the cargo holds and tanks, as well as lockers, stores, ballast and fuel tanks and all void spaces. If forced ventilation is used, there should be at least two complete changes of air. With natural ventilation, this should last for at least 24 hours prior to entry.

A useful method of ventilating ballast tanks is to fill them with clean seawater, then pump them out. Any unsafe atmosphere will be expelled as the tanks fill, and fresh air will be sucked in as the tanks empty.

The OOW should test the atmosphere of the space to ensure there is sufficient oxygen to breathe. The normal oxygen content of air is 21%; if it falls below 18% the atmosphere is unsafe; below 10% causes unconsciousness and death may occur if any personnel are not quickly removed and resuscitated.

He should also test the atmosphere to ensure there are no unsafe levels of hydrocarbon and other toxic gases as appropriate, and that none of the other hazards outlined in section 4.3.2 are present. These tests should be repeated regularly for as long as the spaces remain occupied, taking into account the ventilation provided and any inherent hazards.

4.3.1 Responsibilities of the OOW

The OOW should ensure that:
1. He knows the whereabouts of everyone working on board the ship, as recommended by IMO—see chapter 1.8.3.2.6.
2. Mechanical ventilation is provided to all enclosed spaces in which people are working. The OOW should check on the operation of the ventilation system regularly, as there have been incidents where fans have been inadvertently switched off.
3. A 'Permit to enter an enclosed space' is properly completed on each occasion. For example, the International Chamber of Shipping (ICS) checklist (Marine Safety Card) for entering an enclosed space, or the more comprehensive checklist in appendix X. See also chapter 9.5.3.
4. A permit to work has been issued, and he is aware of the contents of this permit, and its expiry time—see section 4.8 below.
5. An attendant is detailed to remain at the entrance to the space for as long as it is occupied, and a system of communication is established between

this guard and both the OOW and the people inside the space.[91]
6. The hazards associated with particular cargoes are known—see chapter 7.12.
7. If the atmosphere is suspect, and entry is imperative, then those persons entering must wear a harness with a lifeline attached, and breathing apparatus, preferably with two sources of air—a line supplying fresh outside air, and self-contained air bottles.
8. If available onboard, the advice contained in the *Code of Safe Working Practices for Merchant Seamen*[91] should be followed at all times. (See also section 4.13 and chapter 9.)

4.3.2 Examples of unsafe atmospheres

The atmosphere of a compartment may be unsafe in any of the following circumstances:
1. When affected by biological causes—for example, rotting foodstuffs or fermenting grain.
2. When substances which absorb oxygen are present—for example, if the hold contains rusting iron or steel, the rusting process may reduce the amount of oxygen in the atmosphere, and build up the carbon dioxide. There have been several deaths recorded of people entering holds containing pig iron in bulk and rough-hewn timber.

 Any uncoated steelwork of the ship's structure will rust, and absorb oxygen in the process; this can quickly produce an unsafe atmosphere in void spaces, unvented ballast tanks and battened down cargo holds.
3. When substances which emit poisonous gases are present—for example, liquids which readily evaporate giving off toxic gases.
4. When flammable gases are present—for example, if the hold contains coal which may emit methane. In addition to inhibiting breathing, this is explosive. A spark caused by opening the hatch cover has been known to result in an explosion which completely blew off the cover. It is a wise precaution with such cargoes to grease the trackway before operating the hatch opening mechanism.
5. When irritant or choking dust is present.
6. When vapours are present which may displace oxygen—for example, two seamen were reported asphyxiated whilst using a chemical solvent for cleaning an electric motor in a bow-thruster room.[28]
7. When inert gases have replaced the oxygen in the air—for example, leaks from fridge plants or fire-fighting equipment.
8. A toxic atmosphere should be suspected in any space which has recently been painted or subjected to repair work involving burning or welding.

4.4 Dangerous cargoes

Extra precautions are required when handling commodities which are poisonous, or irritate the skin, including those substances which may give off harmful gases. Suitable protective clothing must be worn, and antidote medication should be available.

The OOW must be aware of the action to be taken in the event of any spillage of dangerous cargo—see chapter 7.12.1.

The OOW must ensure that all IMO classified dangerous goods are correctly marked, properly handled and adequately stowed, with suitable segregation from non-compatible commodities. This information is available in the IMO IMDG Code[49]—see chapter 7.12.2, and appendix VI.

4.5 Cargo-handling gear

The OOW is responsible for ensuring that the ship's cargo-handling equipment remains in a safe condition for the stevedores to use.

1. All equipment must be clearly marked with its Safe Working Load (SWL) and an identifying mark, which is used to locate its test certificate. If any parts are changed, the OOW should record the identifying marks of both the old and new parts, and inform the Chief Officer, so that the ship's cargo-handling equipment records can be amended. It is vital that these records <u>always</u> contain details of the current gear in use.
2. All parts should be properly secured—for example: shackles screwed home tight, and moused (the pin fastened with seizing wire); and the ends of all wires fitted with a proper anchorage, which should be checked regularly.
3. All equipment must be in good condition; there must be no signs of excessive wear.
4. All blocks and other moving parts must be free, and should be kept well lubricated.
5. All operating controls should be clearly marked, tested regularly, and switched off when the equipment is not in use.
6. All wires should be free from barbs, broken strands, flattened areas and kinks, and be well lubricated—see also chapter 3.8.
7. All trips, cut-outs, limit switches, over-load devices, slack wire detectors and all other safety and fail-safe features must be functioning, and they should be tested regularly.
8. Any manual vents must be open—for example, those which provide cooling air to the motors.
9. Sufficient power must be available at all times.
10. Brakes should be examined and tested regularly.
11. Lubricating and hydraulic oil levels must be topped up as required, and the oil examined regularly for contamination. Any filters should be cleaned or renewed as necessary. All systems should be checked over regularly for leaks, both of oil leaking out of the system and water leaking in.
12. The access to the control position must be safe, clear and clean.
13. With cranes, the windows should be cleaned regularly.

If the OOW detects any faults in the ship's cargo-handling equipment, the relevant gear should be withdrawn from service, the Chief Officer should be informed immediately, and remedial action instigated. All such facts should be logged.

If the OOW sees any faults in the shore cargo-handling equipment, he should warn the operator, report it to the foreman stevedore, and inform the Chief Officer. He must ensure that dangerous or broken equipment is withdrawn from use immediately. It is good practice to log all such observations, giving full details of the faults and to whom they were reported.

4.5.1 Safe operation of cargo-handling equipment

1. The safe working load of the equipment must not be exceeded.
   The OOW should check not only the weight of items of cargo but also the weight of mobile cargo-handling equipment, such as fork lifts and bulldozers, which is to be lifted by the ship's gear. Often such equipment has a detachable counterweight to avoid overstressing the lifting gear.
2. Controls must never be left unattended, unless switched off.
3. The load must not be left suspended, but should be rested on deck, or some other adequate support, if there is an unexpected delay. This does NOT apply to very heavy lifts, which should be returned to their original position if delays arise.
4. The equipment must be operated by a skilled and experienced person.
5. If the operator cannot see the entire operation (e.g., from the quay to the bottom of the hold) then a signalman must be positioned to cover his blind area. Appropriate communication must be used, with all signals clearly understood by all concerned.
6. The limits of operating angles must not be exceeded.
   For union-purchase rigs, the angle between the wires should not normally exceed 90°. An angle of 120° should never be exceeded as in this condition, the tension in each wire is equal to the load.
7. Slack wires should be avoided, and any slack turns on a barrel must be removed as soon as they are noticed, as there is a danger they may pull out suddenly under load, and maybe cause an accident.
8. Equipment should be operated smoothly, without any jerking; in particular the load should be taken up gradually, as snatching produces excessive strains and stresses in the equipment.
9. The load must not be allowed to pass over personnel. Extraneous passers-by should not be allowed to linger near the path of the load, and those directly concerned with the operation should stand in a vantage point which is well outside this area.
10. Operations such as changing the gearing, or twinning two systems, must only be performed under the direct supervision of the OOW, who should check the manuals or consult the Chief Officer if he is not sure of the procedures or operational requirements.
11. Any limit switches and other automatic control

devices on the cargo-handling gear should be tested regularly, and must not be over-ridden or switched off, except under specific permitted circumstances, when the OOW should directly supervise the operation. Over-ride keys should not be given out to stevedores.

12. The OOW should be capable of calculating the stress in each part of the ship's cranes or derricks and their associated rigging, using the principle of the parallelogram of forces. He should make such calculations whenever the jib or boom has to operate at unusual angles, or with any load which is particularly heavy or close to its safe working load. The OOW must be sure that all parts of the system are operating within their designed limits, if not, parts may fail with possible disastrous results. He should not overlook that the derrick is named after the hangman of the times of (UK) Queen Elizabeth I!

4.5.2 Reminder of crane or derrick stress calculations

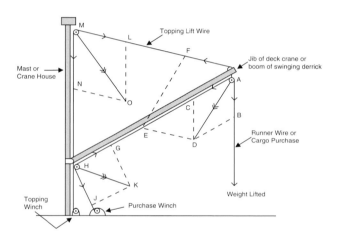

In the diagram, a weight W is lifted by a derrick or crane with a single block at its head, and the cargo hook attached directly to the end of the runner wire. If the lifting rig is a purchase (tackle), the tension in the runner wire AB is reduced by the power gained by the purchase.

REMINDER: The power gained by a purchase is equal to the number of parts of rope at the moving block.

e.g.   Gun tackle = 2,   Luff tackle = 3,
      Double purchase = 4,   Triple purchase = 6.

REMINDER: The tension in a rope increases due to friction when it turns around the sheave of a block. It is usual to allow 6% per sheave.

In the parallelogram ABDC:
  AB = Tension in the runner = W tonnes. to the cargo hook

AC = Tension in the runner = (1.06 x W) tonnes. along the derrick/crane jib
*AD = Stress at the derrick/crane head block.

In the parallelogram ADEF:
  *AF = Tension in the topping lift span.
  *AE = Thrust on the derrick/crane jib.

In the parallelogram GHJK:
  GH = Tension in the runner   = AC. along the derrick/crane jib
  HJ = Tension in the runner   = (1.06 x GH). to the winch
  *HK = Stress at the derrick/crane heel block.

In the parallelogram LMNO:
  LM = Tension in the topping   = AF. lift span
  MN = Tension in the vertical   = (1.06 x LM). topping lift
  *MO = Stress at the masthead topping lift block.

*Indicates can be calculated, or measured using a scale drawing.

4.6 Drink and drugs

Anyone under the influence of alcohol or drugs is a danger to both himself and his workmates. If he suspects someone is under this influence in any way at all, then the OOW must NEVER allow that person to continue working onboard. This applies equally to shore workers and crew members. It is essential that no-one under the influence of drugs or alcohol is allowed to operate any machinery.

Some local laws are very strict on this point. In the USA, ship's personnel are not allowed to consume alcohol whilst on duty, or for four hours beforehand. There are also limits on consumption during off-duty times; the statutory limit can be exceeded by drinking more than one can of beer per hour. There is a maximum fine of $100,000 for operating a vessel under the influence of alcohol; an officer or crew member is considered to be operating a vessel whenever he is on board the vessel [33CFR95.015]. The rationale behind this is that the officer or crew member must always be prepared to respond to an emergency, whether he is on or off-duty, or whether the vessel is under way or not.[28]

Additionally, some ship operators (and charterers) have strict rules, which sometimes involves a complete ban of any form of alcohol on board. Where such rules are in force on his ship, the OOW must be alert for traders from ashore attempting to sell alcohol on board. He should also perform spot checks on crew returning from ashore to ensure they have not purchased any alcohol during shopping trips.

Alcohol is banned in most Moslem countries, and must NEVER be offered to local residents.

The use of drugs is illegal in many parts of the world, and may attract the death penalty in ports such as Singapore.

THE OOW MUST REPORT ALL VIOLATIONS TO THE CHIEF OFFICER OR MASTER, as tact may be required to avoid misunderstandings and disputes, particularly in the case of shore workers. (See also chapter 16.7 on drugs from the security aspect.)

4.7 Fire safety

Fires don't just happen, they are usually caused by people acting carelessly. Fire prevention means recognising a fire hazard and then removing it. The OOW is responsible for ensuring that frequent safety patrols are made of all areas of the ship. He should verify that those people making the patrols understand what to look for, and are instructed to report any fires or fire hazards, as well as any other safety hazards, stressing that they must raise the alarm immediately whenever they detect any signs of a fire. 11% of all high-value claims of the UK P&I Club are attributable to fires.

4.7.1 Theory of combustion

The three elements which are essential for combustion are:

(1) AIR — (2) FUEL — 3) HEAT.

Take away any one of these elements, and the fire is extinguished.

Hence the corresponding three basic methods of fire-fighting are:

(1) REMOVE THE AIR: **Smothering** (CO_2, inert gas, dry powder and foam extinguishers).
(2) REMOVE THE FUEL: **Starving** (remove the combustible material—oil, cargo or stores.)
(3) REMOVE THE HEAT: **Cooling** (water hoses, sprinklers, water extinguishers).

4.7.2 Common causes of fires on board ship

1. Careless disposal of cigarettes and matches.
2. Burning and welding without taking all necessary precautions. (Do not overlook the adjacent compartment).
3. Oily waste, rags or rubbish being ignited, or self-combusting. (Such products should be safely stored in covered METAL containers, and be disposed of at the earliest opportunity).
4. Drips or leaks of oil coming into contact with hot surfaces.
5. Overloaded or faulty electrical circuits.
6. All electrical appliances should be switched off whenever any space is left unattended. Portable space heaters should be prohibited, and the galley range should be switched off at night.
7. Spontaneous combustion of cargo. (Often encouraged by the presence of moisture).
8. Reactions when two chemicals are mixed, producing heat.

4.7.3 No smoking

It is good practice to prohibit smoking on the main deck and in cargo holds at all times on all ships. It is essential when oil, explosives, flammable and all dangerous goods are being handled. It must not be forgotten that some cargo dust falls in to this category. On tankers, smoking is only permitted in designated areas inside the accommodation, see chapter 9.

'No Smoking' signs should be prominently displayed at the gangway and at all approaches to the cargo working area. The OOW should check these are in place and readable. Additional temporary signs should be placed where there is a particularly high risk—e.g., at the bunker connection, at the access to holds containing dangerous goods, next to ventilators exhausting dust (such as during grain loading).

4.7.4 Fire-fighting equipment

The OOW should know the location, present status and condition, and the correct use and operation of:

1. The emergency fire pump.
2. The international shore connection(s).
3. All fire hoses and nozzles - jet and spray.
4. All fire hydrants, and any valves in the lines.
5. All fire extinguishers.

REMINDER:
Red   = Water—a coolant.
Cream   = Foam
Blue   = Dry powder   }
Black   = CO-2   } smotherants
Green   = Halon / BCF. }

6. Fireman's outfits—lamp, axe, helmet, gloves, boots, clothing.
7. Breathing apparatus—smoke helmet, self-contained. (Including spares and the bottle recharging system.)
8. Fire-detecting systems and alarms.
9. Fixed fire-fighting installations.
10. Manual alarms, and the correct signals to use.
11. Emergency muster lists.

4.7.5 Initial response to a fire

The OOW should be guided by the ship's fire response plan, though in general his initial response upon discovering a fire should be:

1. Raise the alarm on board.
2. Tackle minor fires immediately with the correct extinguisher, or smother with a blanket or by other available means.
3. Alert shore fire brigade, port authorities, etc.
4. Restrict ventilation, close all flaps, doors, hatch-covers, etc. Shut down air-conditioning plant.
5. Evacuate unnecessary personnel from the area of the fire.
6. For larger fires, form fire-parties as per the ship's emergency plans. Use hoses with spray nozzles, breathing apparatus, torches, lifelines and portable communications sets as appropriate.
7. Inspect adjacent compartments for signs of fire spreading. Initiate boundary cooling if necessary.
8. Senior officers will decide on subsequent action, particularly the use of fixed equipment like CO-2 flooding, etc., and evacuation of all personnel to the shore.
9. Have the fire wallet available for the shore fire brigade. (There should be one in a waterproof,

clearly marked container near the top of each gangway).

4.7.6 Contents of the fire wallet
1. General arrangement plan—should include location of watertight doors and fire-resistant partitions.
2. Fire-fighting equipment plan.
3. Ventilation plan.
4. Shell expansion plan.
5. Up-to-date cargo plan— with any dangerous goods highlighted.
6. Stability data.
7. An up-to-date crew list.

4.7.7 What else the fire brigade will want to know
1. Location of the fire, both in general and its seat if known, and its severity. What material is burning.
2. How it started, if known.
3. Means of access, to and around the ship, to and around the fire.
4. Present state of accommodation and cargo ventilation.
5. Current fire-fighting measures.
6. Availability and capacity of fire-fighting equipment, including the location of the international shore connection.
7. Location of all oil and ballast.
8. Location of all personnel. (Is everyone accounted for?)
9. Means of communication, onboard and with the shore.
10. Any unusual features of the vessel's design or equipment,
11. Cargo stowage, including details of any hazardous cargo.

4.8 Permit to work
The Nautical Institute recommends the use of permits to work. This is a system of checklists, one of which is produced by the person who orders the job. He sets out the correct methods to be employed to perform the task, and lists all safety precautions. There is a time limit on the validity of the permit, which must not exceed 24 hours. See examples in annexes IX and X.

The person who is supervising the job checks off the list, and signs it when he is satisfied that all is correct. Only then may the work commence.

The supervisor signs the permit again on completion of the task, when he is satisfied that it has been completed—or as much as was possible in the time allowed, and he verifies that:
(a) The locality of the task has been left safe.
(b) All tools and equipment have been stowed away.
(c) The vessel's watertight integrity has been restored.
The permit is returned to the person ordering the job, who should check the above verifications, and file the completed permit.

4.9 Safe use of pesticides
Insects and rodents are objectionable on ships because they are a nuisance, damage equipment, spread disease and infections, contaminate food and may cause damage to cargo that results in commercial loss.

The IMO *Recommendations on the safe use of pesticides in ships* contains sections on prevention of infestation, and its control by the use of contact insecticides, chemical fumigants and baits. Safety precautions are discussed, and the OOW should consult this document whenever pesticides are to be applied by either shore or ship's personnel.[51]

4.10 Safety clothing and equipment
1. The OOW should always ensure that <u>all</u> personnel employed on the ship wear clothing and other relevant protection which is suitable for the job they are performing, and the location in which they are working.
2. Specialised protection is sometimes provided when certain hazardous cargoes are carried, which must be used in the event of a spillage—see chapter 7.12.1.
3. Everyone on deck should wear a hard hat, and safety shoes with steel toecaps, to prevent injury from falling objects.
4. Anyone who has to spend a prolonged period in a dusty area should wear a suitable dust mask.
5. Working clothes should be close fitting to avoid being caught by obstructions or machinery. They should be kept clean, to avoid skin diseases.
6. Clothing should provide adequate protection against strong sunlight, severe cold weather and insect bites, particularly in mosquito areas. There should be sufficient covering to protect the wearer from scrapes, abrasions, spillages and dust. Long-sleeved boiler suits are preferable to shorts and short-sleeved shirts or tee-shirts.
7. Hearing protection should be worn if there are high noise levels around an activity.
8. When appropriate, workers should wear eye, face and hand protection.
9. Anyone working aloft must be provided with a safety harness with a safety line securely attached direct to a suitably strong part of the ship's structure. It is stressed that this applies to all contractors from ashore as well as the ship's crew.
10. Anyone working overside must wear a lifevest and a safety harness attached to a line which is independent of their means of support (stage, etc) and there must be a supervisor watching at all times. Lifebuoys with buoyant lines attached must be readily available.
11. Studded boots or overshoes should be worn by personnel working on timber deck cargoes.
12. High visibility clothing or markings should be worn by all personnel on Ro-Ro ships, or wherever there is a risk of being in collision with cargo-handling vehicles or moving equipment.
13. Gloves should be worn which offer sufficient protection appropriate to the materials being handled—e.g., leather gloves for handling wires, rubber gloves for handling chemicals, specialised heavy-duty gloves when welding, etc.

14. The OOW must report to the Chief Officer anyone who is not using appropriate protection, whether they are shore or ship personnel.

4.11 Accidents involving personal injury

The OOW must immediately respond to any accident in which someone is injured. He should summon sufficient assistance as required, to ensure that all the following tasks are completed:

1. Apply all necessary first aid. The OOW should be aware of the location of all first aid kits.
2. Stop any operations which may make the situation worse.
3. Arrange for the injured party to see a doctor, or for more serious cases, call for an ambulance to take the person to hospital.
4. Inform the Master, or other available senior officer, and the ship's safety officer, if applicable.
5. Take photographs of the scene of the accident, including any broken equipment, and if possible of any injuries to personnel.
6. Remove the hazard, take out of service any defective equipment and renew any broken parts, before resuming cargo operations.
7. Preserve any broken parts or equipment, with suitable identities. Do not allow anyone from ashore to remove these items.
8. Ensure that an accident report form is completed, see Appendix XI. This should include all personal details of injured persons.
9. Record the names of any witnesses, and arrange for their statements to be taken.
10. It is also useful to take statements from people who have knowledge of the area, object or appliance involved in the incident, and also anyone with knowledge of the injured person's activity prior or subsequent to the accident.
11. Do not make any entry in the log book until the wording has been approved by the Master, who may also wish to consult the P&I Club. The OOW should make notes for his provisional report as soon as possible so that nothing is overlooked or forgotten, including:[29]
    (a) How the person was injured (the cause of the accident).
    (b) The extent of his injuries.
    (c) Details of all medical treatment given on board.
    (d) How he was removed from the scene of the accident.
    (e) The weather and lighting conditions.

Most accidents sustained on board ship result in claims being made against the shipowner. Any decisions which the Master (or OOW) may make can have far-reaching effects on the outcome of subsequent claims, and therefore his action at the time of an accident, and its proper investigation and recording, is crucial. The information recorded by ship's personnel is often the most important evidence obtained, because it is recorded immediately after the event, and therefore the importance of full and accurate completion of accident report forms cannot be over-emphasised.[8]

Many of the personal injury claims received by owners are spurious or exaggerated. The accuracy and detail of information that is obtained immediately after an accident is vitally important. It enables the claim to be dealt with properly and fairly.[29]

There are genuine cases of injury which should be, and are, compensated properly. There are also large numbers of claims where the injury is grossly overstated, or where the ship may be unjustly blamed. This occurs in many places, but particularly often in the USA.[25]

All accidents and dangerous occurrences, no matter how minor, should be reported to a senior officer for investigation so that the ship's safety committee can take prompt action where necessary or make suitable recommendations to the shipowners. This process is essential if similar incidents are to be avoided in the future.[93]

4.12 Other safety precautions

1. The OOW must never allow the ship's deck air line to be used to dust off clothing. The pressure of the air can force dust under the skin, which may result in severe dermatitis.
2. Solvents, and other chemicals, must not be used for hand cleaning. This may result in hazardous substances being absorbed by the skin which could severely jeopardise health—for example, they could lead to cancer.
3. The OOW should discourage anyone from walking under a moving load. It is good practice to rope off the shore side of the deck, and make people use the safer offshore side for transit. Slings can part, cargo can slip through nets or fall off pallets, and grabs are notorious for spilling part of their load.
4. The OOW must personally supervise all stages of opening and closing hatches. Trackways should be clear of obstructions, and all personnel should stand well clear—this should be continuously monitored until the hatches are secured. Check wires should always be used if there is a possibility that excess trim or list could cause the hatches to run out of control. It is essential that no-one is permitted to stand on a hatch cover whilst it is moving.
5. Nobody must be allowed to walk on top of hatch coamings. Many crew are fond of doing this when sweeping/cleaning them.
6. Guards must be erected around <u>all</u> openings, however temporary.
7. Lighting must always be switched on before entering darkened spaces such as store rooms and cargo holds. Temporary lighting should be provided whenever there is no permanent lighting available. Portable lights must <u>never</u> be suspended by their cables.
8. Flickering lights usually indicates faulty wiring. The OOW should report this, and ensure it is investigated and repaired.
9. Portable ladders must always be adequately lashed.
10. Nails should be removed from old dunnage before it is reused.

11. Everyone should always use safe lifting techniques:
    - FIRST — Bend the knees,
    - NEXT — Grip the load,
    - FINALLY — lift by Straightening the legs.

    When lifting heavy or awkward loads there should be an adequate number of personnel to assist. Health and safety is more important than 'macho' image!

12. The gangway must be used for all access between the ship and shore; no-one should be allowed to step between the deck and the quay when these are almost level.

13. No-one should be permitted to swim in the port area. Not only may there be strong currents or tides, and a danger from passing craft, but dock water is invariably polluted with some proportion of raw sewage and industrial effluent, posing a serious health hazard.

14. The OOW should check that a safe system of work is used by shore workers unfamiliar with the vessel and its facilities. Recently a USA repair contractor carried a bucket of oil up several deck levels to test a winch. He could have used the ship's crane. Because the ship's crew did not stop or assist him, the shipowner was faced with a claim of over $1 million compensation for his resultant back injury.[22]

15. Whenever the duty engineer is called into an unmanned engineroom by an alarm, he should establish a reporting system to maintain regular contact with the OOW until he vacates the engineroom.

16. Warning notices should be displayed on the radar displays whenever anyone is working close to the scanners.

17. Warning notices should be displayed in the engine control room whenever anyone is working close to the propeller, or close to any overboard discharges.

18. Hazardous clothing must never be worn. This includes:
    - Nylon working gear; this can melt, stick to and burn the skin, and is unhealthy because it restricts ventilation.
    - Short sleeved and short legged working gear, which does not protect the arms and legs.
    - Flip flops, or any other form of soft shoes, which do not protect the feet, and frequently cause slips and trips.

19. Stevedores often throw twistlocks and other container fittings onto the deck when discharging containers. This can cause damage to the ship's structure and severe injury to personnel below. Stevedores should be warned (preferably in writing) that such practices are prohibited. Also, it is important that receptacles in which these fittings can be stowed are provided adjacent to where they are required.

4.13 Further information

Detailed guidance on all safety matters onboard ships can be found in the UK DOT publication *Code of safe working practices for merchant seamen.*[91] Although this is a UK Code, there is no international equivalent; it is most comprehensive and its advice is relevant to all ships, no matter what their nationality.

Specialised advice for oil, chemical and gas tankers can be found in the ICS Tanker Safety Guides,[95,96,97] and other publications listed in appendix I.

Certain cargoes are liable to overheat during the voyage and their temperature should be monitored regularly. See chapters 4.7 and 8.1.1.
Photograph: courtesy of UK P&I Club.

Chapter 5
TAKING OVER THE WATCH
PURPOSE

On completion of this chapter you will be able to explain the principles of taking over the deck watch, and the authority under which this is done.

5.1 STCW Convention

Clauses 96 and 97 of the 1995 consolidated text of the STCW Code provides guidance for the officer about to hand over the deck watch in port:

96 Officers in charge of the deck or engineering watch shall not hand over the watch to their relieving officer if they have any reason to believe that the latter is obviously not capable of carrying out watchkeeping duties effectively, in which case the master or chief engineer shall be notified accordingly. Relieving officers of the watch shall ensure that all members of their watch are apparently fully capable of performing their duties effectively.

97 If, at the moment of handing over the watch, an important operation is being performed it shall be concluded by the officer being relieved, except when ordered otherwise by the master or chief engineer officer.

5.1.1 What the relieving officer should know

Clause 98 states *The relieving officer should be informed of the following by the officer being relieved:*

1 *the depth of water at the berth, the ship's draught, the level and time of high and low waters; securing of the moorings, arrangement of anchors and the scope of the anchor chain, other features of mooring important for the safety of the ship; state of main engines and availability for emergency use;*

2 *all work to be performed on board the ship; the nature, amount and disposition of cargo loaded or remaining, or any residue on board after unloading the ship;*

3 *the level of water in bilges and ballast tanks;*

4 *the signals and lights being exhibited;*

5 *the number of crew members required to be on board, and the presence of any other persons on board;*

6 *the state of the fire-fighting appliances;*

7 *any special port regulations;*

8 *the Master's standing and special orders;*

9 *the lines of communication that are available between the ship and shore personnel, including port authorities in the event of an emergency arising or assistance being required;*

10 *other circumstances of importance to the safety of the ship, its crew, cargo or protection of the environment from pollution.*

11 *the procedures for notifying the appropriate authority of any environmental pollution resulting from ship activities.*

5.1.2 What the relieving officer should do

Clause 99 states *Relieving officers before assuming charge of the watch shall verify that:*

1 *securing of moorings and anchor chain are adequate;*

2 *the appropriate signals or lights are properly exhibited or sounded;*

3 *safety measures and fire protection regulations are being maintained;*

4 *their awareness of any hazardous or dangerous cargo being loaded or discharged and the appropriate action in the event of any spillage or fire;*

5 *no external conditions or circumstances imperil the ship, and that it does not imperil others.*

5.2 Essential communication

When taking over the watch, the OOW must verify which senior officer is available to assist him if required, and who he should call in an emergency. He should know who is the duty engineer, his likely whereabouts during the next watch, and the method(s) of calling him.

If portable radios are in use, the OOW should check the radio batteries are fully charged, and set to the channel currently being used. For efficiency, it is recommended that the OOW, the gangway watchman and the Chief Officer monitor one channel throughout all port operations.

The OOW should know which crew members are on duty, and who is on stand-by to be called to assist if required.

He should make himself known to the duty stevedore foreman or terminal operator, as appropriate, and know how to communicate with them for both routine operations and emergencies. He should also know how to communicate with the operators of cargo-handling equipment.

He should know the location of the nearest shore telephone, and it is helpful if he knows the telephone numbers of:
1. The fire brigade.
2. The ambulance service.
3. The police.
4. The harbourmaster.
5. The ship's agent.
   ● Owner's agent.
   ● Charterer's agent.

He should also know which VHF channel to use to contact any of the above, if such means of communication is available, and which channels to use to contact the pilots and tugs in an emergency.

5.3 Change-over procedure

The OOW must be sure that the relieving officer is capable of performing his watch duties, and if he is in any doubt whatsoever about the fitness of his

relief, he should remain in charge of the watch and report the facts to the Chief Officer or Master.

On taking over the watch, the new OOW should carry out a thorough inspection of all working parts of the ship, which will include the main deck, all open cargo holds, the pumproom or ballast control station, etc. He should check the gangway, ensuring that both the gangway and its net are correctly adjusted and be aware of all operations on the quayside which are relevant to the ship. If he is taking over from another officer, the relieved officer should accompany the new OOW around the ship to point out all activities taking place onboard, and answer any queries he may have. This cannot be done efficiently in the ship's office, or over a cup of coffee in the messroom! It is good practice to make hand-over notes if there is a lot going on, as this helps to make sure that nothing is forgotten.

If the relieving officer is not happy about any operation, he should ask the OOW to correct the fault before taking over. This may include:
- Cargo not being loaded according to the cargo preplan.
- Ballast operations out of step with cargo operations.
- Unsafe practices or hazardous conditions.
- Situations which are contrary to standing orders.

If this problem cannot be resolved, then the Chief Officer or Master must be informed.

5.4 What the OOW should know

In addition to the requirements of the STCW Guidelines outlined above, the new OOW must be totally familiar with the present situation of the items listed below, and what is expected to happen during his period on watch:

1. The cargo plan, and the present state of cargo operations, including any special requirements for cargo handling, stowage, separation and securing. He should be aware of alternative arrangements, know what is his authority to authorise changes, and have a knowledge of the equipment to be used.

   It is good practice for the officer being relieved to update the working cargo plan to show the current stowage of all cargo which has been loaded, or remains onboard (during discharge operations)—see chapters 7, 8, 9, 12, 13 & 17.

2. The ballast plan, and the present state of ballast operations. It is good practice for the officer being relieved to hand over a full list of the current soundings of all ballast tanks and the corresponding tonnages—see chapter 10.

3. Any other operations or activities taking place which may concern the OOW, such a bunkers, stores, repairs or surveys.

4. The number and place of work of all shore staff:
   - Stevedore gangs:
   - Lashing and securing gangs.
   - Repair and maintenance gangs.
   - Surveyors.
   - Miscellaneous visitors.

5. All work being carried out by the ship's crew.

6. All Permits to Work that have been issued.

7. Any valid permission to enter enclosed spaces, and all circumstances surrounding the work being carried on in such spaces.

8. The availability of assistance:
   - Senior officers on board.
   - Crew on duty.
   - Crew/officers on back-up or stand-by.

   including their location, and method of calling.

9. The present status (open, closed, on, off, locked, etc.) of all:
   - Hatchcovers.
   - Cargo compartment accesses.
   - Accommodation accesses.
   - Doors to storerooms, lockers, masthouse, etc.
   - Ramps, side ports, bow/stern doors etc.
   - Cargo and ballast valves.
   - Cargo and ballast pumps.
   - Tank manholes, and doors to enclosed spaces.

   It may be useful to use a checklist for this hand-over, to ensure that no items are overlooked, particularly on complicated vessels.

10. The type of cargo-handling equipment being used, its speed of operation and safe working load, if appropriate, and the settings of any optional controls on the ship's cargo handling equipment. Any limitations, such as reach, movement or extra fittings to be utilised.

11. Any other equipment, gear, stores, etc., which may be needed by cargo or other operations taking place on board during his watch. The OOW should be familiar with where such equipment is currently located or stowed, and the procedures for putting it into service.

12. The present draft, and any draft limits at the berth, including air draft restrictions. The times and height of tide and the directions of tidal set and any currents. The critical stages of the cargo and ballast operations which may be affected by these factors.

13. The weather forecast, and what to do if it rains or there is a strong wind.

14. Security measures—see chapter 16.

15. Anti-pollution measures—see chapter 15.

16. Mooring arrangements, and any extra precautions required—see chapter 3.

17. Arrangements for safe access, including the position and arrangements for adjusting the gangway—see chapter 4.2.

18. The status of any machinery or equipment which is being repaired or serviced, or is temporarily unavailable, particularly if it could be required by the OOW, for example, mooring winches, main engines, etc.

19. Extra safety precautions in force—see chapter 4.

If the Chief Officer has a port or cargo notebook which he uses to pass on orders or information to the OOW, this must be read by the new OOW and signed only when he fully understands its contents. If he is in any doubt, and the relieved officer cannot assist, he must call the Chief Officer immediately to seek clarification.

The relieved officer must make sure that all relevant details of his watch have been recorded in the deck logbook before he retires—see chapter 18.

Chapter 6

COMMERCIAL DOCUMENTATION

PURPOSE

On completion of this chapter you will be able to list the documents which are involved in the carriage of cargo, and explain their significance to your watchkeeping duties in port.

This chapter is merely an introduction to the subject of documentation. It aims to familiarise you with some of the terms involved, many of which you may hear being used on board your ship.

You may learn more details about this subject when you come to study for your Master's certificate of competency. There are numerous commercial publications available if you want a deeper understanding of the terms used in this chapter, including The Nautical Institute's associated publication *Commercial Management for Shipmasters*.[19] A selection of these are listed in the Bibliography in annex I.[83,84,85]

The wording in this chapter is used to explain the meaning in a form which it is hoped will be easily understood by the reader. The author wishes to point out that certain words and expressions may have an exact legal interpretation. Their use in this chapter may not necessarily correspond to such a narrow definition.

6.1 Signing documents

THE GOLDEN RULE IS THAT NOBODY SHOULD SIGN ANY DOCUMENT UNLESS:
1. HE IS AUTHORISED TO DO SO.
2. HE UNDERSTANDS EVERYTHING THAT IS WRITTEN IN THE DOCUMENT. (*NEVER* sign a document in a foreign language unless fluent in that language, or a written translation is provided and attached)
3. HE KNOWS THAT THE STATEMENTS MADE, OR THE INFORMATION PROVIDED IN THE DOCUMENT ARE ABSOLUTELY CORRECT IN ALL RESPECTS.

The OOW should not sign any documents brought on board unless he has been specifically authorised by the clear orders of the Master or Chief Officer. The normal procedure is for the OOW to refer all visitors with paperwork to the Chief Officer or Master. If these officers are not available and the visitor insists on a signature, it may be in order to sign documents with the clause '*FOR RECEIPT ONLY*'. It is a requirement of some charter parties that *all* documents are claused *subject to time-charterer's approval*, and some shipowners require the clause *subject to owner's approval* on all documents.

It is not unknown for an unscrupulous shipper, receiver or charterer to have a junior officer sign a document which appears harmless at first glance, but may subsequently cost the shipowner a considerable sum, for example, by agreeing to offhire for a breakdown of ship's equipment.

In some trades, where there are a considerable number of documents such as tally sheets, the Chief Officer may authorise the OOW to sign these on his behalf, but he must always be convinced of their accuracy first.

No documents should be signed for cargo unless it has been loaded.

6.2 Shipment of goods

Cargoes are carried onboard a ship under a *contract of affreightment*, which may be a *charterparty* (between the *shipowner* and the *charterer*) or a *bill of lading* or *waybill* (between the *carrier* and the *owner of the goods*, or others).

Most cargoes which are transported on ships will have undergone a change of ownership from the *seller*, who may also be the *shipper*, to the *buyer*, who may also be the *receiver* or *consignee*. The cargo may be sold several times during the voyage before it is delivered by the *carrier*, who may be the *shipowner* or the *charterer*.

6.2.1 Contracts of sale

With a *CIF* contract (cost, insurance, freight), the seller contracts to deliver the goods to the buyer at their destination, and so the goods are shipped at the seller's cost and risk.

With an *FOB* contract (free onboard), the buyer takes delivery from the seller before shipment, he is the shipper, and so the goods are shipped at the buyer's cost and risk.

There are 13 standard terms controlling the transfer of goods from the buyer to the seller. They are fully explained in The Nautical Institute's publication *Commercial Management for Shipmasters*.[19]

6.2.2 Freight

The carrier charges freight for transporting the goods from the port of loading to the port of discharge. This is usually on the basis of US$ xx per *freight tonne*.

When the cargo stows at less than 40 cu ft/ton or 1 cu mtr/tonne, freight is usually charged on its actual weight.

Light cargo occupies more of the available space in a ship, which could restrict the carrier's income. Hence with cargo which stows at greater than the above figures, the freight is usually charged on its volume, that is $xx per 40 cu ft or 1 cu mtr, known as a '*measurement ton(ne)*'.

Occasionally the carrier will make one charge for a complete consignment of cargo. This is known as *lumpsum* freight.

If the shipper declares the goods have a high value, he will pay extra *Ad Valorem* freight in return for the shipowner accepting this extra liability.

6.2.3 Shipping documents

When the shipper wants to book his cargo on a ship, he sends a *shipping note* to the shipowner or his agent, which contains a full description of the goods. The compilation of these notes is the *booking list*, which gives details of all the cargo intended for loading. This is sent to the ship to enable the stowage to be planned, and to the stevedore to arrange for the loading.

When the goods are delivered to the ship, they are documented in an advice known as the *boat note*. When the goods are actually loaded, the Chief Officer signs this advice, which then becomes the *mate's receipt*. On many trades, the mate's receipt is issued as a separate document. It is evidence that the specified goods have been received on board the ship.

The shipper exchanges his mate's receipt for a *bill of lading*, which is completed from the details shown on the former document. Often the shipper pays the freight at this time. The bills are consolidated into a *manifest*, which lists all the cargo actually on board. If time permits a copy of this may be presented to the ship, another copy is delivered to the discharge port, to enable the discharge to be planned, and Customs procedures processed.

The bill of lading is delivered to the buyer of the goods; if the goods are sold again whilst they are still on board the ship, the bill of lading is endorsed, and passed to their new owner. At the port of discharge, the final owner of the goods surrenders the bill of lading to the Master, or his agent, in return for delivery of the cargo. As the contract of carriage is now completed, the Master endorses the bill of lading as *Accomplished*. A more detailed description of this process is to be found in section 6.6.

6.2.4 Letters of credit

Where there is an international sale of goods, it is common practice for payment to be made by way of a *letter of credit*. The buyer agrees a detailed specification of the goods with the seller, and agrees to a price based on this specification. These facts are included in the letter of credit which is established between the buyer's and the seller's banks. It will usually state that the goods are *in apparent good order and condition*.

When the bill of lading and certain other documents are presented to the banks, to show that the goods have been shipped, the buyer's bank will transfer the agreed funds to the seller's bank. They will only release the full sale price if the description of the goods in the bill of lading agrees with the description in the letter of credit—i.e., they are *in apparent good order and condition*.

If the bill of lading contains qualifying remarks concerning the quantity or apparent order and condition of the cargo, the buyer's bank may not be prepared to release all the funds, because the description of the goods as shipped may indicate that they are of a lower value.

The process of documentary credit is explained in The Nautical Institute's Nautical Briefing *The Development of Maritime Commercial Practice*—see appendix XX.

6.3 Time charters

When a shipowner hires out his vessel to another operator for a certain period, it is usually done on a document called a time charterparty. As far as the commercial operation of the ship is concerned, the charterer acts likes the owner. He may even sub-charter the ship, or part of it, to someone else. This first (or '*head*') charterer becomes responsible to the sub-charterer for all the owner's obligations, and is often referred to as the *disponent owner*.

A time charter which lasts for several months or years is called a *period charter*, whilst one that lasts for a single voyage is known as a *trip charter*. The shipowner is paid a fixed rate per day for the vessel, known as *hire*, for example $10,000 per 24 hours whilst she is *on-hire* (on charter).

The exact division of responsibilities between the shipowner and the charterer is governed by the actual clauses of the charterparty. Most charterparties are undertaken on standard printed forms to which extra clauses relevant to the particular charter are added. These are known as *rider clauses*. If there is any ambiguity between these clauses and the printed text, then the rider clause will prevail. Also, the printed text may be amended by insertions or deletions.

There are hundreds of different printed charterparties. Some are used on specific trades, or by specific companies. Common standard forms are Baltime 1939, issued by BIMCO (Baltic and International Maritime Council), and NYPE (New York Produce Exchange). BIMCO also issues specialised forms for the liner trades (Linertime) and container trades (Boxtime), whilst the oil majors tend to use their own in-house forms.

6.3.1 Charterer's usual responsibilities

1. Procure the cargo.
2. Load the cargo.
3. Provide all necessary dunnage, securing, fumigation, etc.
4. Pay all port and canal dues, including compulsory tugs and pilots, and compulsory or 'usual' watchmen.
5. Provide the fuel.
6. Discharge the cargo at the destination.
7. Hold cleaning, and disposal of dunnage and securing equipment—but NOT the initial clean at the start of the charter.
8. Pay for all operational communication, and entertainment.
9. Appoint agents to look after their interests at each port.

6.3.2 Owner's usual responsibilities

1. Crew wages, and ancillary costs, such as victualling, medical, reliefs.
2. Maintenance, spares and stores.
3. Fresh water, lubricating oils, and fuel for domestic services.
4. Insurance.
5. Non-compulsory pilots.
6. Appoint *husbandry* agents to look after their interests at each port, though often they pay the charterer's agents for doing owner's work.

It is stressed that in all cases, the actual clauses of each charterparty must be consulted in order to determine the exact division of responsibilities between the owner and charterer for each particular voyage.

6.3.3 Cargo claims

The settlement of cargo claims is usually split between the charterer and owner in accordance with the terms of the charterparty. Some charterparties provide for cargo claims to be split in accordance with the *Inter-club agreement*. This is a formal agreement between the major P&I Clubs of the International Group, which provides for settlement on the following basis:

Claims due to unseaworthiness	100% shipowner.
Claims due to bad stowage or handling	100% charterer.
Shortage, pilferage, overcarriage, and condensation damage.	50% owner and charterer.

—unless any of these are caused solely by the act, neglect or default of one party, in which case he is 100% liable.

Once again, the actual clauses of the charterparty for the particular voyage must always be consulted to determine these responsibilities. See also chapter 7.4.1.

The reader who is interested in learning more about this complicated subject may obtain the text of the *Inter-club agreement* from any member of the International Group of P&I Clubs, such as the sponsors of this publication, the UK P&I Club.

The charterparty will often list commodities which cannot be carried, and there may be specific responsibilities with respect to the carriage of IMO classed dangerous goods.

6.3.4 Delays in port

Routine delays in port—for example, port congestion, stevedores or cargo unavailable—are usually the responsibility of the charterer. However, if the ship or its crew are the cause of the delay, the charterer may be entitled to place the ship offhire and cease paying the daily rate. This will depend on the exact wording of the offhire clause in the charterparty; some examples of when the ship may be placed offhire are:

1. Crew documentation not in order.
2. The ship's statutory certificates not in order.
3. Arrest of the ship due to crew smuggling, including drugs.

4. Ill health of the crew.
5. Breakdown of the ship's cargo-handling gear. If the ship has five cranes and one fails, the ship may be placed one-fifth offhire. Also, the shipowner may have to pay for hiring replacement shorebased cargo-handling gear.

It is essential that the OOW maintains accurate records of all delays to cargo operations. This is so that the shipowner has the means to verify valid claims, or has evidence which he can use to refute improper claims for delays. The OOW should try to find out the cause of all these delays, and make every effort to rectify this if at all possible. He should report all delays to the Chief Officer or Master.

6.4 Voyage charters

When a shipowner contracts to carry a full cargo for one trader, this is often done on a document called a voyage charterparty. In this case the charterer undertakes to find the cargo, and to load and discharge it in a fixed time, known as *laytime*.

The owner is paid freight at an agreed amount per tonne loaded, or occasionally one fixed lumpsum, and is responsible for all other aspects of the ship's operation.

The commonest standard form of voyage charterparty for dry cargo trades is GENCON 1976; in the oil trades, the oil majors tend to use their own in-house forms.

6.4.1 Laytime

The time allowed for loading and discharging the cargo is called the laytime, and its duration is agreed in the charterparty. The actual days used are called *laydays*.

If cargo operations take longer than agreed, the shipowner is paid an agreed rate per day as compensation for the delay, known as *demurrage*. If they are quicker than agreed, the shipowner pays the charterer a bonus known as *dispatch*. Traditionally, dispatch rate is half the demurrage rate.

Sometimes the time saved at one port can be offset against delays at another port, these are known as *reversible* laydays. When they are calculated separately, they are *non-reversible*, which is more common.

Laytime can be a separate figure for loading and discharging, which is the more usual, or a total figure for both. It can be expressed as a fixed number of days, or so many tonnes per weather working day.

6.4.2 Weather working days

Weather working days are 24 hour totals of all periods on which cargo operations are NOT delayed by adverse weather conditions such as:

1. Rain, and other precipitation, which may damage the cargo.
2. High winds affecting the operation of shore cargo-handling gear.
3. Severe cold, which prevents the stevedores from working.

The OOW should always record the times of such weather changes, as this may be required by the Master in order to verify the agent's statement of facts or laytime calculations, though the latter is usually undertaken by the ship operator's commercial staff ashore. If there is a dispute, the times as recorded by an independent authority are usually taken, such as the local meteorological office, airport, or even as agreed by other vessels in the port.

The weather records should continue at all times when the vessel is not working cargo, and whilst at anchor awaiting a berth, as these may be part of the weather working days, depending on the terms of the charterparty.

6.4.3 Notice of readiness

When a ship arrives within the port limits, or some other usually acceptable position, and is *in all respects* ready to commence cargo operations, as described in the charterparty, the Master will present the notice of readiness. The times during which he can present this will be written in the charterparty. Some examples are:

- During normal office hours (0900-1700 local time) Monday to Friday, (these times may vary, part of the weekend may be included such as Saturday morning, and Friday is excluded in many Moslem countries.)
- Any time day or night. This may be qualified by certain abbreviations
    e.g. SHEX (Sundays and Holidays excepted, i.e., not included), or
    SSHINC (Saturdays, Sundays and Holidays included).

Laytime will commence when the shipper or receiver accepts this notice of readiness, or a fixed time afterwards according to the terms of the charterparty. Some examples of this time delay are:

- Start of the next working day,
- Commencement of the next work-shift,
- After four hours.

Sometimes the charterparty provides that laytime will not count during the agreed period of delay *unless used*. This means that if cargo operations commence during this period, then laytime starts to count.

At the loading port, there may be specific requirements in the charterparty before the notice of readiness can be presented. For example, in the grain trade, the holds must have passed a cleanliness survey, and the Master must have proved to a government surveyor that the ship will have adequate stability throughout the intended voyage. With reefers, the holds must have passed a survey for precooling and hold cleanliness.

The charterparty may specify a time and date before which the notice of readiness will not be accepted—though it can be presented before this time. The charterparty may also specify a later time and date after which the charterer has the right to cancel the charterparty if the ship is not ready. The period between these two times is called the *laycan* spread.

6.5 Mate's receipts

The mate's receipt is a document signed by the Chief Officer as a receipt for cargo loaded; it is usually surrendered by the holder in return for the bill of lading. Also, it is evidence of the quantity and the condition of the cargo. Hence, if the OOW observes any damage before shipment, or any shortage, he must report it to the Chief Officer, who should clause the receipt to show this loss or damaged condition.

When the ship is unsure of the quality or quantity, the Chief Officer may clause the receipt *Quality and Quantity Unknown* or add *Said to weigh* or *Said to be* in front of the descriptions printed. **These remarks must not be used when the ship is aware of a correct description, but disagrees with that stated in the mate's receipt.** The clausing of mate's receipts and bills of lading is discussed in detail in chapters 12 and 13.

6.6 Bill of lading

The bill of lading is a document which is signed by the Master once the cargo has been loaded. It is the formal document based on the mate's receipt. Bills of lading are issued for cargo on most voyages, whether they be a liner service or a time or voyage charter. Sometimes it takes a while to prepare these documents, and the Master may empower the agent to sign them on his behalf when they are ready, always strictly *in accordance with the Mate's Receipts*.

To assist with commercial arrangements, it is usual to issue three 'original' bills of lading. Each original may have a number of copies which are sometimes signed individually. The Master may be given one copy of each original, so that he can compare this with the documents presented to him for delivery of the cargo at the discharge port.

Most cargo claims arise as a result of alleged breaches by the carrier of his contractual obligation (in the bill of lading) to carry and care for the cargo whilst it is in his custody.

6.6.1 Functions of a bill of lading

The bill of lading has three functions:

1. **It is a receipt for the cargo, and is evidence of the quantity and condition of the cargo.** (These subjects are expanded in chapters 12 and 13).
2. **It is a document of title.** The reader may think of this as proof of ownership, but in legal terms, it is proof of entitlement to possession of the cargo. As such, it can be passed to someone else if the cargo is sold. At the discharge port, the cargo should only be delivered to the holder of the bill of lading.
3. **It is evidence of the contract of affreightment** (carriage of cargo from one place to another) between the shipowner and the cargo owner. The vessel is expected to proceed between these ports by the most direct route, without deviation, and diligently care for the cargo.

6.6.2 Bills of lading issued under a charterparty

When the Master signs a bill of lading he forms a contract between the cargo owner and the shipowner, *not* the charterer, even though the bill of lading may be on the charterer's forms. The shipowner may be indemnified by the charterers for any resultant claims by clauses in the charterparty.

It is usual when a vessel is on charter for the terms and conditions of the charterparty to be incorporated into the bill of lading by a specific reference to the charterparty in a clause on the bill of lading. Sometimes the terms of the charterparty oblige the Master to ensure that such a specific clause is included in all bills of lading before he signs them. An example of such terms is a *paramount* clause. If the Master gives an agent the authority to sign bills of lading on his behalf, he must include the requirement for such a clause in this authority.

6.6.3 Clausing a bill of lading

A bill of lading which is signed without the Master entering any extra remarks (known as *clausing* the bill) is called *clean*, and this is often a requirement of a bank if the holder of the bill requires payment under a letter of credit—see section 6.2.4. The circumstances in which the Master clauses a bill of lading, and the role of the OOW in providing him with the necessary information, is discussed in chapter 12 for cargo condition, and chapter 13 for cargo quantity.

If the cargo is stowed on deck by agreement, the bill of lading has to be appropriately claused. If there is no agreement, then the carrier can lose some of his legal protection if the cargo is stowed on deck. The OOW must inform the Chief Officer if he observes cargo being stowed on deck which he was expecting to be stowed in the holds.

Without ever seeing the cargo, a prospective buyer often decides to purchase goods on the basis of the description in the bill of lading. Therefore it is essential that this description is accurate, and the ship's staff should check that the amount of cargo and its apparent condition agree with the information in the bill of lading. If there is any discrepancy, the bill of lading must be claused accordingly.

6.6.4 Delivery of the cargo

If the bill of lading states that the goods are deliverable *to bearer*, then the cargo can be claimed by a person who presents an original document. This is known as an *open* bill of lading.

If the bill of lading states that the goods are deliverable solely to a named consignee, then only he can take delivery of the goods. This is known as a *straight* bill of lading.

In most cases, the bill of lading states that the goods are deliverable to a named consignee *or order*. This makes the document *negotiable*, which means it can be *endorsed* to someone else if they buy the cargo. Endorsing means adding a clause to the document and signing it. If the original consignee signs the back, with no other remarks (this is known as *endorse in blank*), the document becomes an open bill of lading. If the endorsement states *deliver to XYZ*, the document becomes a straight bill of lading. If the endorsement states *deliver to XYZ or order*, then XYZ can further endorse it to someone else if they resell the cargo.

At the discharge port, the Master must only deliver the cargo to a bona-fide holder of an original bill of lading. If the bill of lading is open, then he can deliver the cargo to whoever presents the document, provided he has not been informed of any theft or fraud. If the bill of lading is straight, he should check that the person claiming delivery is the same as named in the document. If the bill of lading is negotiable, it is very important that he checks whether the document has been properly endorsed, and that the person claiming delivery is entitled to the goods.

Once he has done this, the Master will endorse the bill of lading as *Accomplished*, and date and sign this remark. At this time, the other two original bills become null and void.

6.7 Cargo quantity

The description of the ship's cargo carrying capacity varies with the type of vessel and commodities to be carried.

- BALE VOLUME is of most interest for general cargo ships,
- GRAIN VOLUME is of most interest for bulk carriers,
- DEADWEIGHT at a given draft is of most interest for heavier cargoes, where the vessel's maximum draft is limited by her loadline, or for set amounts of cargo to/from ports with draft limits,
- TANK (VOLUME) CAPACITY is often used for tankers,
- TEU (twenty-foot equivalent units) SLOTS is the measure used for container ships, whilst
- LANE-METRES (of 3-metre wide lanes) is commonly used for Ro-Ros.

The amount of cargo to be loaded may be fixed by the shipper, or it may be a variable amount, which the shipowner fixes within the range provided for in the contract of carriage. With bulk cargoes, the owner or charterer will always want to carry the maximum cargo commensurate with any limitations of the voyage, such as draft limits at the load or discharge port(s) or enroute—e.g., canal transits or a change of load-line zones.

Frequently, bulk cargoes are shipped in contracts worded such as *50,000 metric tonnes 10% MOLOO*, meaning more or less in owners option. Hence the Master can choose to load between 45,000 and 55,000 tonnes. In such cases, the Master must make a *request for cargo* upon arrival at the port of loading, which is his declaration of the amount of cargo required to load, and that the ship is able to lift. If the ship subsequently cannot lift this figure, then a claim against the ship for *short-shipment* may result. On the other hand, if the shippers cannot provide this quantity, then the shipowner may make a claim for *dead-freight* on the tonnage under shipped. The establishment of the quantity of cargo shipped is fully discussed in chapter 13.

6.8 Damage report certificates

The Master will issue a damage report certificate so that the party responsible for causing the damage is held liable for all the resultant costs. This includes not only the cost of repairs, but also any other relevant expenses such as loss of use, loss of earnings, loss of value and the costs of delays. Such certificates are issued for both damage to the cargo and damage to the ship and her equipment.

The OOW must always report any new damage he notices to the Chief Officer, even if he does not actually see it occur. On some vessels the OOW will be required to complete the damage certificate, on other vessels this is the sole responsibility of the Chief Officer. Even in this latter case, it is good training for the OOW to complete a similar form as the basis of his report to the Chief Officer. An example of such a form is provided in appendix XII.

Most shipowners, and many leading charterers, provide their own blank report forms. If these are not available, then a letter-type report is equally valid. The report should contain full details of where, when and how the damage was caused. A detailed description should be made outlining the extent of the damage sustained, with full dimensions or quantities as appropriate.

Every effort should be made to obtain a signature from those who caused the damage, to show they have accepted the facts in the report. Frequently this is difficult to obtain, in which case the ship should try to obtain a signature *for receipt only* of the report. If this proves impossible, a useful tactic is to have the agent deliver the report, obtaining a signature from him for receipt of the report to forward to the party concerned. This practice will enable the ship to prove the report was written and available at that time.

The document will be more valuable if it is accompanied by dated photographs or videos of the damage, and of any relevant equipment, particularly if this is broken or has been mishandled. Views of the surroundings may assist in identifying hazards—see chapter 18.9.

It is frequently the activities of the stevedore which are the most common cause of damage to either cargo or the ship in port. Many charterparties contain a clause which states that the ship must give a written notice of liability to the stevedore for all damage caused within 24 hours of the incident, otherwise the charterer will not be liable. The idea is to establish clear responsibility for any damage done, but its effect is to encourage the direct settlement of claims between the ship and the stevedore, and not involve the charterer.

The same time limits often apply for notifying the charterer. The Master may fulfil this requirement by faxing a copy of the damage certificate to the charterer, or notifying him of the circumstances by telex. It is essential that the damage is reported within this time limit, otherwise the charterer may repudiate the claim. This is why the OOW's reports are so important, and have to be completed urgently.

If there is a dispute over the facts stated in these reports, including who is responsible, or there are any problems over having them signed, it may be useful for the Master to call for the assistance of the local correspondent of his P&I Club. If the damage may effect the vessel's class, the Master should immediately notify the local representative of the relevant classification society, and the vessel's owners.

6.9 Letters of protest

A letter of protest is a document used to provide a written record of events. They are issued by the Master to draw the attention of some third party to some facts or incidents which the Master believes may affect either the performance of the operations, or the condition of the cargo. The circumstances are usually outside the control of the ship. If the OOW sees any of these, such as in the examples which follow, he should report the facts immediately to the Chief Officer.

6.9.1 Hidden damage

When cargo is loaded very fast, it is sometimes suspected that damage has been caused to this or other cargo, or to the ship, but the damage is now covered by the latest cargo loaded. Such hidden damage will be revealed upon discharge. An example is heavy cargo allowed to fall from a substantial height on to an unprotected tank top by opening the grab as soon as it passes the coaming. It is preferable to persuade the stevedore to lower the grab to the bottom of the hold first, but if he will not do this, then a letter of protest is issued.

6.9.2 Suspected inherent vice

If the cargo is seen to be in poor condition, this must be described in the bill of lading. But if the Master cannot prove the poor condition, but has reasonable grounds to suspect it, he may issue a letter protesting his fears. Also, it may be that the Master suspects the condition of the cargo will cause damage to his ship. An example of this is wet coal, where the moisture may drain off as mild sulphuric acid which can attack the steel structure of the ship. In an extreme example, this acid has corroded completely through the tanktop plating of a new ship.

6.9.3 Cargo quantity in dispute

If the amount of cargo discharged is claimed to be less than that determined by the ship's figures, or calculations, then the Master may issue a letter of protest to declare formally the quantity discharged according to the ship. Where there has been a complete discharge, it is useful if he can have an *empty hold certificate* signed by an independent party, as proof that none of the cargo remains onboard.

Such a letter of protest may be issued when the Master does not agree with a draft surveyor's results, or suspects that his findings are inaccurate. Such letters are not appropriate for loading, as the Master must state what he believes is the correct quantity in the bill of lading (see chapter 13). However, these letters of protest may be an allowable practice in some trades, particularly when the quantity in dispute is less than 0.5% of the total.

On bulkers, a valid letter of protest may be presented to the shippers who fail to provide a full cargo in accordance with the charterparty and the Master's declaration on arrival. Conversely, the ship is likely to receive a letter of protest if it fails to load such a full cargo.

A letter may also draw attention to potential shortages, such as when quantities of cargo are seen to spill during handling or shore transportation, or bulk cargoes are blown away by a strong wind.

6.9.4 Cargo condition in dispute

If the Master and the shipper cannot agree upon the condition of the cargo, or the wording to be used to describe this condition in the bill of lading, the Master may issue a letter of protest stating his assessment of the condition of the cargo. This may also be issued when the Master and the consignee cannot agree upon the condition. In all such cases it may be necessary to appoint an independent surveyor to resolve the dispute, but the ship's personnel must do their best to reduce delays to the cargo operations in these circumstances.

Another example is where the Master is placed under duress when he wishes to add clauses of cargo condition to the bill of lading. He may be forced into signing a clean bill of lading under severe pressure, such as threats of violence or arrest in ports which have an oppressive political regime or where justice in the local Courts cannot be relied upon. Such duress must be real, and a letter of protest issued as soon as possible once the duress is removed, for example it may be cabled or faxed as soon as the ship is clear of the port in question.

6.9.5 Cargo damaged after discharge

Although cargo which is damaged after discharge may not be the responsibility of the shipowner, it is good practice to bring such damage to the attention of all parties concerned. This is discussed in chapter 12.11.

6.9.6 Delays not caused by the vessel

If the actions, or lack of actions, of some third party cause certain operations to be delayed, then a letter of protest is issued, so that the party responsible can be held liable for any extra costs arising from such delay. For example, if the ship is unable to work cargo because the stevedores have failed to inform the ship of some special requirements, and the ship's gear has to be adjusted, or a bunker barge pumps so slowly that the ship takes much longer than anticipated to load the fuel oil.

6.9.7 Receiving letters of protest

The ship is liable to receive a letter of protest if some third party believes they have suffered a loss which they allege was caused by the ship. For example, if some operation is delayed by a failure of ship's equipment, or by the actions or lack of actions of ship's personnel.

6.9.8 Note of protest

The junior officer should not confuse letters of protest with the note of protest which is given by the Master to a notary public as a legal method of stating that the Master is aware of a certain event at a certain time. Such notes are often given after a period of adverse weather when the Master may suspect damage to ship or cargo, but none has yet been found. He is merely stating the facts at a proven time,

when he could not have been influenced by other facts which emerge later—e.g., he is not exaggerating the severity of the weather in order to blame this for cargo he knows to be damaged. Such notes are sometimes used to state the ship's version of the facts after a serious accident, to show that there has been no change of story influenced by facts which did not become apparent until some time later. Notes of protest are not addressed to anyone in particular, and should be given within 48 hours of the event giving rise to the protest, or arrival in the next port.

6.10 Letters of indemnity

A letter of indemnity is issued by a person who declares that he is taking full financial responsibility for certain circumstances. It claims that the person signing the letter will bear any costs resulting from the Master complying with his request. Some examples of circumstances in which these are issued follow:

6.10.1 Clean bill of lading

The shipper may offer a letter of indemnity to the Master in return for a clean bill of lading when the Master wishes to add clauses about the condition of the cargo. To issue a clean bill in these circumstances is considered *fraud*, and such a letter of indemnity is unenforceable.

The GOLDEN RULE is that the Master must never accept such letters of indemnity, as *the courts have regarded this practice as collusion between the shipper and the carrier to defraud the consignee.*[77]

In some circumstances, for example with a regular customer, the Master may be ordered by the shipowner to accept such a letter for reasons of commercial goodwill. This does not change the legal status of such letters, and the shipowner must bear full liability if there is any dispute. In these circumstances, it is essential that the Master has such instructions clearly stated in writing from the shipowner.

6.10.2 Unavailability of the original bill of lading

A letter of indemnity may be presented to the Master as a guarantee at the discharge port, because the original bills of lading are not available for presentation to him. Generally, such a letter is provided by the person receiving the cargo and should be countersigned by a reputable bank. The wording of this letter will have been agreed between any charterers and the shipowners, the text is often in a form suggested by their P&I Club. Although there is no misrepresentation, such a letter may be unenforceable in law. However, the shipowner may be willing to accept it, particularly if it is accompanied by a bank guarantee, for reasons of commercial expediency.

6.10.3 Handling cargo during adverse weather

Some shippers may request the Master to carry on loading during periods of adverse weather, and by signing this letter they take full responsibility for any damage caused to the cargo or to the ship.

A receiver may have urgent need for his cargo, and requests the ship to discharge in the rain. He signs this letter to show he takes responsibility for any damage caused to his cargo. Preferably, this letter should also cover any adjacent cargo which could be damaged by the rain, and may be for a different receiver.

> Again it must be stressed that the Master is fully responsible for the condition of his cargo (see chapter 12), and letters of indemnity which purport to alter this may be unenforceable, and are usually unacceptable to the P&I Clubs.

It may be useful for the Master to consult his owners if he comes under pressure from regular commercial associates of the shipowner, as the owner may choose to accept such a letter of indemnity. Again, this is entirely at the shipowner's risk, though he may be prepared to accept the risk for ongoing commercial reasons.

6.11 Incomplete documents

In some ports the authorities impose very severe penalties if a ship arrives with her cargo documents incomplete, or inaccurately completed. It is reported that a vessel in Algeria was fined $1 million, and the ship and crew detained for one year.[26] Fines can be imposed for cargo which is in excess of the documented quantity in addition to cases where there is a claimed shortage of cargo compared to the documented quantity. Such over-landing of cargo may be regarded as smuggling by the Customs authorities in certain countries.

6.12 Other documents

The OOW should be aware of the functions of:
1. Certificate of origin.
2. Shipper's declaration.
3. Dangerous goods declaration.
4. Certificate of moisture content.
5. Phytosanitary certificate.
6. Hold cleanliness certificate.
7. Certificate of readiness to load.
8. Certificates of loading, and fitness to proceed to sea.
9. Certificates of stowage, trimming and lashing.
10. Certificate of fumigation.
11. Certificate of hatch sealing.
12. Empty hold certificate/Certificate of discharge.
13. Temperature control sheets.

The Chief Officer or the Master should be able to explain the use and contents of any of these documents which are unfamiliar to the junior officer.

A considerable quantity of dunnage is used with a steel cargo, which can be a problem for the crew to dispose of after completion of discharge. See chapter 7.9.3 (6).
Photograph: author.

Chapter 7
BREAK-BULK CARGO OPERATIONS
PURPOSE

On completion of this chapter you will be able to supervise the handling and stowage of the cargo, ensuring this is done safely and efficiently, in accordance with the cargo plan, without causing damage to either the cargo or the ship or injury to personnel.

The basic principles which are outlined below can be applied to all cargo operations, including the specialised vessels discussed in chapters 8 and 9.

7.1 The Hague, Hague-Visby and Hamburg Rules

The Hague Rules (the 1924 *International Convention on the Carriage of Goods by Sea*) establish a uniform code for the carriage of cargo shipped under Bills of Lading; they may also be incorporated into a Charter Party by a clause paramount. Article III, Rule 2 defines the legal obligations of the ship to her cargo, and provides the authority for the OOW's involvement in supervising cargo operations:

> **THE CARRIER SHALL PROPERLY AND CAREFULLY LOAD, HANDLE, STOW, CARRY, KEEP, CARE FOR, AND DISCHARGE THE GOODS CARRIED.**

The carrier is given some defences under these rules, for example he is not responsible for loss or damage arising from insufficiency of packing, latent defects not discoverable by due diligence, and inherent defect, quality or vice of the goods. There are many others, and the reader seeking further information should consult a textbook on the law dealing with the carriage of goods by sea, such as those listed in appendix I.[83,84,85] However, the OOW should not consider that the presence of such exceptions in any way effects his duty to ensure that the cargo is not damaged whilst it is in his custody.

These rules place certain obligations on the carrier in that he must exercise due diligence to make the vessel seaworthy, to properly man, equip and supply it, and to make the cargo holds fit and safe for the reception, carriage and preservation of the cargo ('cargo-worthy') (see chapter 1.5).

The Hague-Visby Rules incorporate amendments to the above convention agreed in 1968; they do not alter the basic advice given here.

The Hamburg Rules (*The United Nations Convention on the Carriage of Goods by Sea, 1978*), which came into force in 1992, have replaced the Hague Rules in those countries which have ratified this convention. At the time of writing (1995), these include few major trading nations outside Africa and South America. Article 5 states that if cargo is lost or damaged, the carrier will be liable if this took place whilst the goods were under his charge, unless it is proved that the carrier took all measures that could reasonably be required to avoid the occurrence and its consequences.

There are fewer exceptions in the Hamburg Rules compared to those in the Hague Rules. The carrier is liable for the entire period during which he is in charge of the goods, whereas under the Hague Rules his liability is limited to the period from 'hooking on' at the load port to 'hooking off' at the discharge port.

7.2 Cargo information

The IMO *Code of Safe Practice for cargo stowage and securing*[54] states in paragraph 1.9 *Before accepting a cargo for shipment, the shipowner or operator should obtain all necessary information about the cargo and ensure that:*
- *the different commodities to be carried are compatible with each other or suitably separated;*
- *the cargo is suitable for the ship;*
- *the ship is suitable for the cargo;*
- *the cargo can be safely stowed and secured onboard the ship and transported under all expected conditions during the intended voyage.*

The Master should be provided with adequate information regarding the cargo to be carried so that its stowage may be properly planned for handling and transport.

In order to plan the handling and stowage of the cargo, the Chief Officer will need to know the numbers, weights and dimensions of all items of the intended cargo, plus details of any fixed lifting and/or securing fittings, unusual characteristics, and the class and exact chemical description of any IMDG cargo.

7.3 Responsibilities of the OOW

The OOW should ensure that:
1. The cargo is handled in a safe manner, and is not damaged.
2. The cargo is stowed properly, in accordance with the cargo plan.
3. The ship's fixtures and fittings are not damaged.
4. Personnel are not placed in any hazard which may cause injury.
5. The quantity and condition of the cargo are accurately recorded.
6. There is co-operation and co-ordination between all parties involved in the cargo operation ashore and on board.

7.4 Conflicts of interest

Ship's personnel must always keep in mind the fact that the interests of the shippers and receivers of the cargo, and of the people employed to load and discharge it, are not necessarily the same as the interests of the ship's operator. What is convenient for one party may be quite the opposite for another.[3]

The carrier's obligation is to look after the cargo properly and carefully, and it will be no defence to a claim for damage to say that the cargo was handled or carried in accordance with the usual practice.[1]

7.4.1 Ships on charter, and the activities of a Supercargo

Many charterers, particularly in the liner trades, appoint a Supercargo to look after their interests. He will often play a leading role in the supervision of cargo operations. His purpose is to assist the OOW with unfamiliar cargoes in unfamiliar ports; he brings local expertise to a vessel with little experience in that trade. He can often provide valuable advice on handling, stowage and securing the cargo, and assist in dealing with stevedores and port officials. His primary role is to expedite the handling of the cargo, assist the ship to arrange stowage to maximise the utilisation of available cargo space, and control costs for the charterer.

However, if there is a difference of opinion as to how to perform some operation, the OOW should immediately inform the Master. The wording of the charterparty must be examined closely so as to discover exactly who is responsible for that operation, and so who has the final say:

A. If the charterparty states that the charterer will load or discharge the cargo *under the Master's supervision*, then the charterers remain responsible for the stowage of the cargo and any loss or damage to the cargo attributable to bad stowage. However, in all circumstances the Master is under an obligation to protect his ship from being made unseaworthy. If he fails to do so then the shipowner may be held liable for any resulting loss or damage. The Master also has the right to interfere with the operation if he thinks it is likely to impose a liability on his owners.

Hence, the OOW should ensure that the cargo is properly stowed and secured so as not to constitute a danger to the ship or her personnel, that is, **the ship remains seaworthy**. He should always ensure that no damage is caused to the ship by the cargo at any stage during the voyage.

The charterers will be responsible for any damage to the cargo caused by their actions (or the actions of their stevedores, or by following the advice of their supercargo) in loading, stowing, trimming and securing. In these circumstances, the OOW must follow the advice of the supercargo or charterer. Otherwise, the Master, perhaps through the OOW, may be deemed to assume responsibility by his actions in over-ruling this advice. If it can be proved by the charterers that the bad stowage was caused only by the orders of ship's staff, and that their own proposed stowage would have caused no damage, then the shipowners will be held liable for any loss or damage to the cargo. This claim may be difficult to disprove.

B. If the charterparty states that the charterer will load the cargo *under the Master's supervision **and responsibility***, then these last two extra words make the shipowner responsible for the planning of cargo operations and the operation of loading, stowing and discharging the cargo. The shipowner can only avoid this responsibility if it can be shown that the charterers have actively intervened or interfered with the operation, and in doing so have caused the loss or damage to the cargo or to the ship.

In these circumstances, the OOW must protest if he thinks the cargo is not being handled or stowed correctly. If he allows a bad practice to continue, even if this was the advice of the supercargo or charterers, or was done by stevedores appointed by the charterers, then the shipowner will be held responsible for any cargo claim, and will be unable to recover from the charterers for any damage caused to the ship.

7.5 Preventing damage to cargo

Approximately half of all claims handled by the P&I Clubs are for cargo. It is the responsibility of the OOW to try to prevent damage being caused to the cargo by:
1. Poor stowage   (16% of all major claims).
2. Poor handling   (8% of all major claims).
3. External factors   (e.g., weather, thieves).

MORE HASTE = LESS CARE
= POTENTIAL DAMAGE.

The best advice to the OOW is for him to imagine that the cargo is his own property, and act accordingly.

It is a good idea for the OOW to be familiar with the value of the main cargoes, so he will appreciate the costs of loss and damage. These values can be obtained from the technical press, or may be known by the Master or senior shore personnel.

The procedures for dealing with cargo which is found to be damaged are discussed in chapter 12.

7.6 Supervising the stevedores

The OOW must supervise the stevedores to ensure that they comply with the requirements of section 7.3 above. In some ports, the stevedores are most professional, and will comply with both the letter and the spirit of this chapter on their own initiative. In other ports, the OOW will have a difficult job to ensure that the cargo operation progresses efficiently. Some common problems he may face with stevedores are:
1. Language difficulties.
2. Lack of suitable equipment.
3. Poorly trained operators of mechanical equipment.
4. Lack of training, and poorly educated cargo handlers, who do not appreciate the finer points outlined in this chapter.
5. Restrictive practices—union or political.
6. Lack of co-operation. Unwilling to try new methods or equipment.
7. Lack of safety awareness.
8. Differing objectives—for example, workers on piece rates may want to handle the cargo as quickly as possible, with no interest in good stowage or damage prevention.
9. Laziness—wanting to do the least work in the easiest way possible.
10. No incentive to work at all! For example if their conditions of employment are poor, or the port is using conscripted or forced labour.

7.7 Cargo handling

Careful supervision by the OOW can prevent much damage. If he is concerned that the methods employed in handling the cargo are causing it to be damaged, the OOW must stop the cargo operation until an acceptable method of handling the cargo is adopted, and inform the Master.[2]

7.7.1 Basics of cargo handling

1. The cargo must be handled in a safe manner, to avoid damage to itself, other cargo, the ship and personnel.
   The operation should be conducted with due care, and without undue haste. Cargo should not be dragged over other cargo or allowed to collide with parts of the ship's structure or fittings.
2. Cargo-handling equipment must be in a safe condition, and operated with safe methods, by trained operators (see chapter 4.5).
3. Employ any specialised equipment available for that type of cargo. (Some examples are given in section 7.7.3)
4. Handling-instruction labels on the cargo must be obeyed.
   e.g., 'This way up' 'Sling here' 'Use no hooks' 'Stow no more than five units high' and of course 'Fragile'.

7.7.2 Basics of safe slinging

1. The load must be as secure in the air as it was on the ground,
2. The load must be adequately secured by the sling.
   (a) It is completely contained by the sling, (e.g., bags in nets).
   (b) Use fixed lifting lugs if available.
   (c) Rope or wire slings are wrapped completely around the load—no loads resting in loose bights of line.
   (d) When using specialised devices, they must be properly attached to the cargo, and the manufacturer's instructions followed.
3. The sling must be adequately attached to the lifting appliance.
4. The load must be slung so that it will not collapse or change form when it is lifted.
   Use forks or special bar lifts for handling pallets. Use specialised frames not wire slings for handling containers.
5. The load must not damage the sling, perhaps causing it to part.
   Use packing or padding at sensitive points or sharp edges.
6. The load must not be damaged by the sling
   e.g., wire rope slings may rip paper, score timber, distort steel, etc.; fibre rope slings can rupture paper sacks.
   Use the type of sling best suited to the type of cargo.
   Wider slings will help spread the load with heavier or fragile cargoes.
7. All lifting parts should act as near to the vertical as possible.

8. Use spreaders where appropriate to even out the load on each part of the sling, and assist with items 4 and 6.
9. Attach a lanyard to heavy, long or awkward loads to assist in controlling its movement.
10. If a single cargo hook is being used, this should be positioned vertically above the centre of gravity of the load. This can be achieved using legs of different length if the CG (centre of gravity) is off-centre.
11. Whenever a shackle is used, any moving part such as the sling must pass through the bow, the pin must only be secured to fixed parts.

7.7.3 Examples of specialised cargo-handling equipment

- Braided steel straps, or 'C'hooks, for steel coils.
- Canvas slings for bagged cargo, frozen meat, etc.
- Can hooks for drums, barrels and cans.
- Forks for palletised units.
- Car slings for vehicles.
- Camlocks for railway lines.
- Grapple hooks for logs.
- Core clamps or probes, for cylindrical cargo with an open core.
- Bale clamps for cotton, pulp, etc.
- Vacuum clamps for newsprint.
- Magnetic clamps for units securely fastened with steel binding tape
- . . . and the whole range of dedicated container-handling gear.

7.7.4 Extra precautions for heavy lifts

1. All equipment should be thoroughly checked prior to each lift.
2. Any extra rigging required by the ship's plans must be in place.
3. Stability requirements should be checked, in particular the angle of heel at the moment the weight is lifted off the quay must be calculated, and the GM at this time proved adequate—see chapter 11.6.
4. As many tanks as possible should be pressed up to avoid loss of stability due to free surface effects—see chapter 11.5.
5. All personnel onboard should be warned, so that no accidents will be caused by an unexpected list.
6. Crew should be in a position to tend to moorings if required.
7. The centre of gravity of the lift should be known to enable the slings to be suitably adjusted to ensure a proper vertical lift.

7.7.5 Fork-lift trucks

It is preferable for trucks which are to be operated on board to be electrically powered. Oil powered trucks are a hazard on board ship:
1. There is an ever-present fire risk from the oil fuel.
2. Good ventilation is essential because excessive fumes may be injurious to personnel.
3. Exhaust fumes may taint sensitive commodities.
4. Oil drips may contaminate the cargo.
   Careless driving can result in cargo damage from collisions between the truck and the cargo and the

ship. It is essential that only skilled drivers are permitted on board, and that particular care is taken on uneven or sloping surfaces, when handling cargo high in a stow, and when breaking out the first unit from a stow. Sufficient personnel should be available to guide the driver, and advise of any obstructions and potential dangers. Speed needs to be supervised, the ILO (International Labour Organization—an agency of the United Nations) recommend a maximum of 25 km/hour on board.

When not in use, trucks should be parked clear of cargo operations, with the brake on, engine off, and forks resting on the ground. They should not be hoisted through the air with their engines running, and it is preferable that all refuelling operations are undertaken ashore.

7.7.6 Handling cargo in the rain

When loading or discharging cargo which is sensitive to moisture, the OOW should stop cargo operations, and cover the holds, during all periods of rain, drizzle, snow, etc.

This standard instruction must be observed at all times, despite pressures from the stevedores or other shore officials to continue cargo operations in the rain. It should only be disregarded if the OOW receives clear authority from the Master or Chief Officer.

It is sometimes suggested that loading of non-sensitive cargoes can continue during rain if any sensitive cargo already in the hold is covered with tarpaulins or plastic. Whilst this may be useful for a very short period, the OOW should be cautious of employing this method for an extended period. First of all rain may collect in the hold, and find a path to run on to the other cargo. More important is the likelihood of condensation forming under this protective layer, and dripping on to the cargo beneath. It has been reported that condensation will form within a few hours, and, for example, start rusting a steel cargo.[20]

Even when rain does not effect the cargo being handled at that time, the accumulation of water in the hold may run on to other cargo causing damage, and may lead to a high level of humidity in the hold once the hatches are secured, which may cause severe damage to other sensitive cargoes, particularly produce. The same arguments apply for rejecting suggestions to continue cargo operations with part of the hatch covered.

Tents can be used to cover the hold during rain. A hatch tent is suspended from the crane or derrick runner wire, and secured around the circumference of the hatch, then the runner is heaved to tighten the tent. This is a quick and easy method of covering hatches where the permanent covers take a long time to operate. It is essential that these tents are examined at regular intervals to ensure that there are no leaks, and that water is not collecting in any depressions. Before removing the tent, any pools of water must be bailed out with a bucket, to prevent such water from falling into the hold and damaging the cargo.

Some ports have huge tents completely covering the hatch and the adjacent area of the quay, and cargo operations can continue under this tent unaffected by the weather.

If cargo is loaded to/from lighters alongside, it is good practice to plug the deck scuppers if rain is expected, to reduce risks of wetting the cargo in the lighters.

In areas such as the tropics, where rainfall is both sudden and very intense, the OOW should run the radar to detect rain in advance, and plot its ETA (estimated time of arrival) at the ship. Precautions should be taken to enable the hatches to be closed rapidly, including having extra crew on stand-by, keep operating wires rigged, continuously running hydraulics, etc. These precautions should be recorded in the log book.

Before reopening the hatch covers after a period of rain, the OOW should ensure that any pools of water lying on the covers are swept off first. A squeegee is useful for this task. Sponges or other absorbent material should be used for emptying any depressions where water collects, such as in container fittings set into the hatch covers. If this is not done, then accumulated rainwater may run off the covers as they open, and run onto the cargo in the hold below.

If rain damages the cargo BEFORE LOADING, the OOW should report this to the Chief Officer, so that it is noted on the mate's receipt and bill of lading. If such wetting is liable to damage other cargoes, by direct contact or by causing condensation in the hold, then the wet cargo <u>must</u> be rejected.

If the cargo is damaged by rain AFTER LOADING, although this is the ship's responsibility, it might be prudent to discharge the damaged portion and reload new cargo, if this is available. This will prevent further damage by moisture migration.[29]

Wet cargo is further discussed in chapter 12.7.

7.7.7 Some examples of damage caused by poor handling

1. Cargo can be stained by driving fork-lift trucks over the stow. Steel plates or floors of (plywood) dunnage should always be used. Staining comes from scuffs, tyres and oil dripping from the engine.

   If the cargo underneath is likely to be damaged by crushing, then this method of handling must not be permitted.

2. If a fork-lift truck is driven carelessly, its forks can pierce packaging and damage the contents. Timber cargo may be split, and unpackaged goods can be scored. Only cargo with integral bearers should be handled by fork-lift trucks; they should never be used to lift flat cargo from a flat surface such as a steel deck or concrete quay.

3. Bands used to bind bundles together must not be broken:
   - Do not lift cargo by attaching sling hooks to such bands;
   - Do not cut them to make the contents fit into an available space;

- Do not allow roughly driven trucks to break them;

otherwise the unit will loosen and the commodity may spill out or be more exposed to damage, for example 'telescoped' steel coils.

Also, loose units could cause the stow to collapse. If the cargo has been compressed then banded, it may be difficult to contain if the banding is broken, and may be difficult to discharge.

4. The use of hooks or pad-eye grips by stevedores can rip the covering of bagged cargo, leading to spillage and loss of cargo.

5. If a sling is overloaded, unpacked goods can be bent, crushed, chafed or scored.

6. If the load is landed heavily, it can be distorted—e.g., steel coils can be 'ovalised' which makes them unable to fit on to machines which unwind the steel, and so require separate processing, which can be an expensive cost which the receiver will seek to reclaim from the shipowner.

7. Cargo can be damaged by oil or grease dripping from cargo-handling equipment, both shore based and ship based.

8. Bulk cargo can be lost from grabs which leak, or do not close properly. Break-bulk cargo can be lost by falling out of insecure slings.

9. If an intermediate bulk container (IBC or Jumbo bag) is pierced, a large amount of cargo can spill out, which may lead to problems in containment, recovery and repacking, particularly if the commodity is IMDG classed.

7.8 Cargo stowage

The correct stowage of the cargo will help to ensure that it reaches its destination undamaged. It is recommended that the OOW makes himself familiar with all the characteristics of the cargo before it is loaded. Prior knowledge of the hazards of spontaneous combustion, self-heating, vapours, fumes, moisture and odours is essential. Ventilation requirements, and compatibility with other intended cargoes should be studied.[23] The complexities of stowage are beyond the scope of this manual, for detailed guidance on individual commodities the reader should consult a definitive cargo manual such as *Thomas's Stowage*[70] and the IMDG Code[49]—see 7.12.

7.8.1 IMO Guidelines

The IMO *Code of Safe Practice for Cargo Stowage and Securing*[54] states the following general principles:

1. *All cargoes should be stowed and secured in such a way that the ship and persons on board are not put at risk.*
2. *The safe stowage and securing of cargoes depend on proper planning, execution and supervision.*
3. *Personnel commissioned to tasks of cargo stowage and securing should be properly qualified and experienced.*
4. *Personnel planning and supervising the stowage and securing of cargo should have a sound practical knowledge of the application and content of the Cargo Securing Manual, if provided.*
5. *In all cases, improper stowage and securing cargo will be potentially hazardous to the securing of other cargoes and to the ship itself.*
6. *Decisions taken for measures of stowage and securing*

cargo should be based on the most severe weather conditions which may be expected by experience for the intended voyage.
7. *Ship-handling decisions taken by the Master, especially in bad weather conditions, should take into account the type and stowage position of the cargo and the securing arrangements.*

Paragraph 2.2.1 states: *It is of utmost importance that the Master takes great care in planning and supervising the stowage and securing of cargoes in order to prevent cargo sliding, tipping, racking, collapsing.*

Paragraph 2.6.1 states: **The principal means of preventing the improper stowage and securing of cargoes is through proper supervision of the loading operations and inspections of the stow.** [i.e., An efficient OOW.]

Specific guidance is given in the annexes of the code for the stowage and securing of:

- Annex 1 — Containers on deck.
- Annex 2 — Portable tanks.
- Annex 3 — Portable receptacles.
- Annex 4 — Wheel based cargoes.
- Annex 5 — Heavy items.
- Annex 6 — Coiled steel sheet.
- Annex 7 — Heavy metal products.
- Annex 8 — Anchor chains.
- Annex 9 — Metal scrap in bulk.
- Annex 10 — Flexible intermediate bulk containers (FIBC).
- Annex 11 — Under-deck stowage of logs.
- Annex 12 — Unit loads.

The OOW should ensure that he reads any annex which is applicable to the cargo to be carried on a particular voyage. If he does not understand any of the requirements, he should seek the advice of the Chief Officer or Master.

7.8.2 Basics of cargo stowage

1. Secure the cargo against movement of:
   (a) the ship; (b) the cargo; (c) other cargo—see chapter 17.
2. Protect the cargo against damage by water.
   - Raise it above the tank top on dunnage, to avoid contact with drainage.
   - Protect it from touching the ship's steelwork, to avoid contact with ship's sweat.
3. Protect sensitive cargoes from chafing against the ship's structure, by the use of flatboard, plywood or inflatable dunnage bags.
4. Provide for means of adequate ventilation:
   - Leave ventilation channels within and around the stow (these can be natural gaps, or constructed using dunnage).
   - Do not block off the ship's ventilator inlets and outlets.
5. Allow access for discharge in the correct port rotation:
   - No over-stow, unless unavoidable, in which case the overstow must be clearly marked on the cargo stowage plan.
   - Safety walkway available, if required (one metre of clear deck space is usually required around unfenced openings).
   - Leave ladder rungs unobstructed if they have to be used.

6. Enable the cargo to be discharged efficiently:
   - Use dunnage so that the sling can be easily attached.
   - Presling the hatch square.
   - Mark the key unit of a stow—the one to discharge first.
   - Maintain access—for example, the flow routes of forklifts should not be blocked off by other cargo which will be discharged later.
   - Stow in a hold served by ship's cranes of adequate capacity.
   - Distribute equally between the holds, so that all holds take the same time to load and discharge. However, the cargo must not be over-distributed—with only small quantities in several holds. Each hold must have sufficient cargo to warrant opening it up and setting the gear, and be more than any minimum quantity in the stevedore gang contract. Otherwise extra compensation payments may have to be made, such extra costs are a waste of resources and a drain on profits.

7. Do not exceed any structural limitations:
   - Bending moments, shear forces—see chapter 11.9.
   - Container stack weights—the OOW should be aware of the maximum values of these restrictions.
   - Allowable deck weights (expressed as tonnes per square metre)—the OOW should be aware of the maximum values of these restrictions.
   - Use timber to spread the weight of point loads.

8. Do not exceed any stability limitations:
   - Excessive deck load with insufficient weights below.
   - Bulk cargoes trimmed level to avoid shifting.

9. Heavy and/or well packaged cargo is given bottom stow, and light and/or fragile cargo is given top stow—whenever possible.

10. Heavy or long cargo, such as beams and pipes, should be stowed fore and aft. Steel coils are usually stowed on the round, in athwartships rows, with their core axis fore and aft.

11. Dunnage should be so arranged that the cargo is well supported in the stow, but is not distorted. For example, dunnage between steel sheets should lie in the same vertical line throughout the stow.

12. Cargoes which may damage each other should not be stowed together. Consider leakage, contamination, taint, chemical reaction, dust, and moisture migration—see section 7.12 for dangerous cargoes.

13. Cargo which is liable to melt, or be damaged by heat, should be stowed away from the engineroom bulkhead and tanks containing oil which will be heated on the voyage. Stowage should be avoided immediately under-deck or in small lockers or other compartments which are difficult to ventilate and which may be heated by the sun.

14. Cargo which is stored in containers such as barrels or drums, which have been filled through a hole, should be stowed with the cap or bung of that hole uppermost.

15. Optimum use should be made of the cargo-carrying capacity of the vessel, in order to maximise its earnings. Traditionally this meant stowing as much as possible in the available space. Modern operating systems require that the time taken to load, stow and discharge the cargo is taken into account. Efficient carriage is a compromise between efficient utilisation of space and efficient utilisation of time.

16. Adopt any special stowage requirements recommended by the shipper.
    It is always good practice to seek further advice from the owner, operator, charterer, local P&I representative, shipper or manufacturer when the ship's staff are unfamiliar with the cargo to be loaded.

7.8.3 Deck cargo requirements

1. Avoid excess loading of the deck.
   The maximum permitted deck load (usually expressed as xx tonnes per square metre) is given in the ship's approved loading manual.
   Decks have been set down and hatch covers damaged and distorted due to having excess weights of cargo loaded on them.

2. Ensure the ship will have adequate stability throughout the voyage, bearing in mind expected wind moments, and changes in weights from the consumption of fuel, the absorption of water and icing.

3. The watertight integrity of the ship must not be impaired.
   Ventilators and air pipes must be adequately protected.

4. The height of the cargo must not interfere with the ship's navigation. Consideration must be given to limiting the blind area forward of the bows which is not visible from the bridge. Vessels with limited visibility may have to employ extra pilots in some ports and canals.

5. Nothing must obstruct safe access around the vessel.
   This includes access between the crew accommodation and the working areas of the ship (specifically the engineroom, steering flat and the fo'c'sle), the pilot boarding area and to ventilators, sounding pipes, air pipes, tank valves, etc.
   A suitable walkway must be constructed over the cargo if necessary.

6. The stow should be as solid and compact as practicable, to produce a self-binding effect, in order to reduce its permeability for seawater, to aid lashing and to prevent them from becoming slack.

7. See chapter 17.8 for timber deck cargoes.

7.8.4 Cargo separations

Sometimes certain cargo in a stow must be distinguishable from other cargo in the same stow. Separations are made to aid discharge, so that cargo for different ports, or different consignees, can be readily identified. It should be remembered that the stevedores in some discharge ports may be illiterate, so may not understand any port name or marking on the cargo. The OOW must be alert to see that the stevedores in the loading port place the separations in the correct locations, otherwise there may be confusion at the discharge port(s), and perhaps the expense of employing extra labour to sort out consignments which have become mixed up.

Incorrect or inappropriate separations can lead to cargo not being discharged at the correct port, either discharged at an earlier port in error, or overcarried to a later port of call. At the discharge port, the OOW should ensure that the stevedores take note of the separations, and do not mix the cargoes, as this could lead to expensive resorting ashore.

Some common forms of separation are:
1. Thin netting (different colours are available).
2. Ropes (different colours are available).
3. Paint (water-soluble if it may damage the cargo—e.g., timber).
4. Marking pens (very suitable for cartons and cased goods).
5. Chalk (but beware as this can be easily erased).
6. Layers of dunnage (flatboard or plywood).
7. Construction of bulkheads from timber or, occasionally, steel plate.
8. Separation cloth (burlap).
9. Plastic sheet (but make sure restriction of ventilation will not harm the cargo).
10. Use of markings (e.g., bags marked on one side can be separated by stowing them mark up/mark down).
11. Natural separation (cargo of different form, shape, or packing).

7.9 Dunnage

The OOW must ensure that dunnage is used in the correct manner, otherwise the shipowner may be held liable for any resulting damage.

7.9.1 Uses of dunnage
1. Prevent chafing of cargo against ship's structure.
2. Spread the weight of the cargo across a large area of the ship's structure, particularly heavy cargoes with small points of contact.
3. Spread the weight of subsequent layers of cargo over a large area of the cargo beneath, to avoid crushing it.
4. Form a barrier between cargo and moisture, both sweat and drainage.
5. Assist with cargo ventilation.
6. Assist to stabilise the stow.
7. Fill in any broken stowage—void spaces within the cargo stow.
8. Secure the cargo—see chapter 17.
9. Form separations—see section 7.8.4.
10. Keep cargo clean.
11. Contain cargo, and assist with the recovery of spills.
12. Enable the easy removal of slings at the loadport, and easy insertion of slings at the discharge port.

7.9.2 Types of dunnage
1. Timber—flat-board, square section, laths, bamboo, pallets.
2. Timber products—plywood, chipboard, hardboard.
3. Paper rolls—kraft, corrugated.
4. Sheeting—burlap, plastic.
5. Mats—straw, dried reeds/grasses/etc., bamboo.
6. Patent devices—inflatable bags.
7. Other commodities—old tyres.

7.9.3 Problems with timber dunnage
1. MOISTURE.
   The moisture content of timber can be measured with a special meter. Moisture can migrate from dunnage into hydroscopic cargoes, such as rice, coffee, cocoa, sugar, tobacco, paper, etc. and damage them.
   Do not use any dunnage with sensitive cargoes if its moisture content is over 15%, especially if it is visibly wet or damp.

2. ROUGH SURFACES
   Timber which is rough sawn may tear bagged cargo, and damage other delicate cargoes.

3. BARK
   Bark may retain moisture, is rough and provides a haven for insects which may migrate and infest a produce cargo, lowering its value, and perhaps leading to extra costs of fumigation.

4. CUTTING TIMBER IN THE HOLD.
   Sawdust may contaminate certain cargoes and it has been reported that it reacted with a chemical cargo, causing a fire in the hold.[20]

5. RECYCLING.
   After use, and before reusing for the next cargo, check for:
   (a) Nails—potential damage to personnel and next cargo.
   (b) Wet—do not stow dunnage on deck unprotected from rain/sea.
   (c) Contamination, including taint—reject any with cargo spills, especially chemicals.

6. DISPOSAL.
   If the dunnage from the previous cargo is not required for the next voyage, and cannot be stowed away on board, or if it cannot be used because of deterioration in quality, then it must be disposed of.
   This can cause problems such as:
   (a) Some countries prohibit the landing of untreated timber.
   (b) Import duties may be required.
   (c) Discharge is difficult to arrange, or highly expensive (e.g., gearless ships at berths with no cranes).
   (d) Discharge is impossible (anchorages or dolphin berths).
   (e) Shore transportation is difficult to arrange or expensive.
   This problem frequently arises on bulk carriers—for example when grain is to be carried after a steel cargo (the weight of timber used can be up to 10% of the weight of the steel cargo.[20]) or after the discharge of grain which has been separated into parcels in the hold. The ship should insist that any

dunnage provided by the charterer is removed by them at the end of the charter.

7.10 Preventing damage to ship

The OOW should supervise the cargo operations to ensure that the ship is not damaged by reckless cargo handling. He must warn the stevedores if he observes any methods being employed which may result in damage to the ship, cargo or personnel, and be prepared to stop cargo operations until a more appropriate method of cargo handling is adopted.

The OOW should pay particular attention to any ramps and doors which open over or on to the quay, and which could be damaged by shore equipment, or by the movement of the ship, including changes of the height of tide, or of the vessel's draft and trim.

7.10.1 Identifying damage

The OOW must be continuously on the lookout for damage to the ship, and he must report any fresh damage he notices to the Chief Officer, even if he does not actually see the damage occur. Every loud bang or unexplained rocking of the ship must be investigated. The OOW should make a habit of regularly viewing all visible parts of the ship's structure as he patrols around the deck. He should pay particular attention to those parts of the structure which are adjacent to cargo-handling equipment.

Crew members can often draw attention to damage that might otherwise be overlooked. It is worthwhile for the OOW to emphasise this to the crew members on duty with him, as often they may not have been encouraged to help in this way in the past. Even shore workers may assist; they often work in close proximity to parts of the ship's structure, and may notice defects, structural failures or previous damage. However, often they may be reluctant to incriminate themselves or their colleagues.

In order to complete the damage report properly, the OOW should obtain accurate measurements of any damaged areas of the ship's structure. On some ships, the OOW will complete the damage report; on other ships this is the responsibility of the Chief Officer. In this latter case, it is both good practice and good training for the OOW to complete a standard damage report form as the basis of his report to the Chief Officer. An example of a damage report form is given in appendix XII.

It should be remembered that damage can spread a long way from the area of impact, so the OOW must always check adjacent structures and compartments. It is a requirement of most charterparties that the ship reports any damage within 24 hours, and holds the stevedores liable, otherwise the charterer may not be held responsible for making good the damage. This is discussed in chapter 6.8.

As with damage to cargo, it is helpful if the OOW is able to take photographs of the damage to the ship or its fittings or equipment. Not only will such photographs provide evidence of the damage, but also they may be extremely useful when organising repairs—see chapter 18.9.

7.10.2 Repairing damage

Many stevedores will prefer to repair any damage they cause with their own labour and materials, to save higher costs and the expenses of organisation and paperwork in the future. The OOW must check that all such repairs are satisfactory; he should be guided by the Chief Officer and/or Chief Engineer as appropriate. These checks should ensure that the correct materials are used, and that the repaired structure is left in a safe condition, with all moving parts tested, and proved to be fully operational. In such cases, any damage certificate must be claused to show the repair was satisfactorily completed, or the report destroyed.

Where the repair is minor, it may not be economical to employ local labour, particularly in high cost areas. Also, there may be insufficient time to undertake the repair or complete it satisfactorily. In these cases, a full damage report must be issued, and full details forwarded to the owners for them to arrange repairs in the future. Often all minor repairs are left until drydock, but it is essential they are properly identified and the records retained, so that costs can be recovered from the party liable, and not left for the shipowner.

Any damage which results in the ship being made unseaworthy MUST be repaired before the ship leaves port. These and all other major repairs must be reported to the ship's classification society, which is usually done by the Master through the shipowners.

7.11 Cargo plan

The OOW must know the exact location of all cargo on board at all times. This is shown on the cargo plan, which is usually a longitudinal section of the ship. Each compartment is shown, with the cargo either in vertical or horizontal plan, according to the practice of the trade, or whichever shows the intricacies of the stow in the clearest way.

7.11.1 Preloading plan

The Chief Officer will devise a planned stowage for the cargo once he receives the cargo booking list. This will take into account the topics outlined in 7.8. He will give a copy of this proposed stowage plan to the stevedores and the OOW. The OOW should study this plan carefully, and if he does not understand any feature of the plan, he must ask the Chief Officer for clarification. The Chief Officer may give some guidance on stowage and separation requirements on the plan, or he may make separate notes on important points for the OOW.

During loading, it is the responsibility of the OOW to ensure that the stevedores stow the cargo exactly according to this plan. He must bring any discrepancies immediately to the attention of the Chief Officer. On some trades, there are likely to be many changes to the initial plan, as cargo bookings change, cargoes occupy more or less space than planned, or the timing of delivery to the quay is altered. In such circumstances, the Chief Officer may delegate some of the minor decisions regarding changes of stowage to the OOW, who should use his initiative and experience. It is always good practice to inform the Chief Officer of any such alterations as soon as it is convenient. The OOW must update his plan as loading progresses, to show the actual stow, particularly when he hands over the watch. Often this is done on a working copy of the loaded plan which is kept in the cargo office.

7.11.2 Loaded plan

During the loading operations, the OOW must record any stowage which is different from the pre-loading plan. In this way, an up-to-date cargo plan is always available. The description and quantities can be added later once this data has been obtained from the tally sheets, but it is essential that the **exact actual** stowage position of all cargo is noted by the OOW. Once loading is completed, a neat final cargo plan can be produced. In some companies, this job is allocated to one of the junior officers, or it may be the responsibility of the OOW at the time.

On some trades, a plan-maker is employed ashore, perhaps as part of the stevedore's organisation. When loading is complete, a copy of this plan is delivered to the ship. It is essential that such plans are very carefully checked by the ship's officers. Usually they will be in a much better position to know the intricacies of the actual final stow, from their regular observations of the cargo holds, rather than the plan-maker, who spends most of his time in an office ashore, and may be relying on second- or third-hand information passed from the stevedores.

It is the ship's officers who have the job of supervising the discharge of the cargo which has been loaded. To ensure the discharge operation is efficient, the stowage plan must be correct in every detail. This is in the officer's own interests; he should remember that the plan-maker has no further interest in the plan once the ship has sailed from the loading port.

With containers, often the loading operation is conducted at such a fast pace that a solitary OOW has not sufficient time to make a note of the stowage of every container, particularly when shore gantries are employed. At such terminals, the ship's staff have no alternative but to accept the validity of the stowage plan provided by the plan-maker. However, it is good practice for the OOW to do spot checks if this is possible, both during the operation and at a convenient time after completion of loading—even if this is undertaken on the next sea passage.

The final plan is copied to send to the discharging stevedore, so he will know exactly what he has to discharge, and from where. It will enable him to organise sufficient labour, suitable handling equipment and appropriate onward distribution facilities. With bulk cargoes and single load and discharge ports, this plan is fairly simple. On break-bulk ships with numerous load and discharge ports, the plan can be extremely complicated. On container ships, each athwartships row of containers usually has its own bay plan.

Traditionally, the cargo plan was drawn on a large sheet of paper, which on complicated voyages needed to be as large as a desk. On modern vessels cargo data may be stored on a computer, and cargo plans can be printed by such systems. This computer is often capable of performing stability and strength calculations, recommending appropriate lashing systems, indicating desirable loading or discharging sequences, highlighting necessary separations and segregations, monitoring limiting factors and maintaining a data base of both cargo characteristics and legislative and regulatory requirements.

7.11.3 Features of a cargo plan

1. The location of each main item of cargo, with a brief description.
2. The weight of major units, and the total weight of each stow.
3. The load port and discharge port of each stow. It helps to show different discharge ports in different colours. Some companies, groups or trades have fixed colours for ports for uniformity, and these should be followed to avoid confusion.
4. The marks of major units.
5. Bill of lading numbers, if appropriate.
6. Location of key units of a stow.
7. Flow-lines for mechanical handling equipment.
8. Details of the type and position of all separations.
9. Extent of any pre-slinging.
10. Remarks on stowage which may aid the discharging stevedore.
11. All overstows must be clearly marked, both to aid discharge of the correct items, and to enable plans to be made for shifting the overstowing cargo. This is especially important when the overstowing cargo needs to be landed, stored ashore, then reloaded, as this can cause problems with the port authorities or Customs, particularly if the goods are consigned to a different country.

Above all, the plan must be easy to read, and capable of being readily understood with no risk of misinterpretation.

7.12 Dangerous goods

The carriage of all dangerous goods onboard ship is governed by the IMO *International Maritime Dangerous Goods (IMDG) Code*[49] and supplements. This publication contains details of the classification of each commodity, and the documentation, labelling and packaging required. Physical and chemical properties are described, and advice on fire-fighting and any limiting quantities is given. Such goods must be appropriately handled, stowed and segregated with regard to the advice given in this code.

The supplements contain information on: reporting procedures, packing guidelines, solid bulk cargoes (BC Code), emergency procedures (EmS Code), and medical first aid guide (MFAG) (for use in accidents involving dangerous goods).

The OOW should make himself familiar with the layout of this publication, including its supplements, so that he is able to extract quickly all information which is relevant to the cargo carried on a particular voyage. Ships which are fitted with computers having a CD-ROM drive may be provided with this publication on disc, for rapid access of the relevant information.

The OOW should read the entry for each item of dangerous goods that is to be shipped, and ask the Chief Officer for clarification of any point he does not understand. With rapid loading, and large quantities of dangerous cargo, the OOW may not have time to read all these entries. It is good training if he reads such entries as soon as he is able. Extra information may be available from the shipper of the goods.

Dangerous goods should be loaded and discharged only under the supervision of the OOW. HE SHOULD ENSURE THAT THEY ARE CLEARLY MARKED WITH THEIR APPROPRIATE CLASS AND IMO NUMBER as described in the IMDG Code, and that they are identified by their CORRECT CHEMICAL NAME and **not** a brand name, otherwise there may be problems in obtaining the correct advice for handling spills or other emergencies.

The goods must be packaged in accordance with the IMDG Code, so that they are capable of withstanding the rigours of handling and sea transportation, taking into account their properties. The classification of each category of dangerous goods, along with the appropriate marking symbol, is shown in appendix VI.

There are specific rules on the separation between different classes of dangerous goods, as shown in the table in appendix VI.[49] It is essential that the OOW checks that all dangerous goods are stowed <u>exactly</u> according to the preloading plan, to ensure that planned segregations are made. He must report any discrepancies to the Chief Officer immediately, to ensure that any incorrect stowage is changed so that incompatible cargoes are adequately segregated.

Empty containers which are being returned to the supplier should be treated as though they contain the commodity which they previously carried, unless the shipping documents certify that they have been thoroughly cleaned and have been examined for contamination from their previous contents.

7.12.1 Spillage of dangerous goods

The OOW should be extra alert if any dangerous goods are spilled from their packaging. He must inform the Chief Officer immediately. The substance should be identified and the spill contained. The IMDG Code must be consulted to ascertain the likely effects of the spillage. Relevant information may be contained in the EmS Code and MFAG supplements. If the chemical is poisonous, gives off toxic fumes, or has any other life-threatening properties, no-one should be allowed near the spill unless they are wearing appropriate protective clothing, and a respirator if necessary. Evacuation of the hold, or the entire ship, may be appropriate.

It should be remembered that substances may be toxic by ingestion, inhalation or even skin contact. It has been estimated that absorbtion of 25 milligrams of the concentrated insecticide Parathion is lethal, and that the contents of one 200 litre drum is sufficient to kill over a million people![20] Decomposition of some chemicals results from contact with air or moisture, or may be instigated by minute contact with organic matter, such as dunnage timbers. This may result in the emission of toxic vapours or spontaneous combustion, which can be so violent as to resemble an explosion.[20] It has been reported that weedkiller from a split bag was absorbed by sacks of flour, resulting in the death of those who ate the bread which was later baked from that flour.[20]

From these examples, it is clear that the OOW must ensure that all dangerous goods are handled with extra care. Any damage must be fully investigated, no matter how minor. All spills of such cargoes and any contaminated dunnage must be properly disposed of, the original packing must be adequately resecured, and the entire area thoroughly cleaned. Special attention should be paid to such areas as the bilges, as there have been cases of the death of crew on subsequent voyages when cleaning bilges into which chemicals had spilt some time before.

A wide-strap sling will prevent damage to delicate cargo. Note also the use of spreader bars to avoid crushing the cargo. See chapter 7.7.2. Photograph: author.

Chapter 8
SPECIALIST DRY CARGO OPERATIONS
PURPOSE

On completion of this chapter you will appreciate the special requirements for keeping a cargo watch on bulk carriers, container ships and refrigerated cargo ships.

8.1 Dry bulk carriers

The officer serving on dry bulk carriers should consult the IMO publication *Code of Safe Practice for Solid Bulk Cargoes*, (The 'BC' Code).[50] This provides detailed guidance on:

1. Cargo distribution to avoid overstressing the ship's structure.
2. The safety of personnel.
3. Trimming procedures, and methods of determining the angle of repose.
4. Cargoes which may liquefy.
5. Cargoes which have chemical hazards.

8.1.1 Hazards of bulk cargoes

Potential hazards associated with dry bulk cargoes include:

1. Movement of the cargo during the voyage.
2. High structural stresses, which can lead to structural failure.
3. Spontaneous heating, which may lead to a fire.
4. Corrosion of the ship's structure.
5. Production of explosive or toxic gases.
6. Absorption of atmospheric oxygen.
7. Health hazards through contact with the cargo.

8.1.2 Loading plan on bulkers

This is not a sectional plan of the cargo compartments, but is the list of the planned sequence of loading the holds, with the tonnage of each pour. Often the ballast plan is contained in the same document. The Nautical Institute recommends that this plan be lodged with the authorities ashore, and has produced a sample pro-forma for this purpose, which is reproduced in appendix VIII—also see chapter 10.4.

8.1.3 Monitoring cargo and ballast operations

In some loading ports, cargo is poured on board at rates in excess of 10,000 tonnes per hour. The International Association of Classification Societies (IACS) has confirmed that these high loading rates in themselves do not cause structural damage to the vessel. However, high loading rates mean that extra vigilance is required to ensure that proper distribution of the cargo is achieved.

It is **essential** that the OOW monitors the loading closely, to ensure that it complies with the preplan. He must also ensure that the cargo and ballast operations are co-ordinated; if they begin to get out of step with each other, the OOW must inform the Chief Officer immediately. Ships have broken their backs when insufficient attention has been paid to cargo and ballast distribution.

With rapid loading and high ballast-pump rates, there is little time available for errors. Shore handling equipment often cannot be stopped immediately, and there may be a considerable quantity of cargo which may have to be run off the belts once the decision to stop loading has been made. Many loading terminals are sited in isolated locations and have no facilities for discharging cargo. If any overloading occurs, cargo which took only a few minutes to load may take several days to discharge. Perhaps this may involve bringing in equipment from another port, and definitely the operation will incur considerable extra costs.

Generally, the cargo discharge rates are not as high as the loading rates. However, the Chief Officer will still produce a plan to ensure that the ship is not overstressed by an incorrect combination of cargo and ballast. The OOW must ensure that the cargo and ballast operations are co-ordinated, and inform the Chief Officer immediately if they begin to get out of step.

See also chapter 10 on ballast operations.

8.1.4 Grain cargoes

When loading grain, all the provisions of the *IMO International Grain Code*[53] must be obeyed. A copy of this should be on every ship which is capable of carrying grain, and the OOW should study this document thoroughly before reaching the port of loading. The Master or Chief Officer will have completed a statutory form to prove that the vessel will have adequate stability at all stages of the intended voyage. This document has to be verified by the shore authorities before they will authorise loading. The leading grain exporting countries have their own forms, copies of which are usually kept on board most bulk carriers.

These forms require the compilation of <u>grain shift moments</u>, and comparing the actual values to maximum limits given in the ship's <u>Grain Stability Manual</u>. The values of these moments vary with the height of the grain in the hold, and whether the ends of the hold are trimmed or not. Junior officers unfamiliar with these terms should ask the Chief Officer for explanation, or see *Bulk Carrier Practice*.[3] It is good training for the OOW to be able to complete these forms.

The holds will require cleaning to the highest standards. <u>All</u> traces of the previous cargo must be completely removed, and there should be no loose rust scale. The holds must be dry and be free of odours, infestation and anything else which could contaminate the grain.

8.1.5 Transportable moisture limit

When a ship vibrates at sea, inherent moisture in the cargo rises to the top of the stow. If this part of the cargo liquefies, it can flow from side to side as the ship rolls. This free surface effect can result in a dangerous reduction in the ship's stability, and has led to ships foundering. Ore concentrates are very prone to such liquefaction.

Such cargoes are allotted a transportable moisture limit (TML) which represents the maximum moisture content considered safe for the carriage of that commodity in ships. It is essential that the shippers provide evidence that the actual moisture content is well below this limit. However, it is good practice for the vessel to perform its own rough tests both before and at regular intervals throughout the loading operation. The OOW may be required to carry out such tests, the procedure for which is described in detail in the IMO *Code of Safe Practice for Bulk Cargoes.*[50] Their purpose is to verify the shipper's declaration, and to establish the effects of any precipitation during preshipment storage or the loading operation. Extra care is needed in very cold weather when moisture may be present within the cargo in the form of ice crystals, and the cargo may not appear as moist as it actually is.

8.1.6 Bulk cargo separation

On bulk carriers, most separations are 'natural' in that different holds are used for different grades or different commodities. Sometimes the quantity of cargo on offer does not match the capacity of the ship's holds and/or tanks available, so a physical separation is required.

On a few occasions parcels are separated by vertical timber bulkheads which are usually reinforced with strong wire lashings. Such separations are used when several small parcels of different grades of ores are required to be carried in the one hold. Because of the difficulty in constructing high bulkheads, this method is only practical for these heavy cargoes, which occupy only a few metres of height in the hold.

If there are only two commodities to be separated, and the hold can be left slack, the first cargo is poured into one end of the hold, and a stout separation cloth is secured over the top of the peak, and draped down the free slope. The next cargo is then poured into the other end, and rests against the separation cloth. Slight mixing at the edges is reported when such simple systems are used.

At other times horizontal separations are made using tarpaulins, burlap, plastic sheeting, dunnage or a combination of these. The OOW must ensure that the first cargo is trimmed level, and that the separation material completely covers the stow, paying particular attention to around obstructions such as hold ladders and vertical framing. There can be several such separations within the one hold, and each consignment can be of any tonnage. In practice, very little mixing of commodities is found when using this system.

In the grain trades from the USA to Japan, this is known as a 'Japanese' separation. The first cargo is bulldozed flat, then levelled by hand using shovels. The cargo is completely covered with one large sheet of burlap, which is itself covered with overlapping runners of plastic sheet. This is covered by plywood sheets with the overlaps nailed together. These methods are only suitable for gentle methods of discharge such as suction, and obviously are totally unsuitable if grabs are to be employed for discharge.

For the contamination of bulk cargoes, see chapter 12.8.2

8.1.7 Trimming the cargo

When cargo is poured on a flat surface, such as the tanktop in the bottom of a hold, it forms a conical heap. The angle between the sloping surface of the cargo and the horizontal tank top is called the angle of repose. If this angle is greater than $35°$, then the cargo is likely to shift, and it is essential that such cargo is trimmed level.

A cargo which is peaked may shift during the voyage. Even where the initial stability is satisfactory, shifting of cargo can cause a dangerous list, which may lead to the vessel capsizing. Certain bulk cargoes are more liable to shift than others, but all are potentially dangerous, and should always be trimmed as level as practicable.

The IMO *BC Code*[50] recommends that **all** bulk cargoes are trimmed level. Unfortunately, often this advice is ignored by many bulk loading terminals around the world. A peaked cargo may settle during the voyage, which can produce a small list if it settles more to one side than the other. This could lead to problems if the ship has been loaded for a limiting arrival draft, or there are draft restrictions on the voyage, such as for a canal transit.

If a bulk cargo is not trimmed so that its top surface is level, there is a risk that the weight of the peaks of the cargo may overload the tanktop. This results in the dishing or set-down of the tanktop plating, and may also cause structural damage. Further, a peaked cargo means that there is more surface area of cargo, which means that more air is in contact with more cargo. With some cargoes, this may mean there is more risk of spontaneous combustion due to absorption of oxygen by the cargo.

<u>Methods of trimming</u>
1. MANUAL—highly labour-intensive and slow.
2. MECHANICAL—use of bulldozers—quick and reasonably effective. There is a danger that cargo may be compressed and this may make it difficult to discharge.
3. SPOUT—the end of the loading spout is moved athwartships and fore-and-aft in order to ensure the cargo fills the space and the surface is as flat as the skill and attention of the operator permits.
4. CHUTE—a deflector plate or similar device is used on the end of the spout to shoot the cargo into the far corners of the hold. These devices can be spun through $360°$, and with a skilled operator can produce an extremely level stow.

8.1.8 Cargo in upper wing tanks

If the cargo in the upper wing tanks (hoppers/topsides) is the same consignment as in the adjacent hold, the bleeder manholes from the wing tank into the hold must be removed before loading, and securely stowed away. On completion of loading, the OOW should ensure that the manholes in the deck used for loading the tanks are properly closed. Failure to follow the following procedure could lead to leaks, ingress of water, and substantial cargo claims.

1. Sweep all cargo residues clear of the manhole,
2. Ensure the surfaces around the manhole and under its cover in way of the gasket are free of rust scale.
3. Check the gasket for damage—replacing it if in any doubt,
4. Tighten the nuts evenly.

At the discharge port, labour must be sent into the tanks to ensure that all the cargo has bled into the main hold, or has been removed by suckers when the commodity is different from that in the main hold. The bleeder manholes must be properly closed following the above procedure, before the tanks are ballasted. Otherwise there is a risk that ballast water will leak from the tank into the hold, perhaps on a later voyage when there is cargo in the hold.

Because of the high costs of the extra labour involved in the loading and discharging of cargo in upper wing tanks, many charter parties provide that all such extra costs are for the account of the shipowner. Because of this practice, and the difficulty in maintaining the tanks in a grain-clean condition, many owners are now reluctant to use these tanks for cargo, and consider them as purely ballast tanks.

8.1.9 Final discharge

During discharge, some terminals will make little effort to remove the final clingage from the holds. The removal of cargo residues remaining onboard after departure is very difficult for the crew, particularly on gearless ships, or during adverse weather. The OOW must monitor the discharge closely, and arrange for any cargo sticking to the ship's structure to be removed whilst it is still easily accessible.

The first approach is for the OOW to request the stevedore to remove such cargo. If the stevedore is unwilling or unable to do this, it may be possible to send some of the crew into the holds during breaks in the discharge of the relevant hold. Although not an ideal solution, most ship's personnel will prefer to do this rather than face increased difficulties during hold cleaning operations at sea. Grain remaining on the horizontal flanges of underdeck beams can be swept off much easier near the start of discharge than during hold cleaning operations. All necessary safety precautions must be taken during such procedures.

Towards the end of discharge, it may be possible to request sweeping gangs from the stevedore to ensure the removal of the last traces of cargo. If not, it is useful to send the crew to sweep the holds whilst the ship is still in the safety of the port. Also, many stevedores can be persuaded to return the cargo-

handling equipment to a hold previously completed in order to recover the extra cargo collected by the crew.

If there is an excessive amount of cargo remaining, the Master should officially inform the terminal, as well as charterers and owners. It is important that they should be told in sufficient time to encourage the stevedores to complete the discharge adequately. It may be possible to hold the charterers responsible for any delays and costs associated with the removing excessive residues. Cargo remaining on board on completion of discharge is lost to the receiver, and may result in him making a claim against the ship for this loss, unless it is clearly documented as abandoned by the receiver.

8.1.10 Heavy grabs

Some aspects of cargo handling itself can cause damage to essential structural components. In response to commercial pressures, cargo grabs have become heavier (there are 40-tonne empty grabs at Rotterdam), and stevedores are under pressure to complete the (un)loading process in as few passes as possible.[71,72] The OOW should be on the lookout for grab damage to ladders, pipe guards, mainframe lower brackets, and the plating of the tanktop, hopper sides, fore and aft stools, and the hatch coamings.

Poor handling of grabs results in cargo spillage, if the grabs are over-filled, not closed properly or swung too fast. With some cargoes this spillage can result in damage to the ship. It may also result in loss of cargo, leading to claims being made against the ship, and to pollution claims.

8.1.11 Hydraulic hammers

In some ports, stevedores discharging bulk cargoes do not take the precaution of knocking down cargo which sticks to the ship's structure as the discharge progresses, whilst it is still accessible. Near the end of the discharge, they attempt to dislodge any remaining cargo aloft by hammering the sides of the holds with bull-dozer buckets, or special hydraulic hammers.

This process should be discouraged by the OOW, as *such harsh treatment can be very damaging, increasing the vulnerability of frames to corrosion, cracking and buckling.*[71] Some ship operators ban this system in their standing orders.

If there are large residues of cargo aloft, some ship's staff are content to allow the use of this hammering to dislodge the cargo. They fear that if this operation is stopped, the stevedores will leave the cargo, and the ship's crew will be unable to clean the holds properly on the next passage, or it will involve a lot of extra effort. The correct procedure is for the OOW to be on the lookout for cargo stuck in the upper parts of the hold, and request the stevedores to remove it whilst it is still accessible—see section 8.1.9.

8.1.12 Further information

For further detailed information and practical advice, the reader is directed to The Nautical

Institute publication *Bulk Carrier Practice.*[3] This is the authority on the operation of all bulk carriers.

8.2 Containerships

Much of the general cargo that was traditionally carried in break bulk cargo ships now travels in containers.

8.2.1 Advantages of containers

1. The handling of the goods between seller and buyer is reduced, leading to less damage.
2. Containers can be handled rapidly with modern high-speed equipment, leading to a reduction in port turn-round time of the ships, and hence better vessel utilisation, and increased efficiency.
3. Pilferage has been reduced by 90%[77] though hijacking of complete container loads is not unknown.
4. Standardisation has lead to a rationalisation of the number and type of cargo-handling equipment required.
5. Goods are protected against the weather at all stages of their handling, and are protected in the stow by the container body, rather than be overstowed directly by all manner of other goods.

8.2.2 Container construction

The IMO *Container Safety Convention*[46] provides for containers to be built to an approved design, constructed within fixed parameters and properly maintained. This is usually achieved by classification society approval of the design and construction, which is indicated by an approval plate fitted on the door end of the container. They are inspected every two and a half years, the date of the last inspection should be stamped on the approval plate. There is also a system for inspection on a continuous basis, known as an accepted continuous examination program. The approval plate is stamped ACEP and is not marked with the inspection dates.

The dimensions of containers have been standardised by the International Standards Organisation. ISO containers are 8ft wide, and usually 8ft 6in high, though Hi-Cubes of 9ft 6in high are popular in the American trades. 20ft long containers have a maximum gross weight of between 22 and 30 tonnes, 40ft long containers usually have a maximum gross weight of 30 tonnes. Some USA operators use containers of non-standard lengths, though usually their lifting fittings are compatible with the ISO standard lengths.

Containers are weatherproof, but not watertight, so they will not withstand the entry of water if they are submerged, or left standing in deep pools of water. They should be capable of withstanding a hose-test.

They are designed to be handled by a vertical lift at the top four corner castings. Hence it is essential that all container handling equipment utilises a spreader, and that loaded containers are **NEVER** lifted by four wires to a central hook. Empty containers can be handled by this method, or by fork lift trucks using the special slots in the base. They are designed to rest on the four base corner castings.

They must not be stowed with any weight resting on the bottom rails structure as this may cause damage by deformation or warping.

8.2.3 Types of container

1. GENERAL PURPOSE. Usually a steel structure with doors in one end.
2. OPEN TOP. The roof is covered with canvas supported by portable cross beams. These containers cater for heavy or awkward loads, which can be lifted in through the top rather than loaded through the doors. They also cater for tall cargoes which can project above the roof, as long as they are given top stow on the ship!
3. OPEN SIDED. The sides are open to permit easy stowage and handling of longer cargoes, and may be covered with netting, PVC curtains, grills or gates. They also cater for over-width cargoes which can project beyond the sides, but these need special stowage slots on board ship.
4. FLAT RACK. This has no roof or sides, and often the end can be folded down to save storage space when they are empty. They cater for heavy, awkward and over-sized loads.
5. BOLSTER or PLATFORM. This consists of the deck structure only. They are used to form a floor for uncontainerable cargo, carried on the ship on a port to port basis. They are also used for large, awkward loads, and for loads which are over-length, over-width, or over-height, or any combination of these, such as unpacked boats, as long as suitable stowage slots are available on the ship.
6. VENTILATED. This has ventilation grills fitted in the top and bottom of the side plating to permit natural ventilation.
7. FANTAINER. This can be fitted with an electric motor to aid air-circulation with the aim of reducing condensation.
8. INSULATED (or CONAIR). This permits the use of cooling air to be blown in from the ship's refrigeration systems, via ducts.
9. REEFER. This has its own built-in electric refrigeration machinery which is capable of maintaining the set temperature to within fixed limits, and control the rate of air changes. Some of these containers are fitted with diesel generators, so that the refrigeration machinery can be operated ashore, and on ships which are not specially fitted for the carriage of reefer containers or in non-reefer slots.
10. BULKER. This has ports cut into the roof to facilitate loading, and a hatch cut into the lower non-door end to facilitate emptying.
11. TANKER. This consists of a tank with a maximum capacity of between 19,000 and 24,000 litres, fitted within a 20ft container frame. It may be specifically constructed to carry a single product, and is often owned by the manufacturer of the product carried. Some of these containers have heating units which have to be plugged into the same power socket as the reefer containers above.
12. SPECIALISED. Containers have been adapted for the transport of live animals, and to provide self-contained accommodation for personnel or offices.

8.2.4 Stuffing containers

'Stuffing' is the term used for loading and stowing goods inside a container. This operation is frequently done away from the port, often by the manufacturer or shipper of the cargo. The same principles which were discussed in chapter 7 for handling and stowing break-bulk cargo in the hold of a ship apply to goods being loaded into a container.

A container which is stuffed by the shipowner, or an agent who groups together small amounts of cargo into one container, is known as a LCL—less than container load. This system is akin to carrying conventional general cargo, as discussed in the last chapter, and the goods are carried at the carriers' responsibility.

A container which is stuffed by one shipper is known as a FCL—full container load. The shipper bears the responsibility for correct packing and securing of the goods within the container, and indemnifies the carrier against all loss, damage, expense and liability which may result from inadequate packing or securing. Also the carrier is not responsible for:

1. Shortage, provided the container is delivered with the original seal intact.
2. The suitability of the goods for carriage in the container.
3. Incorrect setting of refrigeration controls, although this does not remove the requirement for the OOW to check the setting upon loading.

There are built-in securing points provided within the container to which the cargo can be lashed. Other methods for securing the cargo in the container include utilising a locking stow, and using shores and wedges. The interior floor is usually timber, so that timber securing can be nailed to it.

8.2.5 Container seals

Strict monitoring of the seals on the container door must be undertaken at all stages of the transport chain. They should be checked whenever the container is handled. This is to ensure that the cargo is safe from pilferage, and that the container is secure from stowaways and smugglers. It is usually the responsibility of the tally clerk to check that the serial number on the seal is the same as that given in the shipping document. However, it is good practice for the OOW to undertake spot checks to ensure that this number is being verified correctly.

It is recommended that there are strict controls on the issue of seals, to avoid criminal activities. They should be tamper proof, difficult to forge and have a unique code number. They should be fitted by the shipper and removed only by the receiver, who should retain them until he is satisfied with the delivery of the goods. Sometimes, the seals are removed by Customs authorities when they open a container to examine its contents. This may be done on board or ashore, but should always be done in the presence of the OOW or someone else who represents the shipowner. After such inspections, a new seal should be fitted, and a record made of its number on the shipping documents.

8.2.6 Container markings

Containers are identified by a unique ten digit code, consisting of four letters which identify its owner and a six-figure serial number—e.g., OCLU-123456. Other numbers identify the size and type of container. Containers loaded with dangerous cargo must have the correct markings to indicate the IMDG classification of the goods—see appendix VI.

8.2.7 Responsibilities of the OOW

In addition to the guidance offered in chapter 7, the junior deck officer serving in containerships should:

1. Ensure that all containers are stowed in the same positions as shown on the prestowage plan. This is to check that containers are properly separated for each discharge port, and that the weight distribution is compatible with stress and stability requirements. Container stack limits must **never** be exceeded. It is important to check that containers of IMDG cargoes are segregated correctly. Report any discrepancies to the Chief Officer or Master.
2. Examine all seals to check they have not been tampered with.

   Monitor that the tally clerks are checking the seal number against the number declared on the shipping documents.
3. Check all open or unsealed containers, including empties, for stowaways and contraband.
4. Report any damaged containers. Special attention should be given to all containers being stowed on deck, to ensure that rain or seas cannot pass through any damage to the container shell and cause damage to the goods inside.
5. Ensure that reefer and fantainers are connected to the ship's electrical supply as soon as they are loaded, and that the machinery is operating correctly. Check the settings, and verify these agree with the requirements of the shipping documents. Connect any remote monitoring system which may be fitted. It is good practice to log the temperature at the time of loading and discharging.
6. Check that the cargo is securely lashed on all open containers, and that any portable covers are in place and properly secured. It is good practice not to stow any open containers on deck if it can be avoided.
7. Check that any securing arrangements agree with the ship's plans, and that the lashing/securing operation is carried out in a safe manner. Special attention should be paid to access to containers high above the deck, particularly with open-top or other roofless containers—the securing of containers is discussed in chapter 17.9.
8. Check that all containers carrying dangerous cargo are displaying the appropriate labels and placards as required by IMO regulations.[49]—see appendix VI.

8.3 Reefers

Fresh produce is transported around the world in specialised refrigerated cargo ships known as 'reefers'. The cargo may be chilled or frozen, and carried loose, palletised or containerised.

8.3.1 Reminder of reefer basics

Organic matter such as foodstuffs decays in time due to the activities of micro-organisms. These activities are considerably reduced by a reduction in temperature. Hence, refrigeration is a preservative.

Living cargoes generate heat, and emit harmful gases. Both of these must be removed if the cargo is to be transported without harming itself.

> Essentially, the preservation of refrigerated cargo whilst it is on board the ship is dependent on the proper control of both its temperature and the carbon dioxide (CO_2) level in the atmosphere of the cargo compartment.

8.3.2 Controlling the atmosphere

In a modern reefer, air is blown over batteries of pipes containing a coolant. The air is ducted into the cargo compartment through the delivery vents, circulates throughout the cargo, and is then exhausted via the return vents.

To achieve adequate circulation of this air, the stow of cargo must contain channels through which the air can flow. These channels may be natural, formed by the shape of the cargo or the method of stowage. On other occasions, air channels are provided using dunnage, or specially constructed ventilation channels. Some cartons have holes to permit through ventilation, these cartons must be stowed so that their holes are aligned vertically and horizontally so that the air can flow freely throughout the stow.

Humidity also plays a vital part in inhibiting the activities of the micro-organisms. Excess moisture is deposited on the cooling pipes, which have to be defrosted regularly to maintain their efficiency. However, too dry an atmosphere can damage the cargo by causing a loss of both moisture and weight, resulting in shrivelling or brittleness, known as 'freezer burn'. Some modern machinery can provide a degree of control of the humidity of the circulating air. However, it is impossible to control accurately the exact humidity of the atmosphere within a refrigerated compartment.

All living cargo produces CO_2 which could build up to harmful concentrations. In general, the CO_2 level should be maintained at less than 0.5% by the introduction of fresh air once the temperature of the return air is no more than 2°C above the prescribed temperature for the delivery air.[20]

Ripening fruit produces ethylene, which speeds up the ripening process. This must be removed if the cargo is to arrive at its destination undamaged and not over-ripe. Cargoes such as chilled meat benefit from the introduction of nitrogen to inhibit mould growth. The control of gas levels is achieved by the air circulation system. Modern systems can provide a complete change of air up to thirty times every hour.

Sophisticated ventilation capabilities are as vital as temperature control systems.

8.3.3 Controlling the temperature

The temperature of the return air over the delivery air will indicate the effectiveness of the cooling process. As a constant temperature is essential for good storage, this difference should be as low as possible, whilst maintaining the required carriage temperature. General purpose reefers can provide a range of carriage temperatures from –25°C to +12°C, which can be controlled to within 1°C.

The cargo should be presented to the ship pre-cooled to the required temperature for carriage. This is because the refrigeration machinery in the ship (or container) is generally designed only to *maintain* the temperature of the cargo and not to reduce it. Sometimes with fruit, the cargo is loaded at the ambient temperature directly from the orchard, and is cooled on board. This requires that the ship is specially equipped and forewarned, and is clearly stated in the shipping documents.

Some chilled cargoes can be damaged by carriage at too low a temperature. The critical temperature may be the freezing point of its watery contents, or the temperature at which vital enzymes necessary for ripening are destroyed. In such cases, the carriage temperature is the *minimum* temperature at which air must be delivered from the cooling batteries.[20]

For frozen cargo, or others which are not affected by low temperatures, the carriage temperature is the *maximum* temperature of the return air.[20]

8.3.4 Extra prearrival preparations

In addition to the procedures outlined in chapter 2, the following preparations are made on reefers before arrival in port.

1. The cargo compartments must be scrupulously clean and free from taint. This also applies to all dunnage to be used.
   - Tainted dunnage must be jettisoned.
   - Tainted air can be sweetened using an ozonator.
   - Tainted structure must be washed with a suitable cleanser.
2. If carrying frozen cargo, all scuppers in the cargo compartments will have to be sealed with brine. This involves dissolving sufficient salt in a bucket of water to make a solution of brine of the correct salinity, according to the guidelines of the cargo manuals or the Chief Officer. This brine is then tipped down the top of the scupper, and lies in a trap in the pipe, to seal against the passage of air, thus preventing cross contamination of cargo in adjacent compartments. The correct salinity ensures that the trap does not become frozen solid.
3. The entire refrigeration machinery plant must be tested, including the fans and temperature sensors. This procedure must be logged, this entry may be sighted by the surveyor before he issues a preloading certificate of cargoworthiness.
4. The pulp thermometers used by the OOW to check the temperature of the cargo during loading must be tested, and calibrated as

necessary. A quick check can be achieved by plunging them into a bucket of ice.

5. For certain cargoes loaded in certain countries, an ice-test calibration is performed in order to verify the accuracy of the portable and fixed temperature sensors and control equipment.

6. The compartments to be loaded at the next port must be precooled to the correct temperature for the commodity to be loaded. This value should be contained in the shipper's or charterer's voyage instructions, and may be verified from the ship's cargo manuals.

7. It is usual for a thorough preloading survey to be undertaken, to verify that the cargo compartments are clean, dry, free from taint, and at the correct temperature.

8. When planning the stow, cargoes which may contaminate if they defrost should not be stowed with cargoes which are likely to be affected. Cargoes which do not fill the compartment should be stowed at the end nearest to the refrigeration plant.

8.3.5 Extra procedures during loading

1. The OOW should log the temperature of each cargo compartment when it is first opened, and regularly throughout the operations.

2. The condition of the cargo should be carefully monitored, and a continuous record of pulp temperature must be maintained. Any cargo which has a higher pulp temperature than that declared on its documentation should be rejected for loading, as should any obviously wet, damaged, mis-shapen or opened cargo. Pulp temperature is the internal temperature of the product, taken with a spear thermometer. If any cargo is left exposed on the quay for any length of time, the OOW should report this to the Chief Officer, and reject it for loading unless otherwise advised by him.

3. Wet cargo should be rejected because it will freeze together in the stow. This will make the circulation of cooling air less efficient, and may make discharge difficult or cause damage when the pieces of the cargo have to be prised apart.

4. Careful separation may be required, as certain produce can contaminate others. This information can be found in the ship's cargo manuals, or publications such as *Thomas's Stowage*.[70] Foodstuffs have their own unique aroma and flavour, and are of much lower value if they smell or taste like some other food! Cargo can be tainted by the circulation air passing over contaminants such as oil exhausts. It can also be tainted via air leaks in damaged structure, for example a broken sounding pipe.

5. Special attention should be paid to the ship's side insulation to ensure that it is not damaged by the stevedores. This is a common occurrence when using fork-lift trucks to handle palletised cargo, and all such incidents must be reported immediately to the Chief Officer, and a stevedore's damage report completed.

6. Steel plates, or suitable timber boards, should be employed to protect the ship's gratings whenever fork-lift trucks have to drive across them.

7. With some cargoes, special portable recorders are placed in the cargo compartments. The OOW should record their number and location.

8. The delivery and return air vents must always be kept well clear of cargo, to avoid impeding the flow of air. This can be achieved by the careful use of appropriate dunnage. The cargo must be stowed in such a manner so that air can freely circulate throughout the stow.

9. Side access doors and elevator spaces must be kept clear of cargo.

10. When airbags are used to secure cargo, they should be correctly inflated, but there should still be sufficient space left for the free flow of cooling air.

11. The ambient temperature should be logged frequently. This is vital if the air temperature approaches zero Centigrade, as chilled cargoes such as fresh fruit can be severely damaged by such low temperature air.

12. During meal breaks, or other extended stoppages to cargo operations, the cargo compartments should be closed and the reefer machinery run as necessary to maintain the temperature. There have been substantial losses when cargo has partially defrosted when the fans have been switched off to comply with local labour regulations. Every opportunity should be taken to bring the temperature back down as quickly as possible to the proper level.

13. If the loading process is slow, it may be necessary to protect cargo already loaded by means of insulated tarpaulins or other covers. This precaution should be logged, to assist if claims are made later for defrosted cargo.

14. When a hold is only part full, temporarily block off the air ducts in the empty spaces; otherwise the cold air will take the route of least resistance, and bypass the stowed area.[22] It is good practice to cover the cargo already loaded with insulation when the hold is next opened to complete the loading.

15. The OOW should exercise strict control over the stevedores, especially when they are handling cargoes which may contaminate entire holds if they are spilled. Recently an owner faced a claim for $400,000 when barrels of frozen orange juice ruptured, thawed, and leaked through the perforated tween deck onto squid in the hold below. All spills should be cleaned up immediately, because if the insulation becomes contaminated, it may be very difficult to remove, and could taint many cargoes in the future.[22]

16. On completion of loading, all access plugs, and all doors between decks in both holds and battery spaces, must be securely sealed. The reefer machinery is started immediately, to commence the cooling down or temperature reduction period. The OOW must log this time.

17. The temperature alarms on the bridge control panel, where fitted, should be set to the correct values, to ensure that the correct cooling of the cargo is carried out during the voyage.

8.3.6 Extra procedures during discharge

1. Logs of the temperature of cargo compartments, and refrigeration machinery, should be available.

2. If portable recorders have been used, these may be collected by the cargo receivers. The OOW should check and record their number, location and indicated temperature.

3. If local stevedore's regulations require cooling machinery to be stopped, all such stoppages must be recorded, as a defence against possible claims for defrosted cargo. The OOW should ensure that the temperature of the cargo compartments is regularly logged.

4. When any compartment is completely discharged, advise the engineers so that the reefer machinery can be switched off. The OOW should check with the Chief Officer regarding the closing of openings, in case any are to be left open for hold cleaning.

8.3.7 Reefer containers

Along with all other break-bulk cargo, a considerable tonnage of cargo which used to travel loose in reefer ships is now carried in reefer containers. All the advice contained in chapter 8.2 applies to these containers.

It is important to check that the temperature set on the machinery agrees with that given in the shipping document. The OOW should check that the pen on the recorder is making proper contact with the recording chart disc. Air vents should be set to allow gases to exhaust, as per the shipper's instructions. The date, time and temperature should be logged when the container is first connected, and finally disconnected from the ship's power supply. On longer voyages, the chart may require to be renewed; the old chart must be carefully filed. Some operators remove the chart when the container is discharged, whilst others leave the chart in place at all times to produce a continuous record from shipper to receiver.

Regular checks should be made on the temperature recorder. Although specialised staff are required if there is a complete breakdown of the refrigeration unit, frequently minor repairs can be made by ship's staff with simple tools and a basic supply of spares. Some examples are a blown fuse, a broken fan-belt, or a thermostat whose setting has slipped by vibration. If the clock or recorder mechanism develops a fault which cannot be corrected, then a system of regular manual recording must be commenced. *Attention to minor defects can well save a valuable cargo.*[70]

With insulated containers which do not have their own integral refrigeration machinery, the OOW must ensure that they are loaded in exactly their preplanned slot. This is to ensure that they are connected to the relevant manifold delivering air at the correct temperature. He should check that the container has been correctly coupled to the ship's manifold.

What may appear to be relatively minor damage, to a casual observer, such as the scratches/grooves on this steelwork, can result in major claims with sensitive cargoes. The OOW should ensure that all preloading damage—no matter how minor—is reported to the Master so that the bill of lading may be appropriately claused. See chapters 6.8 and 12.
Photograph: courtesy of Brookes, Bell & Co.

Chapter 9
TANKER OPERATIONS
PURPOSE

On completion of this chapter you will be aware of the specialised requirements for keeping a watch in port on a tanker.

This chapter contains reminders of the essential information required for officers keeping a deck watch in port on tankers. It is not intended to be a comprehensive textbook on tanker operations.

9.1 Types of tankers

Although there are a large number of different designs of tankers, essentially they can be summarised under five main headings:-

1. **Crude carriers**—these are mainly the largest type, mostly VLCCs (very large crude carriers), which transport the raw crude oil from the point of production to the refineries located around the world.

2. **Clean or white product carriers**—these are generally smaller and transport spirits, gas oil, diesel oil, kerosene and other refined products that contain little residue. These vessels can often carry a number of different grades at the same time.

3. **Dirty or black product carriers**—these are usually similar in size to clean product carriers but are used to transport fuel oils and other residual products.

Product tankers may alternate between clean and dirty products or carry them in combination. However, when changing from dirty to clean products it is essential that the proper tank cleaning procedures are carried out to avoid the possibility of contamination, as discussed in section 9.19. Under Marpol,[61] a tanker which is designated on her IOPP certificate as a product carrier is prohibited from carrying crude oil, and a tanker designated as a crude carrier is prohibited from carrying products, unless the tanker is specifically designated as a crude/product carrier.

4. **Dedicated carriers**—these are designed and/or operated for the transportation of one commodity, for example bitumen carriers, or used in one particular trade,—for example, specialised lightening vessels and floating storage units (FSUs) at offshore oilfields.

5. **Specialised carriers**—this category includes chemical and gas carriers. A detailed treatment of their highly specialised operational requirements is beyond the scope of this guide. Those readers who require such information should consult some of the reference works listed in appendix I.

Commercially, tankers may be classified according to their size:

VLCC	280,000 tonnes deadweight.	Typically carry 2 million barrels.
SUEZMAX	140,000 tonnes deadweight.	Typically carry 1 million barrels.
AFRAMAX	80-100,000 tonnes deadweight.	
PANAMAX	60-70,000 tonnes deadweight.	
PRODUCT	45,000 tonnes deadweight.	Typically carry 50,000 cu.metres.
PARCEL	20-45,000 tonnes deadweight.	

9.2 Cargo Systems

The arrangements for loading, discharging and tank cleaning are collectively known as the ship's cargo system. Although there are a variety of different systems most tankers will have some or all of the following:

9.2.1 Pipelines, valves and pumps

The arrangements and layout of pipelines vary from tanker to tanker, even between so-called sister ships. Hence, it is most important that the junior officer makes himself familiar with the layout of the pipelines, valves and pumps of each tanker he joins.

Pipelines include main lines (top, bottom and drop lines), stripping lines, drain lines, vent lines and inert gas lines.

Valves include manifold valves, crossover valves, drop valves, and master/isolating valves. These may be butterfly, gate or globe/ball valves, and will be either manual or power assisted (locally or remotely operated). The OOW should be familiar with the operation of all types. Where the valves are hydraulically controlled, the OOW should check regularly to ensure that the system is operating correctly and that the correct level of oil is maintained in the system. Usually the reserve/storage tank is fitted with audible and/or visual low level alarms. Any problems with the hydraulic system, particularly leaks, should be reported immediately and remedial action taken where necessary. Sometimes impurities in the hydraulic oil can cause faults to develop in the control blocks, leading to the valves operating other than as intended.

Traditionally the **pumps** are housed in a pumproom aft, adjacent to the engineroom, for ease of routeing power supplies, etc. In some modern tankers, however, the pumproom has been dispensed with and a deepwell pump has been fitted to each cargo tank. This has significantly reduced the risk posed by pumprooms with regard to fire and explosion. It also reduces the possibility of cargo contamination especially on product tankers carrying several grades. The junior officer should be familiar with the operation of the various types of pumps found on his ship.

9.2.2 Venting arrangements

Insufficient or over-pressurisation of a cargo tank can have devastating consequences such as structural failure. Hence, tankers are fitted with venting arrangements which allow the gas/atmosphere in the tank to escape when loading cargo, and permit outside air to flow into a tank should a vacuum develop in that tank for any reason.

9.2.3 Cargo control room

The OOW should be familiar with the layout of the cargo control room and the operation of all its equipment. This room will contain a cargo pipeline plan, which on modern ships may be in the form of a model or mimic of the ship's cargo tank arrangements and the associated pipelines, valves, pumps and other equipment. Operations are co-ordinated, monitored and controlled from the cargo control room. It is vital that the OOW closely monitors all aspects of the operation in progress, and understands what action is required when an alarm sounds.

Nevertheless, it is essential that the OOW does not spend his entire watch in the cargo control room, but he should make rounds of the main deck and inspections of the pumproom at regular intervals. During these rounds, a duty seaman or pumpman should be stationed in the cargo control room.

9.2.4 Other parts of the cargo system

- Inert gas systems —see section 9.17.
- Ullage gauges —see section 9.18.
- Tank cleaning —see section 9.19.

9.3 ISGOTT manual[65]

The standard reference manual for operating tankers in port is the *International Safety Guide for Oil Tankers and Terminals* (ISGOTT).[65] This publication contains detailed advice on safety procedures and pollution avoidance, and all officers serving on tankers should be thoroughly familiar with its contents. Before cargo operations commence, it is usual to complete the ship/shore safety checklist provided in this manual. **It is good practice physically to check each item on this list, preferably witnessed by the terminal's safety officer.** Completion of this form is a requirement of most terminals in the world before they will permit cargo operations to commence. A copy of this form is reproduced in appendix XIV along with guidelines for completing the form.

9.4 The hazards of petroleum

9.4.1 Petroleum vapour

Petroleum vapour is produced either by heat or by turbulence (i.e., physical disturbance). One or both of these occurs during tanker operations. Volatility is the tendency of a liquid to evaporate, and depends on the temperature and molecular structure of the liquid. Lighter hydrocarbons (kerosene) will evaporate more quickly than heavier structures (fuel oil). Volatility can be measured by either vapour pressure or flash point. Flash point is the lowest temperature at which a liquid gives off sufficient gas to form a flammable mixture.

- Liquids which have a flashpoint above 60°C are classed as **non-volatile**.
- Liquids which have a flashpoint below 60°C are classed as **volatile**.

9.4.2 Flammability

The gases given off by petroleum can be ignited and will burn only when they are mixed with oxygen in certain proportions: if there is too much petroleum gas, the mixture is said to be too rich; if there is too little petroleum gas, the mixture is said to be too lean. The limiting proportions expressed as a percentage by volume of petroleum gas in air are known as the lower flammable limit (LFL) and the upper flammable limit (UFL). For the gas mixtures from the petroleum liquids encountered in normal tanker practice, the overall range of flammability is from a minimum LFL of about 1% gas by volume in air, to a maximum UFL of about 10% gas by volume in air. Combustion cannot be supported outside this range.

9.4.3 Gas density

Gases from normal petroleum liquids are denser (and so heavier) than air and inert gas. The possibility of layering of gases is an important consideration during cargo handling operations, and consideration should always be given to the existence of non-uniform atmospheres throughout the tank. In this respect, the OOW should realise that any measure of tank atmosphere refers only to the immediate vicinity of the sample head, and may not be a true representation of the overall tank atmosphere. For this reason, it is important to take readings at several locations, particularly when deep web frames, or other parts of the structure, divide the tank into numerous 'pockets' where there is a possibility that the circulation of atmosphere is restricted. Strict procedures should be followed before and during entry into enclosed spaces—see section 9.5.3.

9.4.4 Toxicity

All petroleums are toxic in that they are harmful to health if experienced in a sufficiently high concentration. This concentration is measured in ppm—parts per million. There are three routes by which these substances may enter the human body: inhalation, ingestion, and skin contact. There are two possible effects on humans:

ACUTE EFFECT—where the effect is immediate. Comparatively small quantities of petroleum gas can cause dizziness, headaches and eye irritation; larger quantities can cause the body's organs to fail, perhaps leading to death.

CHRONIC EFFECT—where the effect is built up slowly, possibly over long periods, perhaps producing a serious breakdown in health, or even death.

9.5 Tanker Safety

Safety is an area of operations that requires particular consideration since tankers pose threats not present on many other kinds of vessel. The most dangerous time of the voyage is during cargo operations. This section identifies the operational risks posed by tankers and later sections will suggest measures that the OOW can take to minimise these risks.

Moorings should be inspected regularly and adjusted as necessary to maintain the ship alongside and in the correct position in order to avoid excessive strain being placed on the manifold connections. Often the shore connections have a very limited working radius, so the position of the ship is quite critical. For this reason, tankers often use only mooring wires rather than fibre ropes, because wires have less elasticity, and thus permit less movement of the vessel than fibre ropes. Mooring wires may have fibre tails to absorb small changes in tension. Many terminals prohibit tails, which may part in a fire.

9.5.1 Avoiding pressure surges

Incorrect operation of pumps and valves can produce pressure surges. This can cause joints to blow, pipelines to fracture and damage the pump casing. The OOW should ensure that the following precautions are taken:

1. Valves should never be closed against the flow.
2. It is normal to have all valves open before pumping commences, except the pump discharge valve should be left closed until the pump starts to turn.
3. The speed of operation of a valve should be at a controlled rate. The OOW should regularly check that this is within the manufacturer's recommended parameters.
4. During normal operations, there should be no sudden changes in the flow rate. All changes of flow rate should be done with close liaison between the ship and shore personnel in charge of the operations.
5. The lines from the next tank to the pump should always be opened before those to the previous tank are closed.
6. Before opening a pipeline to a liquid, the OOW must ensure that the line is not under vacuum. Otherwise there could be catastrophic consequences such as shattering of valves and springing of pipelines. This is overcome by first opening the tank valve. When setting the valves during the lining up procedure, it should be normal practice to start at the tank and work one's way along the line to the manifold.
7. Always start and end at slow rates of flow.
8. In addition to any limitations on the ship's lines, the OOW should not forget to inquire as to the limitations on the terminal's lines.

9.5.2 Fire and explosion

The primary objective is the elimination of the risk of fire or explosion. This can be achieved by avoiding both a source of ignition and a flammable atmosphere being present in the same place at the same time. Since it is not always possible to achieve these conditions together, precautions should therefore be directed towards excluding or controlling one of them. Inside the accommodation and engineroom, it may be impractical to eliminate all sources of ignition, so it is essential to avoid the entry of gases into these spaces. All external doors, ports, windows and ventilators should be kept closed while engaged in cargo operations.

There is a greater likelihood of flammable gases being present on deck and in pumprooms, so it is essential to eliminate all sources of ignition in these locations:

- Smoking (including the carriage of matches or lighters) and the use of naked flames should be prohibited in these areas.
- All equipment should be approved and certified intrinsically safe, including torches and portable VHF radios.
- Care must be taken with hand tools as incorrect use can produce sparks, through metal to metal contact. These are known as incendive sparks, and have sufficient energy to ignite a flammable mixture.
- No hammering, chipping or blasting should be permitted, nor should any power tools be used, unless a *Permit to Work* has been issued and its terms agreed with the terminal. Most terminals do not allow any work of this type to be carried out while the tanker is alongside.

It is recommended that all maintenance and repairs performed on board are controlled by a *Permit to Work* system. Samples of such forms for *Cold* and *Hot* work are reproduced in appendix IX.

Smoking should only be allowed in designated safe smoking areas agreed between the ship and the terminal. These areas should be clearly marked and have no doors or ports opening directly on to the cargo deck; they should be available for use by all personnel (ship and shore).

As a precaution against fire, regular rounds of the deck should be carried out and any leaks found in pipelines, however small, should be made good immediately. The OOW should pay special attention to the pumproom and the manifold connections. He must be alert for any escaping gas or liquid, and should regard all such leaks as a potential fire or explosion.

Whenever the vessel is engaged in cargo operations the fire main should be pressurised. (Flow can be provided for the pump by opening up the outlet to the washers for the anchor cable, to avoid over-pressurising the line or overheating the pump). Hoses should be run out fore and aft of the manifold and the nearest fixed foam monitors should be directed towards the manifold drip tray. This enables fire fighting equipment to be brought to bear immediately, so maintaining control of any hazardous situation. However, if the system takes some time to produce the first flow of foam, these monitors should be directed overside, and only directed towards any fire once the foam is seen to flow. If water alone is directed onto an oil fire, there could be catastrophic consequences, with explosion and rapid spread of the fire. See also chapter 4.7.

9.5.3 Entry into pumprooms and other enclosed spaces

It is vital that the correct procedures and precautions are carried out on every occasion that personnel are required to enter enclosed and potentially dangerous spaces, as discussed in chapter 4.3. On tankers, such spaces not only carry the special risks of fire or explosion but also the additional hazards associated with the toxic nature of the cargo.

There is the ever-present possibility of entering an atmosphere that is deficient in oxygen. Officers should not be misled into thinking that simply because they cannot smell any gas it is not present. Some gases remove a person's sense of smell so rapidly that an individual would be close to collapse before they realised anything was wrong.

Pumprooms, by virtue of their location, design and operation, constitute a particular hazard and therefore need special precautions:

1. A checklist for entry into enclosed spaces should be completed on every occasion—see appendix X.

2. Before anyone enters the pumproom, the atmosphere must be tested, with special attention paid to the lower levels.

3. Ventilation must be maintained continuously. If the ventilation should fail while personnel are working in the pumproom, the space should be evacuated immediately.

4. Inspections of the pumproom should be kept to a minimum in line with good operational practice. If no problems are encountered during cargo operations, an inspection about once an hour should be sufficient.

5. A harness and lifeline should be rigged and ready for immediate use.

6. Breathing apparatus and resuscitation equipment should be available, and ready for immediate use, close to the entry to the pumproom, whenever personnel are working inside.

7. The OOW must always check that a gas free certificate has been issued and a valid entry permit is in force.

8. Adequate communications must be maintained at all times between personnel working in the pumproom and a responsible person outside. All forms of communication should be tested prior to entry.

9. The OOW must be informed prior to all entries and work in the pumproom. If the OOW wishes to enter the pumproom, he should ensure that a responsible person is informed of his intentions, and he should report regularly during his stay, and on exit.

10. Whilst he is in the pumproom, the OOW should check the integrity of all joints, seals, glands and drain cocks to avoid leaks and spillages. Any defects should be reported to the Chief Officer immediately.

11. It is essential that all machinery and lighting is maintained in first class condition, to avoid sources of ignition. Any defects should be reported immediately they are noticed either to the Chief Officer or the engineer on watch, as appropriate, for remedial action.

12. Any repair and maintenance work must be strictly controlled by a work permit, whose validity should not exceed twelve hours.

13. **If any doubt exists—do not enter.**

9.6 Cargo operations plan

Before cargo operations commence, the following information should be exchanged between the ship and the shore.[65]

1. Cargo and ballast distribution on arrival.

2. Quantity, density and temperature of each grade to be handled.

3. Characteristics of the cargo which may require attention—for example flashpoint, true vapour pressure, sour crude or water content.

4. Ship's tanks to be filled or emptied, and the sequence in which they are to be loaded or discharged. The sequence of various grades.

5. Shore tanks to be emptied or filled.

6. Manifold connections, including reducers, and lines to be used by the ship/shore. (If several grades are to be handled concurrently, then grade name boards should be available to be placed at each connection.)

7. Limitations on the movement of hoses or hard-arms (operating envelope).

8. Initial cargo transfer (pumping) rate for each grade.

9. Maximum cargo transfer (pumping) rate for each grade.

10. Topping off rates, and the notice required for completing each grade.

11. Maximum manifold pressures for each grade.

12. Precautions to avoid the accumulation of static electricity.

13. The venting system to be used. (Taking into account the loading rate, the atmospheric conditions and the true vapour pressure of the cargo.)

14. Sequence and timing of (de)ballasting operations, and tank cleaning, and any restrictions these may have on the cargo operations.

15. The expected duration of pumping each grade, and time of completion.

16. Ship and shore tank changeover procedure.

17. Methods for avoiding contamination of the cargo and/or ballast—e.g., valve separation, dedicated lines, loading over the top, etc.

18. Pipeline clearing for loading/discharging, and methods for separating grades, to avoid contamination (e.g., flushing lines, line pigs, etc.).

19. Other operations which may affect flow/pumping rates.

20. Crude oil washing (COW), or other tank cleaning operations.

21. Normal and emergency communications.

22. Emergency shutdown procedures.

23. Other operations taking place, including those in chapter 14.

24. Names of people in charge of operations ashore/on board.

9.7 Prearrival preparations

Prior to arrival in port it is important that the vessel is ready in all respects to commence operations as soon as she is safely moored alongside. Usually, all preparations are carried out under the direct supervision of the Chief Officer and it is vitally important that both he and the OOW are aware of the current status of all equipment.

1. All fixed and portable equipment that will be required during cargo operations should be tested to confirm that it is working satisfactorily. This includes all antipollution equipment.

2. Ullage gauges should be inspected and checked for accuracy and any differences against the remote readouts made good or recorded.

3. The oil/water interface detector must be checked for accuracy. Modern detectors are multi-functional and can measure ullages and cargo temperature as well as being used as a normal interface detector.

4. Ullage tapes should be checked to confirm that they are in good repair, clean and accurate.

5. Venting arrangements must be inspected and tested for correct operation, and lined up correctly for cargo operations.

6. All cargo alarms must be checked and proved functional—this includes all alarms associated with the inert gas system.

7. If any reducers are required on the manifold connections, these should be fitted prior to arrival if possible. Every endeavour should be made to obtain this information, preferably it should be supplied by the terminal, but can be checked from previous records.

9.8 Preloading procedures

Prior to the commencement of any operations, the *Ship/Shore Safety Checklist* should be completed and signed (see appendix XIV). It is recommended that an anti-pollution checklist also be completed before commencing any cargo operations. An example is provided in appendix XVI.

On older ships, deballasting will commence as soon as the ship has berthed and has been cleared by the authorities. On newer tonnage, cargo operations will start as soon as the formalities have been completed, ballast operations will be undertaken when convenient, according to the Chief Officer's plan. On some VLCCs and other dedicated crude oil tankers, one or two pumps will be dedicated to the handling of ballast. This is due to the need to handle cargo and ballast concurrently. The ballast will be usually clean and can be discharged directly overboard using the main cargo pumps. However, sometimes ballast will have to be discharged ashore to tanks for treatment either because it is dirty or because some terminals prohibit the direct discharge of any untreated ballast water.

Before discharging ballast, the OOW should sight the surface of the water to check for pollution caused by leaking lines or bulkheads. Once proved clean, ballast should be discharged via an oil content monitor with an automatic shut-down device.

The OOW must ensure that the correct lines are connected to the correct manifold, and that the connections are properly made using a safe method. It is a good idea to mark the manifolds with a board displaying the correct grade, to save any confusion. Any manifolds not being used should be blanked and fully bolted. It is important that the engineroom remains informed of all activities that require their assistance. They should be given plenty of notice of the requirements for pumps and inert gas.

Although the ship is now ready, loading operations cannot commence until a surveyor has inspected the vessel's cargo tanks. Prior to any inspection the inert gas pressure should be reduced, unless the tanks are provided with hermetically sealed ullage and sampling ports and the associated equipment. Upon successful completion of this inspection, the surveyor will issue a certificate stating that the ship is fit to load the grades of oil specified and a certificate stating the quantity of oil remaining on board (this is known as the OBQ certificate).

Some special cargoes require the tanks and lines to have all traces of water removed (e.g., lub.oils, aviation spirit, mogas etc.). The OOW should closely supervise any mopping gangs, and will be responsible for testing tank atmospheres and issuing the necessary tank entry permits. Once a tank mopping has been completed satisfactorily, it is inspected by an independent surveyor, who will issue a 'Dry' certificate. Then the tank should be closed and prepared to receive cargo.

Often there will be more than one surveyor, and they may be joint appointments—for example, between the charterer and receiver. Whoever they represent, it is their job to maintain impartiality. All surveyors should be treated with courtesy but the junior officer should not provide answers to questions they may have concerning the quality, quantity or care of the cargo. The OOW should ask the surveyor to direct these questions towards the Chief Officer or Master.

Meanwhile, the OOW needs to make other preparations for loading cargo. The pressure/vacuum (p/v) valves that form part of the venting arrangements should be set so that tanks can vent during loading. If permitted by the terminal, these valves can be set to bypass so that during loading the inert gas in the tanks can be vented to atmosphere as it is displaced by the cargo. Otherwise, the inert gas must be vented to another tank (for example, a tank being deballasted) or to facilities ashore. Ullage gauges should be wound down and a check made that they are reading correctly, by checking the reference reading.

Once the figures have been completed by the Chief Officer and agreed with the surveyors, the cargo system should be lined (set) up to receive cargo. It is always the Chief Officer who is responsible for lining up, though he may delegate this task to the OOW. Lining up should be carried out strictly in accordance with the Chief Officer's operations plan. The OOW must keep the Chief Officer totally informed of all his actions, and should expect the Chief Officer to make spot checks. Lining up involves checking that all valves from the manifold (with the exception of the manifold valve itself) via the deck to the tank, including all those in the pumproom, are either open or shut as appropriate, so that cargo only flows along the intended lines and into the nominated tanks. It is vital that the OOW physically checks that all overboard and sea suction valves are actually shut.

The OOW should regularly check the positions of all valves, to ensure that these remain in accordance with the plan. The status of any manual valves should be kept up to date on the mimic board in the cargo control room. The status of hydraulic valves should be verified against the indicators in the control room as a double check.

If deballasting is to take place concurrent with loading, overboard and sea suction valves may remain open. In this situation, it is extremely important that the systems are carefully checked, and that all operations maintain an adequate separation between ballast and cargo, to avoid contamination and pollution.

The manifold valve should be the last valve opened and this should be done only when the terminal informs the vessel that they are ready to commence loading. The OOW should perform his final checks, open the manifold valve, and confirm this to the terminal.

9.9 Loading procedures

Cargo can be loaded either through the drop lines, which lead directly from the cargo lines on deck (toplines) to the main lines in the tanks (bottom lines), or via the pumproom lines. The former is preferable since it avoids complicated lining up in the pumproom and reduces the risk of leaks in the pumproom and spills overside. It is good practice to have a man stationed at the manifold to check the integrity of the manifold connection.

Loading should commence at a slow rate into one tank in order to check that all connections are tight and that there are no leaks. The OOW should perform an inspection of the deck and the sea around the vessel to confirm that all is well. Once it is confirmed that the cargo is flowing into the intended tank indicated by a reading on the ullage gauge, the terminal operators should be informed that the loading rate can be increased gradually to the maximum agreed rate and further tanks can be opened up. It is important to check that the tanks being loaded are venting correctly via the planned arrangements.

When loading multi-grades, the same procedure should be carried out for each grade ensuring that the required valve separation is maintained to minimise the possibility of contamination. The OOW should ensure that one grade is flowing correctly before starting another.

With some grades there will be a requirement to collect line and bottom samples; this is particularly the case on product tankers. Line samples are taken periodically, according to the Chief Officer's orders, by drawing off a bottle-full of oil from the sampling cock on the relevant line. Bottom samples are usually taken with less than a metre ('2-ft bottom samples') of cargo in the tank but the precise figure will be

advised by the terminal. Loading of the required grades will be stopped while these samples are taken ashore for laboratory testing and analysis. Once a satisfactory result is obtained, loading can recommence. During the time these tanks are not being loaded the manifold valve should be closed and, if necessary, the tanks should be isolated by closing the appropriate valves.

The OOW must follow exactly the Chief Officer's planned loading sequence. An adequate stagger should be maintained between tanks to allow time for unhurried topping off of individual tanks in a logical sequence (see section 9.10 below).

Any significant departure from the planned loading rates agreed should be brought immediately to the attention of the Chief Officer and the terminal and remedial action taken as necessary. The reason for any differences should be sought from the terminal as defence against any possible future claims from the charterer for demurrage.

Ullages should be taken periodically, as advised by the Chief Officer according to the loading rate, and the quantities on board and loading rates calculated. On some ships, it is the operational rule to take ullages from the gauges on deck, as remote readouts should not be relied upon. On ships where remote ullages are taken, it is important that comparisons should be made between these and the primary readout at regular intervals and any discrepancies noted, particularly prior to topping off. It is not unknown for ullaging devices to stick or jam.

Throughout the loading operation, the OOW should regularly check all deck lines, manifold connections, completed and empty tanks, ballast lines and the sea around the vessel, to verify that all is well and there are no leaks. It is worth mentioning again the importance of maintaining a close watch on moorings and the means of access. Special precautions are required during the loading of a cargo with a high true vapour pressure (TVP)—these are outlined in the ISGOTT manual.[65]

9.10 Topping off procedures

When a tank reaches the required ullage as stated in the Chief Officer's plan the tank is said to be topped off. Topping off is the term used to describe the operation of slowly bringing the level of liquid in a tank up to its agreed final ullage. If sufficient manpower is available, more than one tank can be topped off at the same time, but the number is usually kept to a minimum to avoid unnecessary errors in obtaining the final required ullage. Topping off ullages must be corrected, using trim and list correction tables in the ship's tank calibration book, to determine the even-keel figure.

When nearing completion of a tank, it is a good practice to check the operation of its valves, to ensure they are working properly. Similar checks should be done on the next valves to be opened. Both these checks can be made by operating each valve through a small range. They should be made in ample time, so that remedial action can be taken if any problems occur. As topping off approaches, it is good practice to check the accuracy of the ullage gauging system in readiness for completion. This is to avoid the possibility of errors, and should be done in sufficient time. On some ships, it is not possible to take manual ullages during cargo operations. Measuring ullages is fully discussed in section 9.18.

The terminal should always be informed that the vessel is about to commence topping off, as there will be an increase in the back pressure when the ship's valves are being closed. Often, initial topping off can be carried out without reducing the loading rate, provided there is no increase in back pressure in the lines. Nearing completion, the loading rate should be reduced to a safe and practical rate, commensurate with the number of tanks remaining open and the manpower available. The rate is further reduced as the number of tanks being topped off decreases, and the terminal should be informed when you are topping off the last tank. The notice required for stopping a grade will have been agreed with the terminal and the required notice of completion should always be given. Clear communication between terminal and ship is always a vital element but never more so than at this critical stage of the operation.

Some authorities recommend that **all** topping off is carried out at a reduced rate. The OOW should be guided by the system in operation on board his ship, as advised by the Chief Officer. If the loading rate is too high during topping off, droplets of oil may be present in the gas being vented as the oil level approaches the upper tank structure, which can result in pollution. In extreme cases, oil can enter the venting system, preventing the escape of gas; this may lead to overpressure in the tank, and structural failure. It is possible for this to occur before the gauging system indicates that the tank is full, due to the gas pressure building up within the upper tank structure during high loading rates.

When closing the valves of tanks being topped off, the operation should be done gradually, avoiding sudden closure as this could cause hydraulic shocks resulting in a blown joint or a fractured line. The last tank to be topped off should **not** be closed against the flow. When approaching the final ullage, the shore should be told to 'stop loading'. Due allowance should be made for the residual oil flow once the terminal has stopped pumping. The Chief Officer will have enquired what space is required for this residual flow beforehand, and incorporated this into his loading plan.

The cargo tank nominated to receive the oil draining from the lines must be isolated from the IG system. The tank is then depressurised, which allows the oil in the loading arms and lines to drain down. When draining has been completed, the IG valve to that tank is opened up to repressurise the tank. The final drainage can be made into the manifold drip tray. Once the flow has stopped, the terminal will advise the vessel to close her valves. First the manifold valve is closed, and this fact confirmed to the terminal. The OOW should then check that all other valves are closed and indicated as such on the mimic diagram in the cargo control room. The cargo system should be secured, as instructed by the Chief Officer. It may be necessary to allow for line expansion, particularly in hot climates, before closing all valves.

Oil/water mixtures should not be allowed to accumulate in the manifold drip tray. They should be drained into a suitable receptacle and removed for disposal. If the drip tray has a connection for draining to a cargo tank this should not be used during cargo operations for two reasons. Firstly there is the possibility of contaminating the cargo in that tank, which could lead to cargo claims and subsequent financial loss for the shipowner. Secondly, and more importantly, the tank may be inerted and under pressure, opening the connection could lead to a blow-back, with the atmosphere venting through the drains and causing pollution. Many manifold drains are fitted with a U-tube within the tank to which they drain, which in theory will prevent the movement of gas in either direction, but permit liquid to flow. Experience has proved that the OOW should not rely on this system.

9.11 Predeparture procedures

Once loading is completed, the cargo quantity will be calculated by the Chief Officer and probably by an independent surveyor as well. The OOW should offer him every assistance to ensure that the job is carried out as efficiently and effectively as possible. Often the surveyor will bring his own equipment, but it is good practice for the OOW to have prepared the necessary measuring equipment. This includes an ullage tape or UTI, sampling cans and thermometers (where applicable), a hydrometer, a bucket and rags. This all saves valuable time and should be done as a matter of routine. The Chief Officer may on some occasions accompany the surveyor but invariably this task will be delegated to the OOW as the vessel's representative. In this respect, it is essential that the OOW is fully aware of the disposition of the cargo which has been loaded.

It is the responsibility of the OOW to ensure that the surveyor is inspecting the right tanks. He should be aware of the approximate finishing ullages so he can check that the final observations are reasonable. Any significant differences should be cause for concern and a fresh ullage should be taken. Should there still be a difference advice should be sought from the Chief Officer. The final survey may also involve water dips and these, like ullages, densities and temperatures, should be carried out in accordance with the guidance contained in section 9.18 on measuring and sampling.

Once the survey is completed and the figures agreed, and not before, the OOW should supervise disconnection at the manifold. First, the manifold drain cocks, situated on the outboard side of the main manifold valve, should be opened so that any oil that has accumulated in this space can drain off into the manifold drip tray. The OOW should monitor the level in the drip tray and check that the drip tray's own valve is not open, so avoiding any chance of pollution, or contamination if the drip tray drains to a tank—see also the last paragraph of section 9.10.

The OOW should ensure that the gang have sufficient personnel to carry out the disconnection and that this task is carried out in a safe manner, using the correct tools. All the normal safety precautions still apply and the OOW should ensure that these are heeded by the shore personnel. Once all the manifolds have been disconnected, blank flanges should be fitted and fully bolted.

There is nothing more frustrating for a Chief Officer at this busy period than to be constantly pestered by a competent but unprepared OOW about tasks that are quite routine. The OOW is advised to check that he has completed the predeparture checks listed in chapter 19.

9.12 Predischarge procedures

Much of the guidance contained in sections 9.6, 9.7 & 9.8 is also relevant for arrival at the discharge port but with a few important additions. If the vessel has been loaded via the drop lines, it is good practice to flood the cargo pumps with oil, to allow the cargo to replace any gas. This will put a head on the pumproom lines, so as to test them for leaks, etc.

All components of the cargo system will have been tested prior to arrival at the discharge terminal. Such tests will include the cargo pumps, including trips and emergency stops, and all valves, including their indicators. The junior officer should be aware of the procedures involved, and preferably should make sure that he is actively involved in these tests. Only by participating in **all** shipboard operations will the junior officer gain the practical experience necessary to ensure that he is confident of his capability of performing all the tasks required of him.

Vessels fitted with crude oil washing will have tested the system prior to arrival at the discharge port. All lines will have been pressure tested in accordance with the manufacturer's instructions, and the machines tested by turning them by hand. Also, the inert gas system will have been tested to ensure it is operating correctly.

Once again the Chief Officer will have prepared a discharge plan similar to the loading plan detailing the order of discharge, the pumps and lines that are to be used and the manifold connections that will be utilised. It is essential that the OOW is aware of the maximum back pressure and discharge rate that can be accepted by the terminal, which will form part of this plan; he must ensure that these are never exceeded. The plan will also specify details of the ballasting operation. These instructions will be confirmed with the terminal on arrival, and may be amended as required; it is important that the OOW is aware of any such amendments. The *Ship/Shore Safety Checklist* (see appendix XIV), the *Tanker Information-Exchange Checklist* (see appendix XV) and the *Anti-pollution Checklist* (see appendix XVI) should be completed.

Once alongside a surveyor will board to carry out a cargo survey. The OOW should ensure that all the necessary equipment is available and the inert gas pressure in the tanks has been reduced in preparation. Some ships are provided with equipment which can be used without the need to depressurise the tanks, as this is not permitted in certain ports. The ullages, temperatures and densities will be taken with a representative of the cargo receivers, together with an independent surveyor in most cases. Samples of the cargo are taken as part of this procedure; water dips may also be taken. This is because some crude oils carry quite a large quantity of water in suspension which will have settled out of the cargo during transit. (Sampling, dipping and measuring are described in section 9.18.) From the survey an on-board quantity is calculated for each grade and this will be compared with the figures obtained from the final survey at the loading port.

Crude tankers fitted with COW will have prepared a separate, or preferably an integrated crude oil washing plan. It is the usual practice for the Chief Officer to carry out all crude oil washing, while the OOW supervises cargo discharge. Nevertheless, these operations cannot be separated and close liaison should always be maintained between all personnel, including those from the terminal. For further guidance on COW refer to section 9.20.

Prior to starting discharge operations, the OOW should ensure that the ullage gauges are wound down and he should make a comparison of their direct readings with the remote readouts in the cargo control room. If there are any significant differences, or if any problems are encountered when lowering the gauges, these must be reported immediately to the Chief Officer. It is essential to keep the engineroom well informed of all deck requirements, so that equipment is prepared for use in ample time.

9.13 Discharging procedures

The OOW must check that the initial tanks and lines for discharge are properly lined up, with all valves on deck and in the pumproom correctly set. The valves to the first set of tanks to be discharged should be opened to allow the bottom and pumproom lines, and the cargo pumps, to be pressurised. Once this has been confirmed, the OOW should inform the Chief Officer, and then the terminal, that the ship is ready to commence discharge.

Once shore confirm their own readiness, the appropriate manifold valves can be opened and the pumps started one at a time. Pumping is commenced at a slow rate, to allow time for the OOW to verify that checks have been made to ensure that there are no leaks on deck, overside, in the pumproom or at the manifold. A seaman should be standing by at the manifold in order to report immediately should any problems arise.

The OOW should check that the ullages from the nominated tank(s) are increasing, thus confirming that the cargo is being discharged from the intended tanks. Once the terminal has confirmed that all is well with their end of the operation, the pumping rate can be increased, but the maximum back pressure at the manifold agreed between the ship and the terminal must never be exceeded.

With some black products, the cargo is occasionally discharged through a heated line. If not, the terminal should have a procedure to blow the line clear after each use. Otherwise, oil left in the line from a previous ship may solidify, causing a 'cold plug', which can be difficult to move. The OOW should check the back pressure carefully at the initial start of pumping. If this is unexpectedly high, then a cold plug may be present. Pumping should continue at a slow rate, and be continuously monitored until the back pressure suddenly drops—the indication that the plug has cleared.

The OOW should ensure that the tanks which are being discharged are properly supplied with inert gas in order to maintain a slight positive pressure. The OOW should monitor closely the inert gas pressure in the tanks and the oxygen content of the inert gas entering the cargo tanks to ensure the tank atmospheres are maintained in a safe condition. These readings should be logged, preferably in the deck logbook, although some ships have a separate inert gas log. Other ships are fitted with automatic continuous recorders. Inert gas systems are discussed in section 9.17.

In order to maintain optimum performance, it is again important to achieve a good stagger between tanks in order to leave enough time for stripping the tanks towards the end of discharge. Advice should be sought from the Chief Officer in this regard, in particular information about the order in which the tanks are to be stripped.

During discharge the OOW should ensure that ullages are taken regularly. Using these figures, the discharge rates should be calculated on each occasion, as any variation in these rates can be the first indication that something is going wrong. Also, an estimated finishing time should be calculated for each grade. This estimate must take into account the extra time required for stripping in the final stages of discharge. This is an important figure for the terminal who may ask for updated finishing times periodically, in order to plan for the final surveys and the vessel's departure.

Pump temperatures should also be carefully monitored to ensure that they do not overheat. This can be a major problem on VLCCs where the pumps are run flat out for long periods after what may have been weeks of relative idleness between one discharge and the next. A common cause of overheating is over-packing the pump glands with grease. The breakdown of a pump during discharge can prolong the operation with the possibility of claims for demurrage against the ship, which could run into tens of thousands of dollars.

Throughout the discharging operation, the OOW should regularly check all lines on deck and in the pumproom, all completed and empty tanks, ballast lines and tanks and the sea around the vessel, to verify that all is well, and there are no leaks. A note should be entered in the deck or port log to this effect after these rounds have been made. The importance of maintaining clear and comprehensive records being kept cannot be stressed too strongly as a defence against claims for demurrage or pollution—see chapter 18.

If carrying heated cargoes it is most important to remember to shut the heating off before the liquid falls below the level of the heating coils. In some ships the oil is circulated through a heater on deck and this should be shut down before the vessel gets to stripping level.

The order of discharge in the Chief Officer's plan must be adhered to closely, to avoid undue stresses, and in the case of a multi-grade discharge, to avoid contamination. This plan usually allows the main pumps to work for as long as possible, so that the stripping system can be used to drain the last remnants of cargo from some tanks whilst there is still plenty of cargo left in other tanks for the main pumps. This will ensure the maximum efficiency of cargo operations and that in-port time is minimised.

9.14 Stripping procedures

Once the main cargo pumps have discharged the main bulk of the cargo, removing the last remnants of cargo from a tank is referred to as 'stripping'. Different types of vessels can accomplish this in different ways and the OOW should seek advice from the Chief Officer as to what is the normal custom and practice on that particular ship. He should refer to the ship's technical manuals for advice on operating procedures. Some vessels are fitted with separate small bore stripping lines.

Main cargo pumps are not usually used for stripping purposes mainly because when air/gas is drawn into a centrifugal pump, it prevents the pump from developing suction. Once suction is lost, the pump will need to be primed. This can be achieved either with a priming device, or by opening the valve to a partially full tank to provide a head of liquid with which to prime the pump.

However, the main cargo pumps can be used for stripping if they are fitted with a system that removes the air/gas prior to the oil reaching the pump, for example a Vac-Strip or Prima-Vac system. The pump discharge valve should be throttled in to reduce the flow rate through the pump, and reduce the possibility of drawing gas from the tank. The reduction in flow rate gives sufficient time for the remaining cargo to drain back to the suction through the small holes in the stiffening structure of the tank bottom.

Poor stripping performance of a vessel can lead to claims for outturn loss by the receivers when cargo is left in the tanks, or to delays which may result in claims for demurrage. Both of these can run into thousands of dollars. Therefore, the OOW must ensure that stripping is carried out efficiently to avoid any such claims being made against the vessel.

Stripping will require a reasonable stern trim in order to encourage the flow of liquid towards the suction strum. When stripping wing tanks, it is usual to arrange for the vessel to be listed slightly to port or starboard, depending on where the tank suction is located, to assist this flow. This is achieved by using either remaining cargo in other tanks, or ballast if the vessel is discharging cargo and ballasting concurrently. The OOW must not assume that all suctions are located in the same place in each tank, this is invariably not the case, and he must learn their location in each tank, from the ship's plans. If stripping back to holding tanks, it is important that the OOW monitors the ullages in those tanks to avoid any overflows.

Once the last of the cargo has been discharged ashore, all pumps should be stopped and the engine-room informed that the pumps and the inert gas system are no longer required. The terminal should be informed that discharge is complete, and the manifold valves should be closed. Other valves should be closed as advised by the Chief Officer. A survey will be undertaken to establish the remaining on-board (ROB) quantity.

9.15 Ballasting procedures

Ballast operations should be agreed between ship and terminal. Some vessels ballast concurrently with the discharge of cargo, in such cases there should **always** be a two-valve separation between the ballast and the cargo, to avoid contamination and pollution. Other vessels can only ballast following the final survey. The former case includes VLCCs with some permanent clean ballast (although extra ballast may have to be taken on board for heavy weather) and double hulled tankers, with completely segregated ballast arrangements. In an effort to reduce the risks to the environment posed by tankers and the large costs associated with clean-up operations following an oil pollution incident, increasingly tankers are being built with double hulls. On these tankers, the ballasting arrangements are similar to those found on bulk carriers—see chapter 10.

Some tankers still carry the majority of their ballast in cargo tanks previously filled with oil. Ballast loaded into these tanks is termed 'dirty ballast'. Although segregated ballast tanks eliminate the need for tankers to have dirty ballast, because the ballast pipes may pass through cargo tanks, there is still a risk of contamination caused by leaking pipelines. On older ships, contamination can occur due to leaking bulkheads. Prior to ballasting, the OOW must check that the tanks to be ballasted are set to vent to atmosphere during the ballast operation. Failure to do so could result in over pressurisation of the cargo tank and subsequent catastrophic failure of the ship's structure.

The cargo tanks to be ballasted from the sea should be lined up with the relevant pump; it is essential that the OOW carefully checks this lining up. The pump should be started at minimum revolutions, and a vacuum on the pump positively identified, prior to opening the sea chest valve. This is to avoid the possibility of any oil remaining in the tank, the pump or the line from flowing back to the sea chest and thence overside, resulting in a pollution incident. The sea around the vessel should be monitored, and the sea valve should be closed immediately if any pollution is detected. Once it is confirmed that the ballast is entering the correct tanks and there are no leaks, the pump speed can be increased to the maximum rate as advised by the Chief Officer, but never more than the designed loading rate for the number of tanks being ballasted simultaneously.

At the commencement of ballasting, the lines should be flushed through to the furthest tank in the system. This tank should be inspected visually, any oil in the system will have been pushed into this tank, and will be identified during this inspection. The ballast should be constantly monitored to ensure it is still flowing into the designated tanks as well as checking adjacent tanks for any ingress of ballast water. As the ballasting operation nears completion

the pump speed should be reduced in order to stop at the required final ullage. The OOW should ensure that the sea chest is shut as soon as the pump is stopped to avoid any possibility of dirty ballast flowing back to sea from the tanks.

When topping off ballast tanks, the same precautions as for loading oil still apply, due to the potential high risk of pollution. This is particularly true with non-segregated ballast tanks, but even with totally segregated tanks, there is always the possibility of leaks in pipelines or the ship's structure. Oil floating on top of ballast water will always be the first to overflow! It is good practice to visually inspect each of the ballast tanks on completion, to check for any oil which may have leaked into the system.

Once ballasting is completed it only remains to shut down the pumps and the cargo system and prepare the vessel for sea.

9.16 Anti-pollution checklist
- Has the ship/shore checklist been completed? —see appendix IV.
- Has the cargo operations plan been agreed with the terminal?—see 9.6.
- Are all personnel familiar with the oil spill contingency plan?
- Is the spill containment equipment checked and readily available?
- Is the pipeline system lined up as per the Chief Officer's orders:
    - Manifold? ● Deck valves? ● Pumproom?
- Are all deck scupper plugs in place?
- Have arrangements been made to keep the main deck free of water?
- Has the cargo manifold been drained before removing the blanks?
- Are all unused cargo and bunker connections blanked and fully bolted?
- Are pressure gauges in place, and any cocks/drains securely closed?
- Are the relevant valves in the drop lines closed (for discharge), or open (for loading)?
- Are all sea and overboard valves connected to the cargo system confirmed closed and lashed/sealed/locked/immobilised?
- Are engineroom and pumproom bilge discharge valves confirmed closed and lashed/sealed/immobilised?
- Have all hoses and connections been checked?
- Are drip cans or trays in place?
- Is there a multiple valve separation between cargo system and the sea?
- Have the procedures for cargo/bunker/ballast handling been agreed?
- Are the methods for routine and emergency communication between the ship and the terminal fully understood and agreed by all parties?
- Have all emergency procedures been discussed and understood?
- And emergency stops tested?

- **Are the segregated ballast tanks free from contamination?**
- **Is there sufficient planned space in the last tank for draining the shore lines/hoses/arms?**
- **Will the manifolds be properly supervised throughout the operation?**
- **Are sufficient personnel available, with defined and tested methods of communication with the Officer of the Watch?**
- **Will physical checks be maintained on the ullages of all tanks?**
- **Have all valve indicators been checked?**
- **Are cargo pumps to be started before opening the manifold/sea valves?**

9.17 Inert gas (IG) systems

Any volatile liquid giving off flammable gases or vapours poses a considerable risk of fire and explosion. In order to minimise this risk, tankers have equipment to provide inert gas which can be used to fill the space above the liquid and the voids around the tank. This ensures that the level of oxygen is insufficient to support combustion.

Inert gas is supplied in one of two ways. Most tankers make use of the flue gases from the main engine, while other vessels have dedicated inert gas generating plant on board. Most ships use exhaust or flue gases as a source of inert gas because it is relatively abundant, as a by product of normal ship's plant operation. Also it is cheap to obtain, when compared with other inert gases such as nitrogen which have to be purchased and stored. Where flue gases are not available in sufficient quantity, or of the right quality, most ships obtain their supplies from an inert gas generator.

In order to use flue gases the undesirable constituents need to be removed, such as the sulphurous gases, water droplets and small amounts of solids. The gases normally pass through a water spray to cool them, and remove sulphur oxides and ash. They then pass through mesh filters to remove water droplets. If the sulphurous elements and water vapour were not removed they could combine to produce sulphuric acid, a strong corrosive which could do untold damage to tank coatings and ultimately the steel hull of the vessel. Ideally, the most susceptible parts of the IG system should be lined with a protective coating, but frequently this breaks down in time, and the system on older ships is likely to suffer from corrosion failure.

The inert gas system is used during cargo discharge, de-ballasting, tank cleaning and crude oil washing. Besides being used to inert the atmosphere in empty cargo and ballast tanks, the system is also used to purge tanks prior to gas freeing. The system has to be capable of topping-up the pressure in the tanks both on the loaded and ballast passages.

9.17.1 Benefits of inert gas

Besides inhibiting combustion, and preventing the ingress of air, inert gas has other less obvious benefits:

1. A reduction in the oxygen content of the atmosphere inhibits corrosion.
2. The pressure of inert gas reduces the loss of cargo due to evaporation.
3. The pressure of inert gas slightly increases the discharge rate.
4. It enables the transportation of cargoes that react with oxygen.
5. It can be used as a fire-fighting medium.

9.17.2 Instrumentation, monitoring and control

Instrumentation for the IG system in the cargo control room includes analogue and/or digital readouts for the following:
1. Percentage oxygen of the inert gas.
2. Inert gas pressure in the deck main.
3. Inert gas delivery temperature.
4. A schematic diagram indicating the positions of all valves in the system, which usually is automatic.

The pressure and oxygen content of the inert gas in the supply main is recorded continuously on a chart in the cargo control room, engine control room and/or on the bridge . Alarms are also located in the cargo control room, which will provide the OOW with audible and visual warning of any problems. These are duplicates of alarms in the engine control room, where all other alarms and controls are usually sited. The normal system is that the engineers provide the inert gas, the deck department uses it. The pressure and oxygen content of the inert gas will usually be maintained automatically. Nevertheless, it is good practice for the OOW to check the oxygen content of the inert gas supply using a portable analyzer; he should also keep a close watch on all the instruments as a double check, in case the control systems should malfunction.

The inert gas machinery is started shortly before the discharge of cargo or ballast is commenced. The pressure in the inert gas lines must be maintained between set limits. The minimum pressure ensures that there is sufficient inert gas to replace the liquid discharged and to avoid the possibility of creating a vacuum, and the maximum pressure ensures there is no structural damage due to over-pressurising the system. This pressure is usually maintained automatically, but the system has alarms which should be tested regularly.

An alarm will be activated should any of the following occur:
1. High percentage oxygen content.
2. Low deck main pressure.
3. High deck main pressure.
4. Low seal water levels in the scrubber tower and deck seal.

The oxygen content of the inert gas must be maintained at below 8%, and the alarm sounds if this level is exceeded. There is a built-in safety factor, as combustion cannot usually occur when the oxygen content is below 11%. Modern inert gas generating plant can now deliver inert gas with an oxygen content as low as 1%, (3% for ex-flue gas) which in addition to providing an enhanced margin of safety, also further inhibits corrosion.

The inert gas system should shut down automatically in the event of:

1. Low cooling water pressure to the scrubber tower.
2. The scrubber tower water seal level being excessively high.
3. Blower fan failure.
4. The inert gas temperature becoming excessively high.
5. Control power failure.
6. Oxygen content exceeding preset limits.
7. The scrubber overboard valve being closed inadvertently.
8. Deck seal low level.
9. Any manually operated 'emergency stop' being activated.

9.17.3 Action by officer of the watch

If the inert gas system fails to deliver the required quality and quantity of inert gas, or to maintain a positive pressure, or if the system shuts down automatically for any of the reasons mentioned above, then the OOW must take immediate action to prevent loss of pressure and air being drawn into the tanks:

1. Stop all cargo discharge and/or deballast operations.
2. Close the inert gas deck isolating valve.
3. Close any other vent stack valve which may have been in use.
4. Inform the Chief Officer or the Master, and the terminal.
5. Make an entry in the deck logbook.
6. Close the manifold valves <u>after</u> informing the terminal, if the stoppage is likely to be prolonged.
7. Initiate repairs to the inert gas system to correct the faults.
8. Cargo operations should not be resumed until the inert gas system is returned to fully operational status.

With certain combinations of rates of loading/discharging and ballast/deballasting, it may be possible to continue operations for a short time. The Chief Officer will decide if this is possible, for example, when the loading rate is lower than the deballast rate, or the ballast rate is higher than the discharge rate.

9.17.4 Checks prior to discharging cargo or deballasting

1. Check the water level in the deck seal is satisfactory
2. Open the gas regulating valve.
3. Open the inert gas deck isolating valve.
4. Open all cargo tank inert gas inlets and shut all other tank openings (where necessary).
5. Close the mast riser valve.

9.17.5 Checks prior to loading cargo or ballasting

1. Close the inert gas deck isolating valve.
2. Open mast risers or vent risers.
3. Check that flame screens are undamaged and clean. This should usually have been carried out as part of preparations prior to arrival.
4. Open tank isolating valves.

9.17.6 Further information

Inert gas systems vary greatly in their design, although all have common elements required by international convention. Junior officers should familiarise themselves with the inert gas operations manual on their ships. Further information on the principles, design, layout, inspection, maintenance and repair of IG systems can be found in the IMO publication *Guidelines for Inert Gas Systems*[48] and the ISGOTT manual.[65]

9.18 Measuring and sampling

This section addresses the issues surrounding the methods of obtaining the liquid level in a tanker's cargo oil tanks, an 'ullage', and the different devices that are in common use. It offers guidance on when and how to obtain samples of oil and how to obtain cargo temperatures and the devices used.

9.18.1 Gauging systems

Each cargo tank is fitted with a gauge which can usually be read directly at the tank location on deck or from a remote indicator in the cargo control room. Gauges should be checked regularly to ensure that they are functioning correctly and compared against a manual ullage taken with an ullage tape. It is good practice to log all such checks. The OOW should never place too much reliance on the remote readouts.

A manual ullage is taken by hand using a standard ullage tape. This consists of a metal tape with a bob attached, operated using a hand winder. Although this is not a routine necessity on the vast majority of ships today, it is available for obtaining a good check for comparison with the automated gauging systems in use. A detailed description of tank gauging devices, such as the Whessoe Float System, is beyond the scope of this guide, and the reader who requires further information should consult the manufacturer's literature.

Care should be taken when operating these systems manually. When lowering the bobs prior to cargo operation they should never be allowed to freefall. When stowing the bobs on completion of the final survey care should be taken not to wind them up too quickly, especially the last few centimetres, as this can put undue strain on the connection between the wire and the bob. Modern systems have remote readouts in the cargo control room, and can be wound up and stowed from there using compressed air.

Gauges should be checked regularly to ensure that they are reading correctly. The reading of the gauge when it is housed is normally marked on the housing. Hence the actual reading on the gauge should be compared with this value whenever it is wound home. If there is a small difference, say, a few centimetres, this should be applied as a correction to all subsequent gauge readings. Large differences indicate a fault in the system, which should be investigated.

An innovation in manual ullaging took place with the introduction of the ullage/temperature/interface (UTI) detector and similar instruments. These are electronic devices that are designed to be used on modern inerted tankers using a closed ullaging system. The tanks are equipped with hermetically (gastight) sealed openings to which the equipment is connected usually by way of a snap connection. The device provides very accurate readings which are used in conjunction with the tank calibration tables to obtain precise quantities.

Recent developments have seen the introduction of modern technology to obtain the necessary measurements. These include pneumatics, capacitance, ultrasonics and radar, some of which can produce very accurate ullages. This equipment can be interfaced with the main ship's loading computer, so that the computer receives constantly updated and extremely accurate ullages and the status of all tanks is updated on a continuous basis.

9.18.2 Obtaining samples

Whenever oil is transferred between a ship and shore storage, sampling takes place before the operation is commenced and after it is completed. These samples are evidence of the quality of the oil at the time of this transfer, and can be used to settle disputes where one party claims that the oil has been contaminated by the other party. Before a vessel loads a cargo of oil, her tanks are inspected and passed as fit for the particular grade or grades to be loaded. At the same time the oil in the shore tanks to be used is tested to ensure that it is not contaminated or its quality has not deteriorated as a result of storage.

As loading is commenced, samples are taken at the manifold for testing. The OOW should encourage the independent surveyor to obtain these samples. This is because any samples taken by ship's personnel may not have the same value as those taken independently if there is a dispute which goes to Court. The samples are obtained via a small cock on the manifold and collected in sample bottles provided by the surveyor, which are then sealed, labelled and signed by representatives of the ship, the terminal and/or the surveyor.

The terminal will take samples for their own use, which will be laboratory tested ashore. In this way, any drop in the specification of the oil will be checked before too much of the cargo is loaded. If necessary the loading can be stopped whilst the matter is investigated, and remedial action taken to supply cargo of the correct grade. This is particularly important with sensitive cargoes such as white oils like jet, kerosene and lub.oils. Such oils will also be subjected to bottom sampling, which involves sampling the first metre of cargo loaded in each tank. This is done to ensure that the cargo has not been contaminated by the ship's lines or pumps. Loading operations will be halted while these bottom samples

are tested in a laboratory ashore.

Final samples are taken at the completion of loading operations. They are the final check on the quality of the oil loaded, and form the basis from which the chemists obtain the data for the quantity and quality sheet, or specification sheet. A copy of this sheet should be placed on board before the vessel sails. In addition, sample cans containing samples of each of the grades that the vessel has loaded are sealed and dispatched with the vessel to her destination.

There are several different devices for obtaining samples from different levels in the ship's cargo tanks. The principle behind them, however, is much the same in every case. The apparatus usually consists of a bottle or can, which is weighted to allow it to sink to the bottom of the tank. The container is lowered by means of a line which is secured to the stopper as well as the container itself. If the container is lowered gently, the stopper remains in place, but when the container has reached the desired depth, the cord or line is jerked sufficiently hard to remove the stopper, and allow the container to flood. More complex sampling devices allow a single sample to be composed of a one third proportion from each of three different levels in the tank.

9.18.3 Obtaining cargo temperatures

1. Manually, using a thermometer in a sampling container.
2. The UTI detector.
3. Automatic temperature sensors fitted to the cargo tanks which provide the OOW with readings in the cargo control room.

9.18.4 Water dips

Water is sometimes present in the ship's tanks in addition to the oil. This is not usually a problem with cargoes such as heavy crudes which may contain a considerable amount of water in suspension. There can be disputes because the customer does not want to pay crude oil prices for water! However, the presence of water in some products cannot be tolerated, hence the reason, when loading jet oil for example, to have the last remnants of water from tank cleaning removed by moppers before loading is commenced. Claims for water contamination regularly run into thousands of dollars.

Origins of this contaminating water include:
1. Remains of ballast left in the cargo pipeline system.
2. Remnants of tank cleaning.
3. Leaks in the vessel's hull or internal structure.
4. Sea water that has found its way through badly maintained or defective tank lids, ullage ports or Butterworth plates.
5. Water may be present in the cargo when it is loaded and settle out during the voyage.

Water which collects beneath the oil in the bottom of a tank is known as 'free water'. Its presence can be detected with a UTI detector, or by using a sounding rod smeared at the tip with water finding paste. This paste changes colour when it comes into contact with water, enabling the exact level of the water to be read off the scale when the rod is drawn up.

It may be difficult to obtain accurate water dips with black oils such as crude or fuel oil. The rod and line will be coated with a heavy covering of oil which may prevent it registering the correct amount, if it indeed indicates the presence of water at all. A useful tip is to agitate the rod in a bucket of kerosene, which will cause the heavy oil to dissipate, leaving the paste clear so that a reading can be obtained.

9.18.5 Precautions when measuring or sampling

When measuring or sampling oil cargo, care must be taken to avoid inhaling gas. Personnel should stand at right angles to the direction of the wind, and have their heads well back from the ullage port.

Special precautions are required if the tanks are inerted:

1. A minimum positive inert gas pressure must be maintained.
2. No cargo or ballast operations should take place whilst the inert gas pressure is reduced for measuring and sampling.
3. Only one ullage port should be opened at a time, and for as short a period as possible, keeping it closed between different operations.
4. On completion, all openings should be checked to ensure they are securely closed, and all tanks re-pressurised with inert gas before resuming cargo operations.
5. These procedures must not be undertaken on tanks containing cargo whilst the vessel is manoeuvring at the berth.

Some terminals do not permit tanks to be depressurised, so that ships trading to such terminals must be fitted with instrumentation that can be operated whilst the tanks are pressurised with inert gas.

9.18.6 Obtaining a density

A sample of oil should be obtained in the usual way. This can then be transferred to a glass hydrometer jar, long enough to accommodate the hydrometer. Product tankers will be provided with various hydrometers covering a range of different densities. The OOW must ensure that he uses the correct hydrometer, corresponding to the expected density. The actual density is measured using the same methods employed for testing the density of seawater—see chapter 13.9.4.

Density is normally expressed in vacuum at 15°Centigrade.

This is an important task since claims have been made against ships for short shipment of cargo on the basis of a disagreement on densities of different products. The procedure should not be left to a surveyor alone, as is common practice on certain trades. Some claims against the shipowner have been successful because the ship failed to take densities and therefore could provide no useful evidence in defence of the claim. Claims such as this can amount to tens of thousands of dollars.

9.18.7 Example of a calculation of cargo quantity

Observed ullage	1.435 m.
Trim and list correction	– 0.021 m. (from correction tables)
Corrected ullage	1.414 m.
Volume	1623 cu.m.(from ullage tables)
Correction for observed temperature	0.983 (from correction tables)
Volume at 15°C	1595.409 cu.m.
On-board (ROB) quantity (OBQ)	37.514 cu.m.
Volume of cargo loaded	1557.895 cu.m.
Density	0.889 tonnes/cu.m.
Cargo loaded	1384.969 tonnes.

9.19 Tank cleaning and gas freeing

Tank cleaning arrangements vary from ship to ship but consist primarily of fixed or portable machines supplied with wash water from the tank cleaning pipeline system. Some tankers employ a cleaning method known as crude oil washing (COW), which is discussed in section 9.20.

Although the majority of tank cleaning takes place at sea, this chapter would not be complete without reference to this operation as an integral part of preparations for loading a cargo of oil. Tank washing presents the ship with a problem in regard to pollution prevention, as the resultant oil/water mixture has to be disposed of without harm to the environment, and by methods which comply with international laws. This requires specialised monitoring equipment on board, with which junior officers should be familiar.

Tank cleaning is carried out in order to remove any deposits left over from previous cargoes and prepare tanks for receiving the next cargo, so avoiding the possibility of contamination and the commercial repercussions that would entail. It also removes any residues and waxy material, present with some petroleum products, which if left to accumulate would at best reduce the pumping and outturn performance of the ship and at worst would render pumping impossible.

It is generally recognised that tank cleaning and gas freeing is the most hazardous period of tanker operations. This is true whether washing for clean ballast, gas freeing for entry, or gas freeing for hot work. Additional risks from the toxic effect of petroleum gas during this period cannot be over emphasised and must be impressed on all concerned. It is therefore essential that the greatest possible care is exercised in all operations connected with tank cleaning and gas freeing.

Tank cleaning can be carried out in different tank atmospheres and each one requires specific precautions and procedures. It is beyond the scope of this guide to go into any great detail in this respect. However, the author would encourage all junior officers to study the tank cleaning manual on board their ship and familiarise themselves with its contents, particularly with reference to atmosphere control and testing. Washing in anything but an inerted atmosphere imposes certain operating restrictions and junior officers should be aware of these limitations. In an inerted atmosphere there are no restrictions, so long as a positive pressure is maintained and the oxygen content remains below 8% by volume.

Ships are either equipped with fixed or portable machines, the latter gaining access to the tank through openings in the weather deck commonly known as Butterworth plates. They are connected to long hoses that are fed with wash water from the tank cleaning main on deck. If fixed machines are fitted they are also fed from the tank cleaning main. Tanks can be washed with cold or hot water, the latter supplied by passing the water through a heat exchanger. **It is essential that the OOW ensures that the hoses are checked for electrical continuity before being introduced into any cargo compartment.**

If need be, the first tanks to be washed will be the ones required for clean ballast. Once they are completed, clean ballast will be loaded whilst the dirty ballast loaded at the discharge port will be discharged through the oily water discharge monitoring and control system. This equipment records the oil content of the water discharged and ensures that the allowable limits under Marpol 73/78[61] are not exceeded. If the oil content should rise above the allowable limits, the overboard valve is shut automatically, and the dirty water diverted to a slop tank. Once the dirty ballast has been discharged those tanks will then be cleaned.

Water for washing is obtained either direct from the sea or from slop tanks which have been partially filled with water. This is delivered to the appropriate tank via the tank cleaning line and recirculated back to the slop tank. Problems can arise but most of them can be eradicated by remembering a few simple points:

1. Check the machines are well lubricated prior to washing and that they are turning freely. Keep a careful watch on the machines to ensure their correct operation throughout tank cleaning.
2. If using portable machines, ensure the hoses are in good condition and they are flaked out and free from kinks. They should be tested for electrical continuity.
3. Ensure that once washing starts, water is not allowed to build up in the bottom of the tank.
4. Ensure that an adequate trim and, if necessary, a slight list in the right direction is maintained in order that the remaining water flows towards the tank suction and efficient stripping of the remaining liquid is achieved. The list can normally be accomplished by varying the level in one of the slop tanks into which the washings are pumped.
5. Maintain regular checks on the level of liquid in the slop tanks to avoid overflows or over pressurisation of the tank structure.
6. Monitor the inert gas pressure and oxygen content to maintain a safe atmosphere for washing.
7. If using hot water keep a close check on the outlet temperature from the heater.

8. Ensure that the water to the machines is maintained at the recommended pressure commensurate with the size of the tank and the degree of cleanliness required, otherwise washing will be ineffective. The OOW is advised to study carefully the system's operating manual.
9. A bleeder, normally an old Butterworth hose, should be rigged leading overside via a hand valve, to enable the pressure in the system to be released rapidly if required, for example if another hose bursts, or when changing tanks. This is used because the heater cannot be shut down instantaneously.
10. Gas freeing of cargo tanks must be carried out for entry and inspection and if any hot work is required. It is unlikely a ship will be completely gas freed except when going for refit at a drydock.

Further information on tank cleaning and gas freeing is available in the ISGOTT manual.[65]

9.20 Crude oil washing (COW)

A crude oil tanker fitted with an inert gas system and fixed washing equipment in its cargo tanks can use crude oil from the cargo as the washing medium. It is used very effectively to reduce the quantity of oil residues clinging to the sides of the tanks and remaining onboard after completion of discharge.

Crude oil washing has certain recognised objectives:
1. A safer operation which minimises the risk of pollution.
2. A high standard of tank cleanliness.
3. The best possible cargo outturn.
4. The minimum extension of time in comparison with normal discharge procedures.

The advantages of COW over water washing of cargo tanks are:
1. Reduced risk of pollution.
2. Better cargo outturn.
3. Less water discharged to the terminal.
4. Reduced corrosion of the internal tank structure, due to the presence of less sea water.
5. Less slops retained resulting in an affective increase in cargo carrying capacity.
6. Cheaper tank cleaning.
7. Reduced time needed for tank cleaning on passage except those tanks needed for clean ballast, ensuring more time for vessel maintenance, and hence lower overall vessel operating costs.

Further information on crude oil washing is available from the IMO publication *Crude Oil Washing Systems*,[47] the ISGOTT manual,[65] and The Nautical Institute publication *Crude Carrier Practice*.[18]

Crude oil washing must only be carried out under the control of an officer who has been specifically trained and certified in such operations.

Prior to arrival in port where the vessel intends to crude oil wash the vessel must give prior notice to the terminal of at least 24 hours, and seek its approval.

Crude oil washing can only be carried out after this approval has been received. The vessel should also pressure test the crude oil washing lines to approximately 25% above normal operating pressure to confirm its integrity. The exact figure can be obtained from the system's operating manual. Where possible, crude oil should be used for this purpose in order to prevent any water remaining in the line after testing. A record of this test must be entered into the oil record book.

Crude oil for washing purposes can be obtained in one of three ways:

1. Straight from a cargo tank so long as the tank has been 'de-bottomed'—i.e., the lower few metres of the tank contents have been pumped out. This is done in order to remove any free water that may have been present. Crude used for washing must be 'dry' crude. A mixture of crude oil and water can produce an electrically charged mist during washing, which carries a risk of explosion.
2. Transferred to the slop tank(s) specifically to use for washing, provided any slops have been first pumped ashore.
3. Direct from the manifold or topline, if the vessel is equipped with a suitable connection to the crude oil washing line. This is dependent on whether there is sufficient pressure available at the manifold. Care must be taken not to allow the manifold back pressure to fall below the figure agreed with the terminal when using this method.

Crude oil washing must only be carried out with a safe controlled atmosphere in the tanks. It is important that the OOW ensures that the oxygen content in all tanks does not exceed 8% by volume. The OOW should monitor the slop tanks carefully to avoid the possibility of pollution. It is essential that the level in these tanks are checked regularly. Whenever the eductors are discharging into the slop tanks, they should be in the recirculating mode.

During COW operations, some of the cargo lines will be subjected to higher pressures than during a non-COW discharge. The same high pressures are present in the washing mains and feeder lines to the COW equipment. All lines should be frequently checked for leaks, as there is a serious risk of pollution, explosion and fire.

Crude oil washing must be stopped if:

1. The inert gas plant fails or low pressure alarm activates.
2. The high oxygen alarm activates.
3. Any leakage is reported from the manifold or any other lines or joints on deck or in the pumproom.
4. There is an overflow from any tank.
5. There is any indication of leakage from sea valves.

6. The level in the slop tanks rises to the maximum permitted, or there is a failure in the gauging system to these tanks.
7. There is an unexplained change in the level of any other tank.
8. There is a failure in communications between ship and terminal, or between the cargo control room and the personnel on deck.
9. Emergency instructions to stop pumping are received from ashore.

9.20.1 COW checklist

- **The COW/discharge operation discussed with the terminal supervisors.**
- **Ship/shore communications procedures established and tested.**
- **Conditions for aborting COW defined and agreed with the terminal.**
- **All tanks have positive inert gas pressure, and a system in place to monitor continuously this pressure.**
- **A system in place to monitor tank oxygen content, and maintain this level below 8%.**
- **Fixed and portable oxygen analyzers functioning correctly.**
- **The manifold, deck and pumproom correctly lined up.**
- **A responsible person stationed on deck at the tank being washed.**
- **A crew member assigned to check deck lines for leaks.**
- **COW machines set for the required washing pattern.**
- **A system in place to check the COW machines frequently for correct operation.**
- **A system in place to verify the wash pressure regularly.**
- **Float gauges wound up.**
- **A system in place to closely monitor the level in the slop tanks.**
- **Communications checked between the COW team and cargo control room.**
- **A notice displayed at the gangway to indicate that COW is taking place.**

9.21 Further information

The reader requiring a more detailed coverage of the operation of tankers is advised to consult a specialised textbook, such as The Nautical Institute publication *Crude Carrier Practice*,[18] and some of the other publications which are listed in appendix I, including the relevant IMO publications.

Chapter 10

BALLAST OPERATIONS

PURPOSE

On completion of this chapter you will know why ballast is used, why a plan is necessary, and who is responsible for various stages of the ballast operation. You will learn how to pump ballast, understand the importance of monitoring the operation, and appreciate some of the problems involved.

10.1 Importance of ballast

Ballast is used to make the ship safe and more efficient during the different stages of the voyage. Whenever the ship is to load or discharge her cargo, it is likely that sea water will be pumped out of, or into, the ballast tanks. The purpose of this is to ensure that:

1. The vessel remains at a draft suitable for positive ship handling during manoeuvring; if it is too light, the effect of the wind will seriously restrict its manoeuvrability.

2. Sufficient reserve stability is retained in order for the ship to remain seaworthy for the next passage. It must not be too stiff, with a high metacentric height (GM), nor too tender, with a low metacentric height. This will give the ship a comfortable roll, so avoiding damage to cargo and the ship's structure.

3. A seagoing draft is maintained which is deeper than any minimum draft limits provided in the ship's stability book.
   The forward draft must be sufficient for the forefoot to be well submerged, to avoid damage by pounding.
   The after draft must be sufficient for the engine cooling water intakes to be underwater. There are often two sets of these, one high for fully loaded, and one low for lightship. Even the lowest must not be too near the bottom of the hull to avoid sucking up mud in shallow water.

4. The propeller is operating efficiently—when the ship is empty and without sufficient ballast, the propeller is often partly out of the water, making it very inefficient.

5. Bending moments and shear stresses remain within allowable limits. Ballast can be used to compensate for uneven loadings, particularly on voyages with many ports, or during complicated loading procedures.

6. The vessel remains upright. This may be a continuous process on ships such as containerships which may be fitted with large side tanks which are used to compensate for lists introduced when heavy cargo is loaded or discharged from one side of the ship.

7. A required trim is maintained, for example, to ensure that cargo tanks are fully pumped out.

8. Any required maximum air draft is not exceeded, so that the ship can safely pass under obstructions such as bridges.

9. Any required maximum coaming air draft is not exceeded, so that shore cargo handling equipment is able to reach into the holds.

10.2 Ballast management

On some ships, the OOW will have little involvement with the ballast operations, whilst on larger ships, particularly bulk carriers, he plays a major role in such operations. In this chapter it is assumed he will be heavily involved by basing the text on the usual practices on board large bulk carriers.

Where it is the responsibility of the OOW to control the ballast operation, sometimes he will be required to operate the pumps and the valves. He must have a basic understanding of the principles involved, if equipment is to be operated safely and efficiently, without causing damage to the system, the ship or its cargo, or delay to the port turnround time.

Because ballast has to be used to ensure optimum performance, the ballast sequence has to be managed carefully. The role of the OOW is most important because the consequences of not controlling the operation effectively can be catastrophic, causing both damage and delay.

Some examples of faults which have led to serious incidents, sometimes with loss of life are:

1. Vessel capsized—insufficient ballast, or pumped at the wrong time.

2. Vessel broken in two—incorrect combination of cargo and ballast.

3. Vessel grounding at the berth due to ballast being pumped out much slower than planned, combined with a high load rate and inattention.

4. Lighters alongside sunk by being filled with discharging ballast.

5. Cargo damaged by flooding from ballast.

6. Cargo and/or ballast contaminated due to operating valves in the wrong sequence.

7. Tanks ruptured due to pressure or vacuum build up.

8. Pumps burnt out due to inattention.

9. Undercarrying cargo due to inability to deballast fully.

Therefore it is vital to check all ballast lines and valve settings before every operation, and to have an agreed safe setting for all valves to which they must be restored on completion of every ballast operation. It is essential for the OOW to monitor closely the ACTUAL movement of ballast at all times, so he always knows what tonnage of ballast water is in which tank. This goes hand-in-hand with his monitoring of the cargo operation, and his checking the ship's draft regularly.

10.3 Minimising the amount of ballast

The main purpose of a ship is to earn money from carrying cargo, so the Chief Officer will be constantly alert to the need to minimise the amount of ballast on board, retaining just enough to comply with the requirements listed in section 10.1. Excess ballast means a higher displacement, so that more fuel is burnt to propel the ship through the water, and the speed may be reduced. Also, if there are limiting drafts at any stage of the voyage, excess ballast will mean less cargo is being carried. In these circumstances, it should be remembered that every tonne of ballast that remains on board on completion of deballasting is one tonne of freight sacrificed if cargo has to be shut out.

Correct loading and distribution of the cargo often enables the required draft and trim to be obtained without the use of extra ballast. On ships which are provided with optimum trim/displacement/speed tables, a small amount of extra ballast may be used to achieve the required minimum fuel consumption, as indicated by these tables.

10.4 Ballast plan

On bulk carriers large quantities of ballast water have to be pumped quickly to compensate for the rapid loading or discharge of the cargo. The Chief Officer will have produced a ballast plan, which will ensure that the sequence of pumping ballast corresponds with the sequence for loading or discharging of the cargo, in order that the bending moments and shear forces are kept within acceptable limits—see also chapter 8.1.3.

For bulk carriers, The Nautical Institute has produced a cargo operations control form which it recommends is lodged with authorities ashore. This shows the planned sequence of loading each hold, with the tonnages for each pour, and the associated programme of deballasting each tank, to the same time scale. Corresponding drafts and stresses are tabulated to prove that the operation is being carried out within safe limits. The form is also to be used for discharging operations—see appendix VIII.

Throughout the ballast operation, the OOW should know the tonnage of ballast in each of the tanks at all times. It is his duty to ensure that the ballast plan is adhered to strictly, to avoid excessive stresses being placed on the ship's structure.

WHENEVER HE DETECTS THAT THE BALLAST AND CARGO ARE OUT OF STEP FROM THIS PLAN, THE OOW MUST CALL THE CHIEF OFFICER IMMEDIATELY.

The Chief Officer may calculate that a change of ballast or cargo sequence is required, but in some cases the cargo or ballast operation must be halted to allow the other to catch up. Some Chief Officers will require the OOW to update the ballast input on the stability machine regularly, so that an up-to-date picture is always available. Other Chief Officers do not permit anyone else to touch this machine, in order to avoid errors caused by too many people interfering with his settings. The OOW should check these requirements when he first joins a new ship, and when there is a change in personnel.

The Nautical Institute has recommended for bulk carriers that whenever possible the 'At Sea' stress limits are not exceeded in port, thus permitting a greater margin of safety than is given by working to the higher 'In Port' limits.

10.5 Ship's ballast system

When he first joins a ship, the junior deck officer should learn the layout of all the tanks onboard, the route taken by their associated pipelines, and the location of each sounding pipe and tank valve.

10.5.1 Tanks and pipelines

Ballast tanks may be double-bottom, side, topside (upper wing or 'saddle'), or fore and aft peaks. The lines may be separate to each tank, or form port and starboard mains, or ring mains. Some ships may have a ballast duct formed from part of the double-bottom structure in lieu of pipelines. Some vessels also have certain holds which are of reinforced construction to allow for them to be filled with ballast. These are used to achieve sufficient immersion of the hull to prevent the bow slamming and the propeller racing if adverse weather is encountered.

10.5.2 Pumps

There are usually two large capacity ballast pumps, which can be used either singly or together, and also it may be possible for a general service pump to be connected into the system. The OOW should learn the capacity of these pumps, both their theoretical figures and their practical capabilities. Larger vessels also have stripping pumps or eductors, to assist with the removal of the last traces of water. These connect in to the same lines on most ships, so that stripping cannot be done at the same time as the main pumping. A few ships have separate stripping lines. There are variations; the Chief Engineer will be able to explain which combinations are possible, and when these can be used.

10.5.3 Pumping ballast

Nearly all ballast pumps are centrifugal in operation. Pumps work in one direction only, meaning that water always comes in through the inlet side and is forced out of the outlet side. Hence the direction in which ballast is pumped, in or out of a tank, is determined by the operation of valves in the lines around the pump.

10.5.4 Speed of ballast

With bulk carriers, there is often a clause in charterparties, and sometimes in the contract with the loading terminal, that the ship must be able to deballast completely within a specified time—e.g., 24 hours for a Panamax bulk carrier. If the ship is unable to achieve this, she will suffer financial penalties; hence the need for the OOW to ensure that the deballasting operation is efficient. A knowledge of pumping capacities can be used to determine the time required to fill or empty each tank, and enable the OOW to monitor the operation efficiently.

10.6 Ballasting responsibilities

The duties of the OOW regarding ballast operations vary from ship to ship, so, when he joins each new ship, the junior deck officer must enquire of the Chief Officer as to the exact details of the methods employed, and who performs each operation.

10.6.1 Centralised controls

On some ships, the ballasting operation is performed entirely by the duty deck watchkeeper, or by the Chief Officer assisted by the OOW. This is often the case on new ships with centralised ballast controls, which may be in a deck pumproom, cargo control room, engine control room or the bridge. The ballast pumps, and valves for each of the ballast tanks, various sections of the ballast lines, and sea-suctions or overboard discharges, may be remotely controlled from these rooms. There will be indicators showing the setting of each valve (open, closed or part-way), and gauges showing the performance of each pump. Such a system also features remote reading gauges which show the level of the contents of each ballast tank. This system is similar to that found in the cargo control room on tankers—see chapter 9.

10.6.2 Local controls

On other ships, part of the operation is performed by the duty engineer, or pumpman, with whom the OOW must maintain a close liaison. Tank valves may have to be manually operated from the deck, whilst valves in the pipelines may have to be operated from a part of the engineroom. Pumps may have to be set up locally from a pumproom or from the engine control room. A tank such as the fore peak usually has a manual valve on deck, where the pipeline penetrates the collision bulkhead, in addition to any remote valves. This should ONLY be opened when filling or emptying, to avoid being unintentionally left open when the ship proceeds to sea.

10.7 Basic ballast procedures

The following procedure describes the steps to take to pump out a ballast tank. It should be remembered that this is usually done in pairs of port and starboard tanks, so it will be necessary to duplicate this procedure. Filling a tank is basically the same, with the water flowing in the opposite direction.

1. Confirm with duty engineer that there is sufficient power available to commence and complete the operation. With electrically driven pumps he may need to start up an extra generator.
2. Check all valves on the system are closed.
3. Open the valve to the tank.
4. Open any necessary valve(s) in the lines between the tank and pump.
5. Open the pump suction valve.
6. Open the overboard discharge valve.
7. Make any checks on the pump required by its operating instructions.
8. Open the pump discharge valve until it is about 20% open.
9. Start the pump.
10. Gradually open the pump discharge valve further until its gauge reading reaches the manufacturer's recommended discharge pressure.
11. Check the tank is emptying, as described in the next sections.

10.8 Monitoring the ballast

Whatever the system of operation, the monitoring of the ballast is usually the responsibility of the deck watchkeeper. This means that the OOW must ensure that the tanks in use are regularly sounded. On those ships fitted with remote reading gauges, this simply involves observing the readings frequently. Such gauges must be checked regularly to ensure they are operating correctly, and that their readings are accurate. On older ships, this will involve manual sounding of the tank with a hand line. Often the duty seaman can be delegated to perform this task, but the OOW should monitor him closely. It is good practice to record the soundings and the corresponding tonnages in a 'ballast book' on a regular basis—see section 10.20. This will alert the OOW to any problems as soon as they occur.

The monitoring of the ballast operation is an important part of watchkeeping duties in port. If the OOW fails to detect a slowdown in the programme, particularly when deballasting during a rapid loading, then it may prove impossible to make up the lost time. The cargo loading may need to be halted to allow the deballasting to catch up, and the ship will suffer financial loss.

The OOW must always call the Chief Officer immediately if he becomes aware of any delays he did not anticipate.

10.9 Hand soundings

The OOW should check the final sounding on completion of each tank when deballasting, as an accurate reading will be required as part of the Chief Officer's draft survey. Gauges are indications of readings, and should never be relied upon as being absolutely accurate. They can be used to monitor the progress of the ballast operation, but hand soundings should always be used to obtain the final figures, or whenever an accurate tonnage is required.

10.10 Checking air pipes

Whenever starting to ballast or deballast a new tank, the OOW should develop the habit of feeling around the air pipe to that tank, to check there is a flow of air in or out—the opposite direction to the water. This will confirm to him that:
1. The pump is working and the correct lines are open.
2. The correct tank is being pumped.
3. The tank is being filled or emptied, as intended.

This procedure is especially important in very cold weather, particularly if the ballast is fresh water. There is a possibility that fresh water ballast can freeze in the air pipe, causing a blockage. If the ballast is being pumped out, a vacuum can be created in the tank which can lead to structural failure by implosion.

10.11 Checking adjacent hold

It is also good practice to sight the adjacent holds and void spaces when first starting to ballast a new tank, and to repeat these observations regularly for as long as ballasting continues. Occasionally wet damage has been caused to cargo by ballast seeping from manhole lids which have not been properly secured, or through leaks in the ship's structure caused by previously unnoticed damage or rusting through of the steelwork or welds. It is not unknown for a hold to partly fill with water from a ballast tank via a hold bilge sounding line which has rotted or broken where it passes through the tank.

10.12 Rechecking soundings

Sometime after completion of deballasting a tank the OOW should recheck the sounding. This is best done whilst there is still a good stern trim, and if any water is found, there is an opportunity to strip it out. Water may have been lying at the forward end of a tank when the vessel was near even keel, or perhaps did not flow aft very quickly because some of the drain holes were blocked (with sediment, or loosened scale). Occasionally the tank may have been refilled by someone operating the wrong valve.

When a double-bottom tank is emptied, generally the tank valve should be closed before stopping the pump. Some engineers may claim that this should be done in the reverse order, arguing that closing a valve against the pump will harm the pump. However, if the pump is stopped first, sea water can gravitate back into a double-bottom tank which has just been emptied, so defeating the object of the exercise. Manufacturers confirm that it does no harm to leave the pump running for a few seconds whilst the tank valve is closed. Some pumps wind down slowly, and there is no back flow when they are first switched off, giving ample time to close the valves later.

On completion of filling a tank, the correct order of operation is close the sea suction valve, stop the pump, then close the tank valve.

10.13 Using gravity

For simplicity and economy, the force of gravity is used to assist ballast operations whenever possible. When deballasting, this means that topside tanks are allowed to drain out naturally before so much cargo has been loaded that the dock water level reaches the level of the lowest point of these tanks. When ballasting, double-bottom tanks are flooded naturally before so much cargo has been discharged that the dock water level reaches the level of the highest point of these tanks.

Using gravity makes the operation easier to control, as the flow of water will stop naturally. If there is no pressure of time, it may not be necessary to monitor the soundings so frequently. Also, it is free—no energy is used to operate pumps. An advantage when ballasting double bottoms is that no water overflows on deck where it may cause damage, and that the head of water pressure is not excessive. On ships with common topside and double-bottom tanks, the OOW should monitor the soundings so that the pumps are activated once gravity stops assisting.

10.14 Over-pressurising tanks

When filling a ballast tank, the OOW should take care not to over-pressurise the tank, as it can be structurally damaged if it is filled faster than the air can escape, or faster than the excess water can overflow. All ballast tanks are fitted with air pipes at their forward and after end for this purpose. These air pipes can become blocked by damage, or by the freezing of water. On some older vessels the air pipe cowl may need to be opened manually before ballasting operations begin.

On modern vessels the air pipes are permanently open, and are fitted with a nonreturn float. This float is fitted to prevent seawater from entering an empty tank in adverse weather, which would cause the ship's draft to increase beyond that planned (and perhaps beyond her loadline limit). This could lead to the ship capsizing. It is good practice to regularly check that the nonreturn float in the air pipe is working correctly by feeling the flow of air in or out of the pipe during ballast operations. On some ships access to the float is easy, and its operation can be checked by hand.

Overflowing double-bottom tanks puts an unnecessary extra pressure on the tank structure due to the extended head of water to deck level from the top of the tank, and such practices should be avoided. When deballasting, if the air pipe is blocked, the resultant vacuum can cause severe structural damage, too, by implosion.

10.15 Avoiding a list

The port and starboard tanks should always be (de)ballasted together. If the ship develops a list due to unbalanced ballast, the stevedore may try to correct it with the cargo. This may lead to an unbalanced loading of the cargo, which places additional stresses on the ship's structure due to twisting. It can also cause distortion of the hatch opening, leading to difficulty in closing and securing the cover.

When stripping double-bottom tanks, some Chief Officers introduce a slight list in order to help the remaining water run towards the ballast line suction. This assists the removal of the final few tonnes of ballast. This operation is only done when loading is slow, with plenty of time to spare to complete the deballasting programme, and a maximum cargo lift is essential. It must only be attempted with the complete knowledge of the stevedore to avoid him taking remedial action with the cargo. For this reason, the OOW must never try to perform this exercise on his own initiative; the Chief Officer must always give his approval first.

10.16 Blocked sounding pipes

Sometimes the sounding pipes can become blocked, commonly with the lower links or end bobs of broken sounding rods, or occasionally with rust, scale or sediment. Whenever sounding a tank, it is good practice to note the reading on the sounding line at the top of the sounding pipe when the bob just touches the striking plate. This reading should be checked against the true distance ascertained from the ship's plans or tank calibration tables. Any difference means that the sounding pipe may be blocked, and will need to be cleared. If this practice is ignored, the tank may appear to sound empty when it still contains some ballast.

10.17 Dumping valves

If the topside tanks are fitted with dumping valves, the OOW will need to check that the ballast water being discharged is not causing damage to cargo in barges alongside, or on the quay, or to fittings on the quay such as electrical connections, motors, or even loosely laid cobblestones. Each of these examples has resulted in large claims being made against the ship. Usually such vessels are provided with chutes to redirect the outflow close to the hull, these must be used to good effect whenever necessary. The OOW should check regularly that such chutes are having the desired effect, and see that they are adjusted as required.

On completion of dumping, the OOW should always check that these valves are properly closed. Otherwise if there is just a slight gap, seawater can flood back into the tanks once the ship has loaded enough cargo to submerge the dumping valve over-side outlet. This could lead to serious overloading and overstressing of the ship. Because there have been a number of cases when one of these valve has been overlooked, it is a good idea to lash the operating wheel to the ship's rail whenever this valve is closed. This will provide a visual reminder. The Nautical Institute recommends that the final closing of dumping valves is logged.

10.18 Filling topside (upper wing) tanks

When filling topside tanks, it is good practice to stop when the water level is just short of the top of the sounding pipe. This will ensure that an accurate sounding or ullage can be taken, and so the most accurate tonnage of ballast water attainable can be computed. This system also prevents water from overflowing on deck where it may cause damage to the quay, barges or spilt cargo not yet swept up. The tanks can be topped up once the vessel is under way, to avoid water sloshing around and perhaps causing structural damage, and reducing the ship's stability by its free surface effect.

Some shore authorities who may have little knowledge of the ship's characteristics frequently ask for ballast tanks to be overflowed, in order to assist with draft surveys. This is undesirable, as it could lead to excessive pressures within double-bottom tanks, and may prevent the accurate measurement of the quantity of ballast in topside tanks. An overflowing tank does not mean that the tank is 100% full, as it fails to take into account that there may be voids at the top of the tank where air is trapped, so the actual volume of ballast is not the same as the book figure for a full tank. This is particularly noticeable when the ship has a large trim; as much as 10% of the tank capacity may be occupied by air.

10.19 Ballast holds

Where vessels have one or more ballast holds, the shipowner will endeavour to include a clause in the charter-party to allow the vessel to present Notice of Readiness even though the ballast hold may be still filled and the ship is not strictly *ready to load in all respects*. The Master will make the decision when to pump out the ballast holds, taking into account the terms of the charterparty. He also has to consider the allowable stresses on the ship, the predicted weather, the likely duration of any delays awaiting a berth, the draft required for safe ship-handling, and the time required to pump out the ballast hold(s) compared with any contractual allowable time.

The ballast hold(s) may need to be filled before departure from the discharge port—for example, to achieve a lower air draft, or when bad weather is expected on sailing. The Chief Officer will have discussed this with the stevedores to ensure that this hold is emptied early in the discharge programme. The OOW must check that all cargo residues have been removed, so that the suction lines are not blocked when deballasting. He should also check that any blanks in the bilge, ballast or fire-smothering lines have been set to their correct position.

Whenever the ballast hold is filled or emptied, the OOW should check that any pressure release valves are operating correctly, or that any extra ventilation requirements are provided. On some ships, a vent in the coaming or a manhole in the hatchcover has to be opened.

10.20 Ballast book

The OOW should always complete a ballast book during all ballast operations. This book need only be a rough note book, but should show the current position of all ballast valves, and the current soundings and tonnages of water in all ballast tanks. The OOW should update these readings regularly. If this system is followed, the Master, Chief Engineer, pumpman or anyone else interested in the progress of the operation, can obtain accurate up-to-date information without having to chase up the OOW. The reader should remember that a well completed ballast book is the sign of an efficient OOW.

Some authorities recommend that the ballast book should include records of ballast pump gauge readings, times of opening and closing of ALL valves in the system, and details of pumping rates observed. The OOW should enquire as to these requirements when he first joins a new ship. On some ships, a blackboard with the tanks permanently stencilled on is used, and updated as necessary. However, this system does not provide a permanent record, which can be referred to when resolving problems.

One vessel loading grain suffered delays while attempting to remain within draft/airdraft limits. The charterers alleged that the delay was due to mismanagement of deballasting; with no ballast records available, this claim was extremely difficult to resist.[25]

The keeping of such a ballast book does not affect the requirements to maintain records in the deck logbook as described in chapter 18.

10.21 Final ballast remaining

The draft surveyor should be requested to attend the vessel when all the ballast has been discharged, and the ship has a reasonable stern trim. His early presence will expedite the final draft survey, and produce a more accurate result.

The advantage of this arrangement is that a much more accurate measurement of the final ballast remaining on board can be made whilst the vessel still has a good stern trim. This is because when the ship has a large trim, any remaining ballast should have flowed aft in the tank to the area close to the sounding pipe. Also, with a large trim, a large change in sounding represents only a small change in tonnage, so any slight inaccuracy in reading the sounding will not greatly change the accuracy of the tonnage of ballast remaining.

However, at even keel, a small change of sounding represents a substantial change in tonnage. Hence any inaccuracy in the soundings taken at this time will give a much less accurate indication of the tonnage of ballast remaining on board. Also, larger ships are often sagged in the fully loaded condition, which may mean that water lying at the forward end of after tanks remains undetected, and that there is a false increase in the soundings of any water lying in the after end of forward tanks.

Unfortunately, it is often the practice that surveyors only attend for the final survey on completion of loading, when the vessel is usually at even keel. Sometimes this can lead to a dispute between the ship's officers and the surveyor over the quantity of ballast remaining. Occasionally, a draft surveyor will accept the ship's figures if he sees that well presented records are being kept.

10.22 Deballasting problems

Usually, fewer problems arise during ballasting operations. Discharge of cargo is usually slower than loading, giving more time for the ballast operation. Also, the end results are not so critical, in that a small percentage under-ballasted causes no ill effects, and can soon be remedied by topping up the slack tanks. However, deballasting is much more critical, as any extra ballast remaining may deprive the owner of revenue if cargo has to be excluded, and could affect the departure, if there are any draft limits. Also, experience has shown that there is more likelihood of mechanical problems arising during deballasting.

In practice, most problems due to ballast arise when pumping out double-bottom tanks. They are more difficult to strip out, especially if the vessel has only a small stern trim, because of their extensive flat bottom. A small sounding represents a large volume. Topside tanks and peaks taper down to small space, and are less trouble to strip as the final few centimetres of sounding usually represent only a very small tonnage of ballast remaining, and can be accepted.

10.23 Leaking ballast lines

Many vessels have expansion joints in their ballast lines, which allow for the bending of the ship. In time these joints may leak, and allow air to be sucked in, which reduces the efficiency of the pumping system. The same result occurs if a hole develops in the line. Where the pipes pass through adjacent tanks, these leaks can be difficult to locate. They only become apparent once the water level in the tank drops to below the level of the leak. Signs to look out for are changes in the contents of a tank further along the line when another tank is being pumped, or continued difficulty in pumping out certain tanks below a fixed sounding. It may be possible to identify the location of the leak by comparing the pumping rates of different tanks on the suspect line. If the tanks can be opened up, it is sometimes possible to hear the air bubbling around the leak during deballasting, or spraying out from the leak during ballasting.

An emergency first aid measure is to wrap the leak with plastic or cloth coated in grease. Later the nuts on the expansion joint bolts can be tightened if possible, but most likely the entire set will need to be replaced. A well managed ship will carry spare sets of these bolts. For a hole in a small diameter pipe, a piece of jointing rubber can be placed over the leak, and held in place with a Jubilee clip. For larger pipes, an old tyre inner tube can be wrapped around a fracture in an emergency.

A hole can be welded over, but it may be best to replace the entire section of pipe, to prevent reoccurrence. Complete gas freeing will be required before welding is undertaken on vessels which are carrying, or where the relevant tank has carried, any hazardous cargo. Some ships have a programme of turning (rotating) all easily-accessible water pipes, particularly those on deck, in order to equalise the wear or rusting all around their circumference.

10.24 Pumps tripping

When a pump runs faster than its designed speed, it is liable to overheat, and automatically stop. This is known as cutting out or tripping. Its purpose is to prevent the pump from seizing up solid.

10.24.1 Gauge settings

Gauges will show the pump suction and discharge pressures and the electrical load. Good pumping is achieved when the pump discharge pressure is steady at the manufacturer's recommended level and the suction pressure is steady. As the level of water in the tank falls, the pump discharge valve should be closed gradually to maintain the maximum back-pressure on the pump and hence the maximum rate of pumping. If this valve is closed too much, the pump is likely to overheat and trip.

10.24.2 Gassing

When the water level in a tank is very low, the pump will begin to pump air as well as water. Modern pumps are fitted with degassing devices known as vacuum pumps, the purpose of which is to remove the air from the main pump, and so enable it to continue pumping water without tripping.

10.24.3 Cracking another valve

To reduce the problem of pumps gassing up, some officers recommended slightly opening ('cracking') an overboard valve to provide another head of water to the pump. The idea is that it will continue to pump the last of the water from the tank as well as pumping water from overside, and so not trip.

The danger is that it is possible that the pump only draws water from overside, and not from the tank. Meanwhile, all the pump gauges will indicate that all is well, which can lead to a false sense of security. In effect, water could be pumped from over one side of the ship to the other. This reinforces the importance of carefully monitoring the tank soundings, as this will soon show when no ballast is being pumped out of the tank. The valve to another fuller tank may be cracked open, to provide a similar head. The danger here is that water may run from the full tank into the near empty tank if suction is lost, so this practice is not recommended.

10.24.4 Blocked lines

The system may appear to be functioning perfectly, but, despite this, ballast is prevented from being pumped out by a blockage in the line. The usual cause of this is mud or sediment in the tanks, and the only long-term answer is to have the tanks thoroughly washed out in dry-dock. One short-term solution is to flood seawater back into the tank to agitate the sediment, and hope that it subsequently pumps out.

On a loaded passage, it may be possible to introduce a small amount of ballast to a tank with a suspected large deposit of sediment. As this swills around with the ship's motion, it dissolves the sediment which can then be pumped out. This operation can only be undertaken if the ship will not be overloaded or overstressed. There is often a reluctance by ship's staff to introduce ballast on a loaded passage with draft limits at the discharge port in case the ballast cannot be pumped out completely. Changing ballast on passage should also reduce any sediment remaining in the tanks.

Another cause of blocked lines is loose scale when the tank coating breaks down. The remedy for this is regular internal inspections of the tanks, with an accompanying programme of regular maintenance.

IF THE PUMP KEEPS TRIPPING, OBTAIN ADVICE, OR CALL THE CHIEF OFFICER.

10.25 Ballast pollution

An increasing number of countries place restrictions on ships deballasting in their ports because unwanted organisms which can cause health problems are being introduced into their waters. This subject is discussed in chapter 15.3.

When filling any ballast tank, the OOW should monitor the adjacent holds. Note also the use of a 'cherry-picker' to examine the structure closely. See chapter 10.11 and appendix V.
Photograph: courtesy of Brookes, Bell & Co.

Chapter 11
STRESS AND STABILITY
PURPOSE

On completion of this chapter you will appreciate the effects of cargo and ballast operations on the strength and stability of the ship.

This is not a stability textbook, and it is assumed the reader has a basic knowledge of ship's stability. The text is a reminder of some of the considerations the OOW should take into account whilst on duty in port.

The reader who requires a more detailed explanation of the theories and calculations involved should consult a stability textbook.[88]

11.1 Importance of stress and stability

If insufficient attention is paid to the ship's strength and stability during cargo and ballast operations, the results can be catastrophic—for example:

1. A ship with insufficient stability may list excessively during cargo operations, resulting in damage to the ship and to shore installations.
2. A ship with insufficient stability could be swamped by heavy seas.
3. On a ship with excessive stability the cargo could shift, and there is a risk of structural damage, due to heavy and violent rolling. Either of these may lead to the ship capsizing.
4. A ship which has adequate stability at the start of the voyage may become unstable during the voyage as bunkers are consumed. This needs to be taken into account when planning the cargo stowage.
5. A ship which is stressed and strained by excessive bending moments or shear forces may suffer structural failure. This can occur immediately, but more likely a long term build up may result in sudden failure on future voyages when there may be no excessive stress.
6. Incorrect calculation of drafts may lead to the ship grounding, or being refused permission to sail if her loadline is submerged.

11.2 Reminder of stability basics

In the diagram, when the ship is inclined by an external force, the waterline changes from WL to W'L'. The ship's centre of buoyancy moves from B to B', such that BB' is parallel to bb', where b and b' represent the centre of buoyancy of the emerging and immersing sections of the hull respectively.

A ship is **HEELED** when she is inclined by an external force—e.g., wind.

A ship is **LISTED** when she is inclined by an internal force—e.g., cargo shifting.

The **CENTRE OF GRAVITY** (G) is the point through which the total weight of the ship, and all weights on board, may be considered to act vertically down. Its vertical position (VCG or KG) is calculated by arithmetically summing the moments about the keel of all known weights and then dividing by the displacement. Its horizontal (or longitudinal) position (LCG) is calculated by arithmetically summing the moments of all known weights about either the aft perpendicular, or more usually nowadays, about amidships—see section 11.4.1.

The **CENTRE OF BUOYANCY** (B) is the point through which the total force of buoyancy may be considered to act vertically up. It is the centre of gravity of the underwater volume of the ship, and

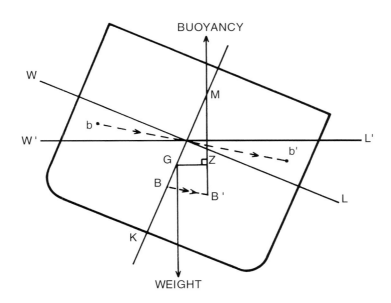

both its vertical position (KB) and horizontal position (LCB) are listed for a range of drafts in the ship's stability manual or hydrostatic particulars—which may be tables or curves.

ARCHIMEDES' PRINCIPLE states that when a vessel floats in water, she displaces her own weight of water. To remain at rest, the centre of gravity must be in the same vertical line as the centre of buoyancy.

The **METACENTRE** (M) is the intersection of the vertical lines through the centres of buoyancy in the initial and inclined positions. It is a function of the underwater shape of the ship, the larger the beam, the higher the metacentre. Its vertical position (KM) and horizontal position (LCM) are listed for a range of drafts in the ship's stability manual or hydrostatic particulars. The transverse metacentre governs the transverse stability and the ship's rolling; the longitudinal metacentre governs the longitudinal stability and the ship's pitching.

The **METACENTRIC HEIGHT** (GM) is the vertical distance between the metacentre and the centre of gravity. It is often used as a measure of the ship's stability. International regulations provide that a vessel can put to sea only if her metacentric height exceeds certain minimum values.

A ship has **POSITIVE STABILITY** if she tends to return to the initial position when inclined; this occurs when M is above G.

A ship has **NEGATIVE STABILITY** if she tends to heel over further when inclined; this occurs when G is above M.

The **RIGHTING LEVER** (GZ) is the horizontal separation of the forces of gravity and buoyancy when the ship is inclined. GZ = GM x Sin(Heel)

The **MOMENT OF STATICAL STABILITY** is the moment which acts to return the ship to the upright when it is inclined. It is the mathematical product of (GZ x Displacement).

11.3 Behaviour of a ship at sea

The **period of roll** is the time taken by the ship to roll from one side to the other and back again to the original position. It is a function of both the GM and the ship's beam. The ship may have tables which tabulate the rolling period for different values of GM.

A ship with a large GM is called **STIFF**; she will try to return to the upright position quickly when inclined. Her period of roll is quite short. This results in a rapid and jerky roll, perhaps rather violent, which may cause the cargo to shift or structural damage.

A ship with a small GM is called **TENDER**; she is sluggish returning to the upright position when inclined. This results in a long, slow roll which may lead to large volumes of water being shipped on deck. Any changes in weights have a marked effect, and could cause the ship to become unstable.

As the OOW has no control over the position of M, the major factor determining the ship's stability is the position of G. This is governed by the vertical distribution of the cargo, and by the contents of the tanks:

● Additional weights stowed lower in the ship, and weights removed from higher in the ship, both increase the ship's stability. This occurs when a ship takes on bunkers during the voyage, or discharges her deck cargo at an intermediate port.

● Additional weights stowed higher in the ship, and weights removed from lower in the ship, such as consuming bunkers from double bottom tanks during the voyage, both reduce the ship's stability.

This is important on containerships which carry a large proportion of their cargo on deck, which may lead to a high KG. It is vital that the weights of the containers on the top tiers are efficiently monitored in order to ensure that the GM does not fall below any required minimum value. It is also important on ships carrying timber on deck, which may absorb moisture from rain and seas on the voyage, thus increasing the weight on deck and so the KG, and consequently reducing the GM.

On ships which are likely to have critical GMs, it is essential that the value of the GM is known, and so should be recalculated regularly throughout the cargo and/or ballast operations.

11.4 Stability calculations

The calculations listed below relating to the ship's stability are usually made by the Chief Officer. It is both good practice and good training for the OOW to make these calculations too. If he is not sure of the theory, the OOW should consult a textbook on ship's stability, such as *Ship Stability for Masters and Mates* by D.R.Derrett.[88] If he is not sure of the procedures, the OOW should ask a senior officer to explain the calculations, and show him how they are made on board his ship. He should know where to obtain the required information, and should make himself familiar with the contents and layout of the ship's stability manual and hydrostatic particulars/tables.

1. The effect of loading / discharging fixed amounts, say, 100 tonnes on small ships and 1,000 tonnes on larger ships, at each hold, deck, tier or tank on:
   (a) KG.
   (b) GM.
   (c) Draft. REMINDER: Sinkage = $\dfrac{\text{Weight added}}{\text{TPC*}}$
   (d) Trim.

   REMINDER: *(for small weights)*
   Change of Trim =
   $\dfrac{(\text{Weight added x Distance from Centre of Floatation})}{\text{MTCT 1 cm*}}$.

   For large weights, the full calculation must be performed, see 11.4.1.
   *Obtained from the ship's stability tables, for the initial draft.

2. The effect on KG, GM, draft and trim of filling or emptying each of the tanks onboard—ballast, cargo, fuel and water, including their free surface effects when partially filled.

3. The correction of observed draft for density. Although the fresh water allowance (FWA) is given on the loadline certificate for the summer displacement, at all other drafts it should be calculated using FWA = $\dfrac{\text{Displacement}}{(4 \text{ x TPC*})}$.

   REMINDER : DWA = $\dfrac{\text{FWA x } (1025 - \text{Density})}{25}$

The officer should be able to calculate both the CHANGE OF DRAFT and the CHANGE OF TRIM when there is a change of density.

REMINDER:

Change of trim = $\dfrac{\text{Displacement x Shift of LCB}}{\text{MTCT 1cm.}}$

(If LCB moves aft, trim is by the head)

4. The transverse movement of the ship's centre of gravity due to loading or discharging cargo away from the centreline, and the resultant list—see section 11.6.

(It should be remembered that for a given offcentre weight, the list will be greater the lighter the ship is. The OOW should be alert to pairs of port and starboard tanks having unequal contents. When the ship is deep, it may appear to be upright, but as discharging continues, a list appears.)

5. The calculations produce a mean draft and trim, which must be proportioned to obtain the fore and aft drafts.

REMINDER:

TRIM FWD = (TRIM/LBP) x (Distance Fore Peak to Centre of Floatation)

TRIM AFT = (TRIM/LBP) x (Distance Aft Peak to Centre of Floatation)

11.4.1 Procedure for calculating the ship's stability

1. List all the compartments on board the ship, with the values of their vertical centre of gravity (VCG), longitudinal centre of gravity (LCG), and free surface moment, which are obtained from the ship's stability manual. Then enter the weights of cargo or liquids contained in each one, including lightship, stores, and constant.

   The LCG may be measured from the after peak (always positive), or from amidships (usually positive if forward, negative if aft—but check the ship's tables as differences do occur).

2. Multiply the value of each weight by its centre of gravity to calculate the horizontal and vertical moment for each compartment.

3. Add up all the weights to calculate the ship's DISPLACEMENT.

4. Add up all the vertical moments to calculate their sum.

   Add up all the horizontal moments to calculate their sum. (pay close attention to signs if distances are measured from amidships)

   Add up all the free surface moments to calculate their sum.

5. KG = (Sum of vertical moments) ÷ displacement.

6. Obtain the following values from the ship's hydrostatic tables, by looking up their value against the displacement:

- KM   (height of the metacentre above the keel)
- LCB   (position of the longitudinal centre of buoyancy)
- LCF   (position of the longitudinal centre of floatation)

   {LCB and LCF are tabulated either from midships or the aft perpendicular}

- MTCT 1cm. (the moment to change trim one centimetre)
- Draft   (this is draft at the LCF)

7. The metacentric height GM = KM – KG.

8. The virtual rise in the centre of gravity due to the free surface effect of partially filled tanks is referred to as GG" (see section 11.5).

   GG" = $\dfrac{\text{(Sum of free surface moments)}}{\text{Displacement.}}$

9. G"M = GM – GG".

   where G"M is the metacentric height corrected for free surface, often known as the virtual metacentric height.

10. LCG = $\dfrac{\text{(Sum of horizontal moments)}}{\text{Displacement.}}$

11. TRIM = $\dfrac{\text{(LCG-LCB) x displacement}}{\text{MTC 1cm.}}$

12. The fore and aft drafts are calculated from the trim and the draft at the centre of floatation by the method shown in step 5 in 11.4 above.

A worked example of this calculation is provided in appendix XIII.

11.5 Free surface effect

Whenever a liquid can move in a tank, there is a reduction in the ship's stability. This free surface effect is caused by liquids sloshing around in partially filled tanks, known as *slack* tanks. The wider the tank, the greater the effect—it is a function of the cube of the tank's beam. This effect occurs irrespective of the position of the tank in the ship. It is convenient to regard this loss of stability as a virtual rise in the ship's effective centre of gravity, and hence a virtual reduction in the ship's metacentric height GM, as shown in the diagram at the foot of page 104.

As the ship heels, the level of the liquid in the tank changes as shown, and its centre of gravity moves from g to g'. The ship's centre of gravity moves from G to G' (Note GG' is parallel to gg'). The new righting lever is G'Z', which is equal to G"Z", so the ship's effective metacentric height is G"M.

It is usual to refer to GG" as the virtual loss of stability due to the free surface effect.

Whilst it is possible to calculate the value of this reduction in GM, many ships will have the values tabulated for each tank in their stability tables. This is the maximum value, in practice this figure is used whenever the contents of the tank is between 5% and 95% of their maximum capacity. It is a safe figure to use, as no matter what the actual level of liquid in the tank, the resultant reduction in GM will never be more than this maximum figure. Outside of this range, i.e. when the content of the tank is less than 5% or more than 95% of its maximum capacity, it is usual to ignore the free surface effect.

On other ships, the free surface correction is given as a "free surface inertia moment". Once again, only the maximum figure is tabulated. The sum of these moments for all slack tanks, divided by the ship's displacement, gives the virtual reduction of GM. The OOW should make himself familiar with the method used in his own ship's stability book.

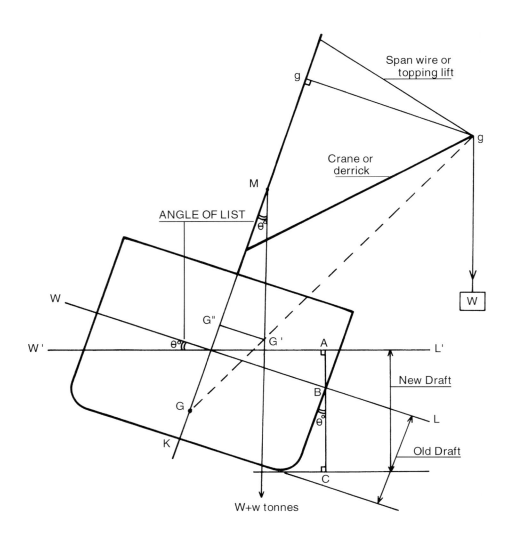

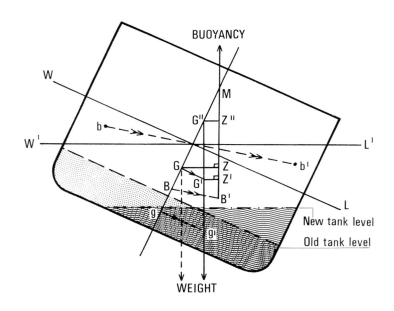

11.6 Effect of heavy lifts

When a ship uses its own cargo handling equipment to load a heavy lift, the critical stage occurs when the lift is just clear of the quay. In this position, the centre of gravity of the ship will have moved up from the keel, so reducing the ship's stability, and moved out from the centreline, so producing a list. These effects can be calculated using simple beam theory by taking moments about the keel (to find the rise in G) and moments about the centreline (to find the athwartships movement of G).

REMINDER $GG'' = (w \times Gg'') / (W + w)$.
$G'G'' = (w \times gg'') / (W + w)$.
Tangent (angle of list) $= G'G''/G''M$.

It is important that such calculations are made, so that the OOW can predict the behaviour of the ship. In order to reduce the adverse effect on the ship's stability, all tanks should be as full as possible to eliminate the free surface effect. On some ships, it may be necessary to fill some double bottom tanks to ensure the centre of gravity remains below the metacentre. It should be remembered that the resultant list causes an increase in the ship's draft, as shown in the diagram.

REMINDER:

New Draft = ½ Beam x Sin (List) + Old Draft x Cos (List)
 [AC]   [AB]   [BC]
[In diagram on left]

11.7 Effects of fire-fighting

A substantial quantity of water may be pumped into the ship during a fire-fighting operation. This can have a considerable effect on the ship and its stability, due to:
1. Change of the ship's centre of gravity, and associated change of the ship's metacentric height.
2. Free surface effect of the added water further reducing the stability.
3. Increase in the ship's draft.
4. Change of trim, and/or list.
5. Overloading decks.
6. Overstressing the ship's structure.

These effects will be governed by the quantity of water added, and the position and dimensions of the compartments concerned.

When considering holds which are loaded with cargo, the permeability of the cargo will have to be estimated. This is the percentage of the loaded compartment not occupied by solid cargo, and hence which can be occupied by water. Consideration should be given also to water which may be absorbed by the cargo. The adverse effect of free surface is reduced if the compartment contains large blocks of impervious cargo.

11.8 Investigating lists

Throughout cargo and ballast operations, it is usual to arrange for the ship to remain upright. If the ship develops any unexpected list, the OOW must investigate, and identify the cause. This may be due to:

1. Cargo not loaded evenly about the centreline.
2. Cargo shifted in a nonworking compartment.
3. Ballast pumping at uneven rates in pairs of port and starboard tanks.
4. A valve leaking on a tank not in use.
5. A compartment flooded due to structural failure or some other accident.
6. The ship grounding on the inshore side.

During loading, particularly on bulk carriers, it is important that the stevedore is informed about any list which is **not** due to cargo, otherwise he may try to correct the list with cargo subsequently loaded. This could result in the ship being subjected to twisting stresses, which can weaken the ship, and in extreme cases can lead to structural failure. Some ships have flashing lights on the bridge front to indicate list.

The list is obtained by reading the inclinometer, the longer the pendulum arm the greater the accuracy. Some ships construct their own instrument by pinning a line to the top of an athwartships bulkhead, and suspending a weight from the line near the deck. A scale is drawn on the bulkhead using simple geometrical calculations. **The most accurate indication of list is obtained by comparing the port and starboard drafts amidships.**

11.9 Reminder of strength and stress basics

The dimensions and configuration of the components of the ship's structure determine its strength. The item of most concern to the OOW will be the load on each deck or tanktop. This is expressed as so many tonnes per square metre, and maximum limiting values are stated in the ship's approved stability book. The Chief Officer will have considered these figures when planning the stow. The OOW should be aware of these limitations, in order that he remains alert to the possibilities of overloading the ship's structure if the cargo is not stowed exactly according to the preplan.

The strength of the ship's structure will govern the maximum forces of stress it is able to absorb in safety. The two forces which concern the OOW are those of **SHEAR STRESS** and **BENDING MOMENTS**. These can arise from the uneven distribution of weights throughout the ship, or the uneven distribution of buoyancy of the ship in large waves.

The shear stress at any point is that force within a material which tends to break (shear) the material across, it is equal and opposite to the load applied at that point. It is expressed in tonnes. (Diagram A on next page).

The bending moment at any point is the total moment tending to alter the shape of the structure, it is equal to the algebraic sum of the moments of all the loads acting between that point and one end of the structure. Bending moments tend to cause the vessel to bend along its length, producing a HOG or SAG. They are expressed in tonnes-metres. (Diagram B on next page).

The bending moments and shear forces are normally calculated on the ship's stability computer. They may also be calculated longhand using data and

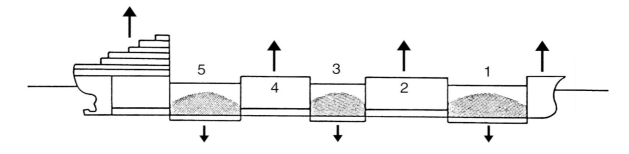

A: Shear stress.

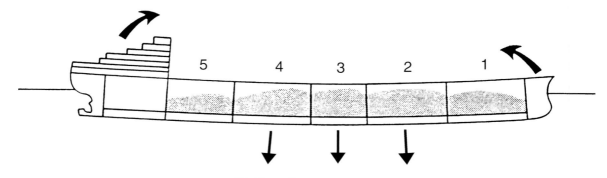

B: Bending moments.

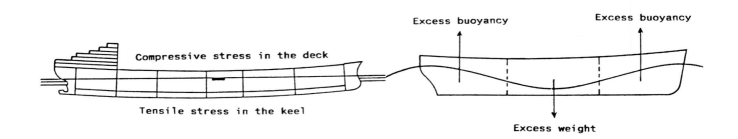

C: Sag.

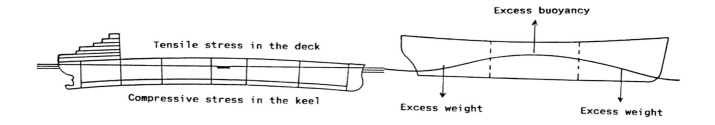

D: Hog.

a proforma which are to be found in the ship's stability manual. It is both good practice and good training for junior officers to be able to perform such calculations. Worked examples are given in appendix XIII.

When a ship is subjected to uneven forces along its length, the hull takes the shape of a complicated curve. It as a convenient common practice to consider this shape as a simple smooth curve, where the midships draft is greater or less than the mean of the forward and aft drafts.

If the mean of the forward and aft drafts is LESS than the midships draft, the ship is said to be **SAGGED**. This occurs when most of the weight of the cargo is placed in the middle of the ship. For most ships with their accommodation aft, this is the more usual loading. When loaded to her marks, a ship which is sagged will lift a lower tonnage than indicated by her deadweight, because she displaces less water at her fore and after ends.

Also, a ship is subjected to sagging forces at sea when the crests of waves support each end of the ship, and a trough lies amidships. (Diagram C).

If the mean of the forward and aft drafts is MORE than the midships draft, the ship is said to be **HOGGED**. This occurs when most of the weight of the cargo is placed near the ends of the vessel. When loaded to her marks, a ship which is hogged will lift a greater tonnage than indicated by her deadweight, because she displaces more water at her fore and aft ends.

Also, a ship is subjected to hogging forces at sea when a crest of a wave supports amidships and each end is in a trough. (Diagram D).

The degree of hogging or sagging is dependent upon the bending moments, though there is no exact relationship which can be readily calculated onboard. Once a ship is hogged or sagged by a certain loading condition, it may take some time for the hull to change to the hog or sag corresponding to a subsequent loading condition. Thus during rapid cargo operations, the hog or sag at any time may bear no relation to the actual loading condition at that instant of time. It is not unusual for a ship to sail from one port with one hog/sag, and arrive at its destination with a very different hog/sag.

11.10 Stability computers

If the ship has a machine to assist with stability calculations, then the OOW must be proficient in its use and operation. He should read the manuals, and ask senior officers for guidance. In learning to use such machines, it is important that the OOW does not disturb information which the Chief Officer may have entered in readiness for cargo or ballast operations. The OOW must always ask the Chief Officer if it is convenient before he practises using these machines. During cargo operations, he should be guided by the system in use on that ship,—if the relevant data are to be updated by the OOW or only by the Chief Officer.

The OOW should be able to:
1. Switch on and set up the machine.
2. If it is a general purpose computer rather than a dedicated stability machine:

(a) Understand the operating system.
(b) Load the stress/stability programmes.
(c) Use the help system.
3. Enter data for ballast, cargo, fuel, fresh water, stores, and dock water density.
4. Understand which units are used.
5. Appreciate the method of assessing the centre of gravity of partially filled compartments.
6. Appreciate how the free surface effects are allowed for.
7. Obtain the results for:
  (a) Draft and trim.
  (b) Stability: (i)   GM.
                   (ii) the area under the GZ curve.
                   (iii) grain shift moments.
  (c) Shear forces.
  (d) Bending moments.
8. Understand the difference between IN PORT and AT SEA conditions.
9. Appreciate the limitations of the system.
10. Use the test cases to check its performance.
11. Save and retrieve data.
12. Predict the effects of filling/emptying all ballast tanks.
13. Predict the effect of filling/emptying cargo compartments.

11.11 Levelling bulk cargoes

In order to minimise the risk of bulk cargoes shifting during adverse weather, the IMO *Code of Safe Practice for Solid Bulk Cargoes*[50] recommends that **all** bulk cargoes are trimmed level on completion of loading before the vessel leaves port. Unfortunately, this practice is often ignored, and has resulted in ships developing lists during the voyage when the cargo shifts, or settles more to one side than the other, occasionally with disastrous consequences.

11.12 Grain stability

The free-flowing characteristics of grain reduces the stability of the ship; grain which does not completely fill a compartment displays a free surface effect similar to a liquid in a partially filled tank. As the ship rolls, the grain is likely to flow to one side of the compartment, where it will cause the ship to list, and perhaps capsize. The OOW must ensure that all compartments which are planned to be filled have **all** the spaces under the decks and hatch covers filled as much as possible. Any compartment which is to be partially filled must have the surface of the grain trimmed absolutely level.

One of the basic requirements of the IMO Grain Regulations[53] is that the Master must demonstrate that at all times during the forthcoming voyage the vessel will have sufficient stability to take into account the adverse heeling effects caused by an assumed pattern of movement of the grain in the holds. This is usually accomplished by completing the calculations on special forms provided by the marine safety agencies in the loading port. The reader wishing to obtain further information on this subject is advised to study The Nautical Institute's publication *Bulk Carrier Practice*.[3]

11.13 Keeping to the pre-plan

On larger ships, the Chief Officer will have constructed his pre-loading/discharging plan to ensure that the ship remains within her allowable maximum values of shear forces and bending moments at all times. The OOW must ensure that the planned sequence of ballast and cargo operations is strictly maintained. If these two operations are permitted to get out of step, the ship may be subjected to unacceptable stresses, which could lead to structural failure. **It is essential that the OOW informs the Chief Officer immediately if he detects that the cargo or ballast operations are not keeping to the preplan**—see also chapters 8.1.3 and 10.4.

11.14 Damage control

The permitted maximum values of shear forces and bending moments apply to the dimensions of the ship's structure as she was built. Hence it is important for the OOW to report any damage or decay (heavy corrosion, detached parts of the structure, etc) which he sees, as this could effect the validity of such values. Guidance on what to look for is contained in appendix V. A ship which is damaged is not as strong as it was, and it is more likely that the structure could be overstressed or overloaded.

The OOW should be aware of the effects of stress on the ship's structure when any compartment is flooded. He should also understand the use of ballast to change the ship's trim or list in an emergency.

This cargo is stowed on a dirty quay in the open. The OOW ought to report these facts to the Master so that the bill of lading is claused to show that the cargo was loaded wet and contaminated by an unknown chemical. See chapter 6.6.3 and chapter 12.
Photograph: courtesy of Brookes, Bell & Co.

Chapter 12

CARGO CONDITION

PURPOSE

On completion of this chapter you will be able to describe how to establish the condition of the cargo, and list the precautions you should take to ensure that the cargo is delivered to the consignee in the same state as it was received from the shipper.

12.1 Importance of cargo condition

The cargo must be delivered to the consignee in the same condition as it was received by the vessel. The description of the cargo in the bill of lading is evidence of its condition at the time of loading. Thus it is important to establish the actual condition of the cargo at this time, in order to verify that the description in the bill of lading is correct. If there is any discrepancy, the bill of lading must be claused with appropriate wording to indicate the true condition of the cargo.

If the cargo is not delivered in the condition described in the bill of lading, then the cargo owner may claim compensation from the shipowner. So for example if the OOW fails to notice some preshipment damage, then the receiver of the cargo may claim that this damage was incurred during transit, and hold the shipowner liable. In particular, if the cargo has been sold, the new owner will have made his purchase on the basis of the condition as described in the bill of lading, and will claim against the shipowner for any variation from this description when he receives his goods.

Further, if any defective condition is known, or should have been known, and is not noted on the bill of lading, the shipowner's insurance with his P&I Club could be prejudiced.[2] This means that the shipowner may be uninsured for any claims which may arise due to the condition of the cargo. This restriction would also apply if a clean bill of lading is issued despite the mate's receipt being claused. In such circumstances, the issue of a clean bill of lading can lose the shipowners their right of indemnity against the charterers.[77] Hence the OOW has a vital role in ensuring that the description of the cargo in the bill of lading reflects its true condition, to avoid unnecessary claims being made against the shipowner.

Cargo which is in a dangerous condition, and which could damage the vessel or adjacent cargo, should **never** be loaded. This is especially true for cargo which may cause fires, such as damp cotton and hot coal.

With reefer cargoes, the temperature of the cargo at the time of shipment is an essential part of its condition. Cargo which is found to be not at the temperature shown in its shipping documents must be rejected. Also, if there is evidence that the cargo may have spent some time at a warmer temperature, and then recooled, this must be reported to the Chief Officer and such cargo must be rejected. Obvious signs include stained or mis-shapen cartons or wrappings of frozen cargo.

12.2 Cargo care

The ship's personnel have a legal duty to take care of someone else's goods whilst in their custody. Whenever cargo is being loaded, and discharged, the OOW must ensure that it is not damaged by poor handling, poor stowage, or adverse weather. These are the areas of responsibility of the shipowner, and are discussed in chapter 7.

Should anyone other than ship's staff damage the cargo, it is essential that they are held responsible. This includes damage done before, during or after loading or discharging the cargo. The OOW must continually look at the condition of all the cargo to discover if there is anything wrong with it, and report any faults he finds.

12.3 Preloading damage

Cargo which is received in an unsound condition clearly cannot be delivered in a sound condition. It is therefore essential for the OOW to keep a careful watch for damaged cargo during the loading operation.

- The golden rule is that if any cargo is observed to be damaged before loading, then it should be rejected. The shipper must be given the opportunity to replace such cargo with undamaged goods.
- If the rejected cargo is not replaced, the OOW must ensure that the tally is adjusted accordingly. He should always advise the Chief Officer so that the quantities stated in the mate's receipt and bill of lading can be checked.
- If the shipper insists the cargo is loaded, then the OOW must advise the Chief Officer. He will need to obtain accurate details of the condition of the cargo, including numbers and dimensions of any damaged areas. This will enable the mate's receipt and bill of lading to be claused with an appropriate description of this condition.

In many instances, the division between pre-shipment damage and damage during or after loading is clearly defined, but sometimes there are differences of opinion, particularly where this occurs on the quay close to the ship. Usually, the ship's responsibility commences as soon as the loading operations commence. This is deemed to be the moment the goods are hooked on to the gear (whether this be shore or ship's) and ceases when the goods are unhooked from the gear at the discharge port.[74]

12.3.1 Examples of preloading damage

1. Unpacked goods which are clearly broken, dented, spilt, twisted, chipped, torn, distorted or otherwise damaged.
2. Packed goods where the contents are visible and clearly damaged.
3. Packed goods where the packaging is damaged to such an extent that the goods inside are likely to have been damaged.
4. Cargo which has obviously been tampered with.
5. Wet, mouldy or ripped bags or bales.
6. Stained or contaminated goods, including cargo which is coated with unidentified substances.
7. Cargo which appears to have been handled previously in a manner contrary to instruction labels attached to the cargo.
8. Leaking containers and packaging—dry or liquid cargoes.
9. Discoloured bulk cargo, or containing foreign material.
10. Rust on metal goods, particular attention should be paid to vehicles, and all steel products—see section 12.4.1.
11. Frozen cargo which has partially thawed.
12. Packaged goods which are obviously light, partially empty, or other signs that some or all of the contents are not in place.

   Cargo which has been partially lost or stolen is to be treated as damaged cargo—the establishment of the quantity of cargo loaded is discussed in chapter 13.

12.3.2 Damaged or inadequate packaging

It is good practice to examine the packing of all cargo before it is loaded, to ensure that it is suitable for the planned method of handling. Damaged packaging must be noted in the same manner as damaged cargo. Some examples include insecure straps, ripped plastic covers, cartons torn or cases broken.

If at all possible, damaged packaging should be repaired before the cargo is loaded and stowed, to avoid further loss before delivery. Where it is suspected that part of the cargo is missing, the packaging should be opened and the contents checked and tallied. This should be done by a responsible person, and preferably witnessed by the OOW or some other ship's officer.

Packing costs money, so frequently the minimum necessary is used, which the manufacturer or shipper hopes will be sufficient to withstand the rigours of handling. Often goods packed for inland transportation are subsequently sold on, and are then presented for carriage on ships with this same packing, which may be totally unsuitable to withstand normal marine cargo-handling and stowage techniques. Cargo which is obviously inadequately packaged is likely to be damaged or lost before delivery. To protect the shipowner from claims for losses which seem inevitable, the bill of lading should be claused with a description of the unsatisfactory packaging.

Plywood is often presented for loading in bundles lacking rigidity, this may result in the bundles becoming loose, with considerable damage being caused to the edges of the plywood sheets. Similarly rolls of steel with broken banding may become loose; this not only increases the likelihood of the edges of the steel becoming damaged, but also may lead to the stow becoming insecure and collapsing.[20]

Palletised cargo should have the individual pieces in a locking stow, glued together or adequately strapped to provide a secure unit. Shrink-wrapping is a popular method of reducing contamination and opportunist theft. However, unless they are additionally secured by some other method, it does not stop the individual pieces moving within the unit, which could lead to the collapse of the palletised stow.

12.3.3 Clausing the shipping documents

Whenever the cargo is found not to be in the same condition as described in the mate's receipt or bill of lading, these documents must be claused with suitable wording which accurately reflects the apparent condition of the cargo at the time of loading.

The purpose of these remarks is to prevent the receiver of the cargo from claiming that the damage occurred during transit, and so hold the shipowner liable. It is useful extra evidence if the OOW is able to take photographs of all pre-shipment damage—see chapter 18.9.

The description of the goods in the bill of lading is supplied by the shipper. Their condition could have changed since they left his premises, for example, they could have been damaged by handling en route to the port, or by contamination during storage at the port. Also, there could be an inaccuracy in the original description, which may be accidental due to carelessness, but could be deliberate fraud.

These clauses should reflect not only the physical condition of the cargo, but also any apparent defects or structural abnormalities, or any contamination by extraneous materials, including moisture. They must be accurate and detailed, so the OOW should be able to provide information such as the numbers of pieces affected, the dimensions of damaged areas, the extent of contamination, etc.

With reefer cargoes, if the shipper insists that the cargo must be loaded even though it is found to be **not** at the temperature in its shipping documents, then it is essential that the actual temperature of the cargo at the time of loading is inserted in the mate's receipt and bill of lading. This is to protect the shipowner against any claims for defrosted cargo which may be made later.

Comments should be confined to pre-shipment conditions, and must never contain any reference to damage which occurred during or after loading. This area is the responsibility of the carrier, and references such as *Loaded during rain*, *Dented by stevedores* or *Grooved by slings* are extremely damaging to the carrier's interests, as they are an admission of failure to care. It is correct to hear such clauses referred to as *Own goals* or *Self-inflicted wounds*.

Some examples of appropriate and valid clauses for steel cargoes are given in appendix II. These are given to illustrate the type of remarks which are required, so that the OOW will know what to look out for, and what sort of information is required. Similar clauses are valid for all cargoes.

12.3.4 Rejecting all damaged cargo[30]

On certain voyages, the Master may order the rejection of all cargo which is not in apparent good order and condition, without exception. This should be the case when the charterparty contains a clause which obliges the Master to issue only clean bills of lading. In such cases, the OOW will need to be extra vigilant in monitoring the condition of the cargo, because there is no opportunity to defend the shipowner's interests by inserting a clause in the bill of lading to reflect its true condition. He must ensure that the stevedore does not load such cargo, or discharges it as soon as the condition is noticed.

If any difficulty is experienced, the Master should be informed immediately, so that he can take this up with the owners and their local P&I Correspondent. He may need to issue a letter of protest to the stevedores, shippers and/or charterers. It may be necessary to appoint an independent surveyor to resolve any disputes; in the meantime the ship's personnel must do their best to reduce any delays caused by these circumstances.

12.4 Preshipment surveys

In some trades with a long history of claims for damaged cargo, notably the carriage of steel products, it is usual for the shipowner's P&I Club to arrange to have the cargo examined by independent surveyors before it is loaded on board. For large shipments, a team of surveyors may be employed. Their purpose is to assist the vessel in establishing the true condition of the cargo as presented by the shipper. It is realised that the OOW has many other duties, and cannot spend his whole time examining every item of cargo before it is loaded. Also, loading operations may commence immediately the vessel has berthed, so there is no time available for the ship's staff to inspect the cargo prior to loading. Further, these surveyors may have vast experience of the commodity in question, so they should be able to recognise defects quickly, understand the system of cargo marking in that port, know which wording is most appropriate, and be familiar with the local methods of notification. With reefer cargoes, these surveys establish the actual temperature of the cargo at the time of shipment.

Further information on these surveys can be found in The Nautical Institute's publication *The Work of the Nautical Surveyor*.[10]

12.4.1 Steel cargoes

Preshipment surveys are common when steel products are to be carried, because rust and deformation are major problems, and there is a long history of substantial claims. Many officers are confused over the correct terms to use to describe various types of rust. The International Group of P&I

Clubs has produced a recommended list of such terms, to help ensure consistency in describing 'rust' on steel cargoes—these terms are reproduced in appendix II. The same surveyor will often inspect the hatch covers prior to loading, and report any deficiencies to the Master (and his owner and their P&I Club).

For further information, the reader should consult the publication *Steel, Carriage by Sea*[74], which is the standard reference work on this subject, and contains a wealth of information and photographic examples.

12.5 Preloading inspections

Whenever possible, the OOW should make his own brief examination of the cargo before it is loaded in order to establish the condition of the cargo as received by the vessel. The OOW is not expected to be an expert with regard to the quality of any particular cargo. But he is expected to be capable of carrying out a <u>reasonable</u> inspection and noting any <u>obvious</u> defects.

Defining these two terms is not easy, but the OOW should remember that the Bill of Lading normally states the goods were *shipped in apparent good order and condition*. If he is in doubt, the OOW should ask himself 'does this description accurately describe the cargo?' If the answer is *'no'*, then he should inform the Chief Officer so that either the cargo can be rejected, or a more suitable description can be inserted on the mate's receipt and bill of lading.[2] If a much more detailed inspection would have been necessary to discover a defect, then the shipowner is not liable if the Master signs the Bill of Lading unclaused.[11]

The OOW can have no idea of the condition of totally enclosed cargoes, but he should be suspicious of the condition of cargo when the outer packaging is severely damaged, stained or wet. He will be able to make a superficial examination of unpackaged and bulk cargoes.

12.5.1 Cargo quality

Neither the OOW nor the Master is expected to be an expert in the quality inspection of any particular cargo. They are not in a position to verify if grain is *Prime No.2*, steel is *Grade B*, or manufactured goods are technically identical to the description in the shipping documents. If there are questions of quality such as in these examples, the dispute should be resolved between the buyer and the seller. It is a problem of the contract of sale, not the contract of carriage.

Discrepancies from *apparent good order and condition* are distinct from the actual quality of the cargo. They should be noted by the OOW, and would include such examples as torn bags, dented machinery, leaking drums, scratched vehicles, ripped covers, telescoped coils, and wet or contaminated goods, as discussed in this chapter.

12.6 Sampling on tankers

In order to provide evidence of the condition of the cargo loaded on tankers, it is important that cargo samples should be drawn at the manifold at the start of loading, and thereafter at regular intervals. Samples should be labelled and clearly show when and from where they were drawn. It is preferable to have this operation undertaken by an independent surveyor, and witnessed by a representative of the shippers. This subject is discussed fully in chapter 9.18.

12.7 Wet cargo

Cargo handling during rain is discussed in chapter 7.7.6.

It is essential that cargo which is known to contain moisture or can be damaged by moisture during the voyage (by 'sweat'- see section 12.7.3) is given appropriate ventilation both on the voyage, and during prolonged periods in port. A full and detailed treatise on the ventilation of cargo holds is beyond the scope of this manual. However, this is a subject which the junior officer serving on dry cargo ships should study in depth. Guidance can be obtained from such publications as *Thomas's Stowage*.[70]

12.7.1 Loading wet cargo

Cargo which is found to be wet before loading should be rejected if there is any possibility this will cause damage to other cargo, or to the ship itself, or its own condition will deteriorate. Some examples are:

1. Wet timber should not be stowed in the same hold as produce, paper, kiln-dry timber, or any other cargo whose quality is degraded by absorbing moisture.
2. Wet reels of paper or linerboard, even when dried, cause many problems due to distortion of the cargo, which makes it impossible to use with automated processes. As such they are virtually worthless to the receiver.
3. Wet bags of produce will develop mould, which may spread to other parts of the consignment.
4. Wet grain, and most other organic cargoes, will begin to heat due to the chemical reactions associated with oxidisation.
5. When moisture drains from wet sulphurous coal it forms sulphuric acid which will cause the steelwork of the ship's structure to rot.
6. Wet pulp will expand, and if the stow is tightly packed, this may result in structural deformation of the hold.
7. Wet cotton is liable to heat and deteriorate, which may lead to spontaneous combustion if any oil or grease staining is present.

If the shipper insists on loading the cargo, the OOW must inform the Chief Officer so that the mate's receipt and bill of lading may be appropriately claused. The Master may need to give a letter of protest—see chapter 6.9.

In some trades, it is the normal practice to continue loading in the rain, for example timber loaded in North-West North America is invariably loaded wet. Because this can lead to staining from rust or fungus, mould growth, or even cargo rot, it is recommended that the carriage documents are claused to show the true state of the cargo, such as *Wet before shipment*, or *strapping bands rusty*.[20]

12.7.2 Moisture content of produce

All produce has some moisture present as part of the composition of the natural raw material. On short voyages, this does not change the quality of the cargo whilst it is on board the ship.

However, on longer voyages, this natural moisture will migrate from the warmer centre of the stow to the cooler outside of the stow. What happens is the warmth of the centre causes the moisture to evaporate and raise the relative humidity of the air in between the granules of cargo. The increase in vapour pressure will drive this moisture to the outside of the stow where the vapour pressure is lower. The increase in moisture content of the outside of the stow will encourage oxidisation, fermentation and mould growth, with the associated rise in temperature. This can develop into a major problem when discharge is delayed, perhaps by port congestion. Often this phenomenon (known as moisture migration) is misidentified as sweat. With bagged cargoes, proper ventilation can assist in removing this damp air, but there is little that can be done with bulk cargoes.

The main concern during loading is to ensure that the moisture content of the cargo is below the value at which this process will commence. Often the only guide available to the OOW is the value declared by the shipper, though if he suspects the cargo is damp, the OOW should advise the Chief Officer, who can request an independent surveyor to establish the true moisture content of the cargo. The critical value of the moisture content varies with each commodity. Some examples are 8% for cocoa, 12% for oil cake expellers and 13% for most grains.

There are a lot of problems with produce cargo which is damp and mouldy before shipment, but the bags appear to be sound. The damage only manifests itself during the voyage. Recently a surety of over $30 million had to be given when the receiver alleged that mould damage to a cargo of ground nuts from China was caused during transit. Bags of produce which are mouldy, wet, moisture-stained or show signs of infestation, including larvae or pupae, must be rejected by the OOW. It is good practice for the OOW to take the temperature of as many bags as possible using a 'spear' thermometer to reach the inner cargo, and record these readings. It is useful if he can find out and record how and where the cargo was stored before being loaded.[22] If possible, photographs should be taken of the cargo in the storage area (but see chapter 18.9). Advice on ventilation requirements should be sought from the shippers, and it is important that proper records are kept of such ventilation.

12.7.3 Discharging wet cargo

Cargo can be damaged on board by seawater leaking into the holds during adverse weather; the securing of hatch covers is described in chapter 19.5.

Another cause of cargo becoming wet on board is inadequate ventilation during the voyage, which results in the formation of sweat. **Ship's sweat** is formed when the air in the hold is damp, and as the ship's structure is cooled, for example during a voyage to colder climates, so moisture forms on the steel surface and may run onto the cargo if it is not adequately protected. **Cargo sweat** is formed when warm damp air is introduced into the holds, for example as the ship passes into the tropics, and moisture is deposited on the cooler surface of the cargo.

Whenever wet cargo is discovered in the hold an investigation should be made to discover the source of the moisture, and the facts must be reported to the Master. He will decide whether it is necessary to call in a surveyor from the P&I Club to assess the damage. This surveyor will be able to perform a silver nitrate test to establish if the damage has been cause by salt or fresh water, as this can be important when the shipowner is defending a claim for damaged cargo. Silver nitrate is a clear liquid which turns milky on contact with any trace of salt.

If wet damaged cargo is discovered during discharge, it is essential that the damaged portion is separated from the sound cargo. If it is not, the receiver may claim that the whole consignment is damaged, or a much larger proportion than in fact. This is particularly important for bulk cargoes.

Cargo can be damaged by direct contact with wet dunnage. This can be the result of rain falling on dunnage when it is being stored on deck unprotected, or when it is laid out in an uncovered hold. It may also be caused by moisture inherent in the timber used for dunnage. In one case reported, this was as high as 28% of the weight of the dunnage.[28] Such dunnage should never be used for cargoes sensitive to moisture.

12.8 Cargo contamination

Contamination is a form of damage, and the cargo owner may claim loss of value for any cargo contaminated by an incompatible substance.

12.8.1 Contamination by spillage

The OOW must be alert for a spillage of one cargo which may contaminate another cargo. This applies not only to physical mixing, but also to taint, and change of chemical or physical state. For example dust or leaks from bags of chemicals or fertiliser may cause rust damage to steel if there is any moisture present. All cargo spills must be contained, returned to their original consignment, and the packaging repaired to prevent any further spillage. If it cannot be repackaged satisfactory, the spill must be removed, and stowed in an alternative safe place. Even with cargo of one type, a lower grade consignment can contaminate one of a higher grade. Special care is required with cargo in bags having a loose weave, where contamination can easily reach the product.

It is good practice to cover any sensitive cargo with canvas or plastic whilst handling other cargoes which are suspected may cause contamination. This covering should be removed on completion of cargo handling to avoid any problems caused by restriction of ventilation to the cargo underneath.

The spillage of dangerous cargo is covered in chapter 7.12.1.

12.8.2 Contaminated bulk cargo

Bulk cargoes are sometimes contaminated by other cargoes during their handling ashore before reaching the vessel. This can occur during:

(1) Transportation to the port.
(2) Storage in areas within the port.
(3) Handling by equipment on the quay (especially conveyors) which have not been cleaned after the previous cargo.

The OOW should always watch the first pour of a bulk cargo carefully for signs of other commodities, especially if other cargoes are known to be handled at a terminal, or can be seen in storage nearby. Particular caution is required if the previous ship on the berth loaded a different cargo, as there is a chance that any conveyor system may not have been cleared of that commodity. If he sees a different cargo enter the hold, the OOW must stop the loading operation and call the Chief Officer.

Grain cargoes can be contaminated not only by different types of grain but also by different qualities of the same commodity. The OOW should report any sightings of large quantities of other grains, but the correct grade can only be identified by a qualified inspector. There have been cases where a ship has had to shift to another berth, discharge part of her grain cargo, which was then returned to the silo, and the ship reloaded part of it mixed with other grains to achieve the required grade as per the contract of sale.

Grain, and other bulk foodstuffs, can be contaminated by moisture, insect infestation, animal droppings and garbage. This latter item can effect all bulk cargoes, where the cost of the contamination may not be a lowering of value of the product, but the repairs necessary when shore cargo-handling equipment is damaged:

1. If a conveyor belt is ripped, very high claims will be made for the cost of both a new belt, and the delay to the operations whilst it is fitted.
2. Suction equipment can be jammed by short lengths of rope or sacking.
3. Sensitive handling equipment designed for light cargoes can be wrecked by steel parts which become detached from the ship's structure.

Examples of extraneous materials discharged along with the cargo include:-

(a) Ropes and wires from securing arrangements ashore or on earlier transportation.
(b) Remnants of empty jute bags from cargo bulked on board by bleeding a cargo delivered in bags.
(c) Parts of the ship's structure removed in error—bilge cover plates and steel protection bars which were not properly secured, or knocked off by grabs or bulldozers.

12.8.3 Contamination on tankers

Different products or different grades can be spoilt commercially by contamination with one another. This may be caused by inadequately cleaned pipelines, or incorrectly manipulated valves—see chapter 9.

12.9 Stevedore's damage

The cargo owner will claim compensation from the shipowner if the condition of his cargo deteriorates after it was shipped. Thus if the stevedore damages the cargo, either during loading or discharging, the cargo owner will claim from the shipowner. This does not mean that the shipowner has no redress, but it does mean that he cannot ignore claims from the receivers by referring them to the stevedores, or to any other third party which has caused the damage.

Hence it is vital that all damage done by the stevedore is noted by the OOW and properly reported, so that the shipowner can reclaim this compensation from the stevedore in due course.

This is discussed in chapter 7.

12.10 Cargo damage discovered at the discharge port

The OOW should be equally vigilant in noting the condition of the cargo during discharge. If he discovers any damage which has not been noted previously, he must make full notes of the condition of the cargo, and notify the Chief Officer. This will provide the shipowner with some defence against any exaggerated claims which may be made later. However, it must be stressed that it is unlikely that the ship will be able to disclaim responsibility for any such damage that should have been obvious during loading, but was not noted at the time. The ship may be able to disclaim responsibility if it can be proved that the damage could not have been seen by a reasonable inspection of the cargo during the loading operation. Furthermore, the shipowner may be able to invoke various defences which are provided in his contract of carriage—e.g., perils of the sea, inherent vice, etc.

For serious damage, the shipowner will arrange for his P&I surveyor to attend, who will advise on the best way to minimise any claims. Damaged cargo should be separated from sound cargo in order to prevent any increase in loss. This is particularly important with bulk commodities, where a small portion of damaged cargo could easily lead to a much larger proportion of the cargo being contaminated by mixing. It is better to bear the extra cost of arranging for a small portion to be discharged by a different method, than to face a substantial claim for loss of value if all the cargo is discharged together.

It is important that the contents of damaged cases are tallied, so that the exact extent of the loss during transit is known. Many broached cases are later claimed to be empty—there may well be further thieving after discharge, but this did not occur during transit, and may not be the responsibility of the shipowner.

Sweepings from torn bags, etc. must be collected and rebagged, and their discharge tallied with the original cargo. With produce costing between $200 and $500 per bag, the OOW can substantially help to reduce claims by ensuring that any spilt cargo is not discarded.

In order to protect his interests, the receiver of the cargo may appoint a surveyor to establish the condition of the cargo at the discharge port. The OOW must seek guidance from the Chief Officer or Master as to what access is allowed to such surveyors. The shipowner may require his own surveyor to accompany surveyors representing other parties, in order to safeguard his own interests.

12.10.1 Causes of damage to cargo on board

The causes of all damage to cargo which occurs onboard must be properly investigated in order to enable any necessary remedial action to be taken to prevent a recurrence. Some examples of causes of cargo damage are:
1. Wet stained cargo may indicate leaking hatch covers, manhole lids, pipelines, a structural fault, or a lack of, or inappropriate ventilation during the voyage.
2. Oil stained cargo may indicate a damaged hydraulic line.
3. Failure of lashings or other securing devices.
4. Failure of the ship's structure, fittings or machinery.
5. Contamination from other cargoes.
6. Failure to care for the cargo according to the shipper's recommendations or owner's instructions.
7. Poor handling—see chapter 7.7.

12.11 Damage after discharge

Although the ship may have no control over the cargo once it has been discharged, and usually no longer has any responsibility for it, the OOW should take note of any obvious deterioration in the condition of the cargo on the quay, and record all relevant facts in the log book. If possible, the facts should be brought to the attention of a responsible person ashore.

Some examples include cargo which is:
1. Deposited in pools of water or mud.
2. Loaded into dirty or wet trucks, waggons or lighters.
3. Left unprotected against the weather, includes rain, wind and heat. (One Master reported ice cream left for an hour on the quay in a port in the tropics whilst the stevedores took a meal break!)
4. Contaminated by mixing with other commodities.
5. Physically damaged by rough or inappropriate handling.
6. Bulk cargoes spilt from shore handling equipment.
7. Stolen. Ship's staff are advised not to intervene in acts of rampant pilferage ashore for their own safety in ports where shore security is lax.

It is useful if the OOW is able to take photographs of such damage, and in all cases the OOW should report the facts immediately to the Chief Officer or Master so that a letter of protest can be issued. Such evidence may be vital for defending the vessel's interests if it is later claimed that the damage was caused by the ship. In extreme cases, it may be advisable for the shipowner's P&I surveyor to attend to witness the events.

Chapter 13

CARGO QUANTITY

PURPOSE

On completion of this chapter you will be able to describe the methods used to establish the quantity of cargo loaded, and appreciate their limitations. You will be able to assist with making a draft survey.

13.1 Importance of establishing cargo quantity

The same quantity of cargo must be delivered to the consignee as was received by the vessel from the shipper.

The carrier has to verify this quantity at the time of loading, to ensure that the figure stated in the bill of lading is correct. This can be achieved by counting the cargo (tallying), using measuring or weighing devices, or calculating the total on board (draft survey) or in each hold or tank (using the ship's calibration tables).

The shipowner may face a claim for shortage if the figure for the quantity discharged is less than the figure contained in the bill of lading. This applies even if all the cargo which was loaded on board has been delivered. In the bulk trades, it is useful to obtain an *Empty Hold Certificate*, preferably signed by the receiver or an independent witness, to show that there is no cargo remaining on board the ship.

Hence it is essential for the OOW to check the quantity of cargo loaded is accurately recorded to enable the Master to verify the bill of lading figure. It is equally important for him to check that the quantity of cargo discharged is accurately recorded, so that the Master can prove that all the received cargo has been delivered.

13.2 Clausing shipping documents

In chapter 12, it was shown that the mate's receipt and bill of lading must be claused to show the true condition of the cargo at the time of loading, where this condition was observed to be different from that stated in these documents. In the same way, these documents must be claused to show the true quantity loaded, if the figure stated in the document is found to be incorrect.

Where the ship has definite knowledge of the quantity loaded, this figure <u>must</u> be stated in the bill of lading. Where there is some doubt over the figures, the wording of the clause should reflect the observed discrepancy. Such doubts are more likely to occur in the bulk trades.

One leading bulk ship operator provides the following guidance:

1. If the difference between the ship and shore figures is less than 0.1%, then this is accepted as normal errors of measurement.
2. If the difference is between 0.1% and 0.5%, the bill of lading is claused *Said to weigh....* and the Master has to issue a letter of protest to the shipper stating the ship's figures.

3. If the difference is over 0.5%, the bill of lading has to be claused *x tonnes on board according to the ship's figures* and *quantity in dispute, if on board to be delivered.*

The Hague Rules provide that *no Carrier or Master shall be bound to state in the bill of lading any marks, numbers, quantity or weight which he has reasonable grounds for suspecting do not accurately represent the goods actually received, or which he has no reasonable means of checking.*

Hence 'one container' is an acceptable declaration of quantity, but reference to its contents should be claused *said to contain...*, because the ship's staff can have no knowledge of the quantity of goods inside a sealed container.

Other clauses which are used when the Master is in doubt over the quantity are *Said to weigh...* and *Quantity and weight unknown.* It is stressed that these should only be used where there is some genuine doubt, and *not* when the Master has definite knowledge that the figure stated in the bill of lading is incorrect.

13.2.1 Anticipated losses

If the packaging of the cargo appears to be too weak to withstand the rigours of handling during loading, stowing and discharging, and of the normal stresses during the sea passage, then the cargo should be rejected, just as if it were already damaged—see chapter 12.3.

If the shipper insists the cargo is loaded, then the OOW must advise the Chief Officer, so that appropriate clauses can be inserted in the mate's receipt and bill of lading. These should clearly indicate the inadequacy of the packaging, so that the carrier is protected should there be a loss of cargo which can be attributed to such packaging, before delivery to the consignee.

Occasionally cargo is manufactured, packaged and sold for domestic use, and is subsequently resold for export. The original packaging may have been sufficient for inland road transport, but may be wholly unsuitable for further transportation by sea. Inadequate packaging increases the possibilities of the cargo being both damaged and lost. When bagged produce is carried, the stow should be surrounded by burlap, so that spills may be easily collected, and these 'sweepings' discharged as part of the cargo. To assist with this rebagging, it is useful to carry a number of spare empty bags. Note also the examples given in section 13.4, paragraph 5.

13.3 Incorrect declarations

The weight of cargo shipped in units is often wrongly declared by the shipper. This may be due to ignorance or laziness, when he has not bothered to declare a weight accurately. It can also be due to fraud; when the freight is based on declared weight, it is in his financial interest to underdeclare the weight. Many times a fork-lift truck of ten tonne capacity has struggled with a container declared to be five tonnes! If the OOW detects such an inaccuracy, he must inform the Chief Officer. This is specially important with deck containers, when the ship's stability can be adversely affected by too much unplanned weight too high in the stow. Also, damage can be caused to the hatchcovers or tanktops if the allowable container stack weights are exceeded.

13.4 Cargo shortage

Claims due to shortage of cargo may be caused by:
1. Inaccuracies in establishing the quantity of cargo loaded or discharged.
2. Errors in recording the quantity of cargo loaded or discharged.
3. Cargo discharged at an earlier port, or left on board, and perhaps discharged at a later port.
4. Preshipment loss, where the correct number of items have not been shipped, or some of the contents of individual units is missing.
    The OOW should make spot checks to ensure that for example all bags are full—they are not obviously loose and underfilled, and cartons are not empty or have part of their contents removed. This does not mean there are obvious signs of the outer packing being tampered with, as the loss could have occurred at the manufacturers or packers.
5. Handling loss, where part of the contents spills out and is either lost or discarded, or is not able to be recovered. This may occur when the cargo is inadequately packed, for example insecure boxes and improperly sewn bags, or the packing is unsuitable—for example bags with too loose a weave or crates with large gaps so the cargo spills out from the undamaged packing.
6. Operational loss, such as residues which come off the cargo and are left on board, for example, bark falling off logs.
7. Weather loss—for example bulk cargo blown away by the wind before or during loading, or during or after discharge.
8. Natural or inherent loss—for example moisture which evaporates from within a cargo during ventilation on the voyage, or water which drains from the cargo into the bilges, and is pumped overside.
    This latter case is common with certain coal cargoes in bulk, and it is recommended that records are kept of all water pumped from the bilges during the voyage, to explain any differences in arrival and departure draft survey figures.
9. Pilferage ashore or on board.
    - Pilferage on board is a security problem, over which the OOW may have some control.
    - Pilferage before loading should be detected by the system used to establish the quantity of cargo loaded. Hence it is important to check such figures against those stated in the bill of lading.
    - Pilferage after discharge should not be the responsibility of the carrier, provided he has a reliable system for establishing and recording the quantity of cargo discharged to prove when the loss occurred. Ship's staff are advised not to intervene in acts of rampant pilferage ashore for their own safety in ports where shore security is weak. However, they should record all relevant facts, and photograph the activity from the ship if it is safe to do so.
10. Fraud.
11. A 'paper' loss, where there is no actual physical shortage, but certain paperwork does indicate a shortage. So although the consignee may actually receive the correct quantity, a claim for shortage can be made if the paperwork indicates otherwise.

13.5 Cargo tallies

On many break-bulk trades, the individual units of cargo are counted on and off the ship by a tally clerk. The written record of his count is made on a tally sheet, which will contain the 'marks' on the piece(s) of cargo, and the number of pieces of that mark. At the end of his shift, the tally clerk may require the OOW to sign his book of tally sheets. The OOW must be very sure that this cargo has been loaded or discharged exactly as described on the tally sheet before he signs it. This is achieved by monitoring the performance of the tally clerks throughout the cargo operations to ensure that no inaccuracies arise from the reasons listed in section 13.5.1.

The tallying operation should be performed on board the ship, so that there is less chance of cargo 'going missing' after it has been checked. Tallying cargo on a truck or a lighter, particularly when only part of its load is being delivered to this ship, is tempting loss.

The tally sheets are used to check the quantities stated in the mate's receipts and Bills of lading at the load port, and to confirm the quantity unloaded from the ship at the discharge port. The ship's copies of the loading and discharging tally sheets should be filed away on board so that they can be retrieved as evidence should there be a dispute over the cargo out-turn.

When the likes of bagged cargo is tallied on board, the correct quantity for insertion in the bill of lading is 'x' bags. The weight of each bag is unknown, so any reference to this in the bill of lading should be claused *said to weigh....* Also, because the quantity is so many bags, then all bags must be discharged and tallied, even if they are partially filled or empty.

13.5.1 Inaccurate tallies

If tallies are incorrect, then a claim for shortage may be made against the ship. The OOW should supervise the tally clerks to ensure that an accurate count is made. Reasons for inaccuracies in tallying include:

1. Fatigue—tally clerk falling asleep.
2. Overwork—cargo operations conducted so fast that the tally clerk cannot keep up with the stevedores.
3. Insufficient manning—one tally clerk trying to count for several gangs of stevedores, or for one gang working as several groups.
4. Incorrectly assuming that the number of units in each sling, net or pallet, or on each lorry, is the same as previously counted.
5. Copying the tally from another source (e.g., the delivery note.)
6. Poor location—the tally clerk cannot clearly see the cargo.
7. Damaged units incorrectly accounted for.
   For example, if bags of produce are torn or wet damaged, the routine may be to reject them, and then they will be automatically replaced by the shipper with sound units. How are these rejects tallied?
8. Fraud and corruption—deliberate over/under counting.
   This was once very common in ports where the cargo-handling operations were influenced by the criminal underworld, and any 'excess' cargo not tallied was sold locally.

13.6 Shore scales

The quantity of cargo loaded or discharged is often obtained from measurements made ashore. Sometimes this can be highly accurate; other times the shore figures are highly inaccurate, and, even worse, are often inconsistent.

13.6.1 Accuracy of the figures[20]

1. Grain loaded from an elevator, where the weight of each bin can be known to the nearest pound, may be accurate to within 0.1%.
2. Other automatic load-cell weighers, used for powdery type commodities may be accurate to within 0.2%.
3. Units loaded via a weigh-bridge may be accurate to within 0.5%. However, the system must be properly indexed for debris, weather, temperature, etc. which if ignored or improperly set can seriously effect the results. There must be an efficient system for ensuring all the shore transport uses the weigh-bridge both when full and empty.
4. Cargo loaded using a crane with a load recording device may be accurate to within 0.5%.
5. Vibratory feed high-speed weighers are used for coal and coke, and may be accurate to within 1%.
6. Belt weighers are notoriously unreliable and inconsistent, and are likely to be accurate only to within 2%, though 0.5% may be claimed.

13.6.2 Sources of inaccurate figures

1. Any system which is not properly maintained by qualified staff in accordance with manufacturers recommendations.
2. All systems which are not tested frequently.
3. Systems used with a commodity other than those for which it was designed.
4. History of the system—the OOW should seek candid advice. This is best requested from an equipment's operator or surveyor, rather than the foreman or terminal manager who may be tempted to provide an 'ideal' figure rather than a more realistic one.

13.6.3 Inconsistent figures

These are the worst problem for the OOW, as he cannot rely on what quantity of cargo is being delivered on any one occasion. It is not unheard of for the shore figures to be up to 10% low compared to ship's figures, then a few hours later 10% high. The OOW must never rely solely on these figures, they should be treated only as a guide to the weight loaded. He should be particularly careful on bulk carriers loading for a limiting draft. **In all cases, the final check is always the ship's draft—see section 13.9.**

13.7 Space measurement

If all else fails, a very rough approximation of the quantity of cargo can be obtained by measuring space. Traditionally, this method was used to assess the amount of cargo that could be loaded at a subsequent port. For small consignments, it may be possible to measure the actual dimensions of the space occupied by the cargo. For large consignments, measurements are taken of the space remaining after the cargo is loaded, and deducted from the total cubic capacity of the hold, to give the space occupied by the cargo.

Space occupied divided by the stowage factor gives the weight of the cargo. The stowage factor may be determined by shore measurement, but this is only a theoretical figure. It is expressed as so many tons per cubic foot, or so many cubic metres per tonne. The actual stowage factor is found by taking into account any unoccupied space within the stow, and parts of the cargo compartment which cannot be used for the particular commodity—for example, when there is not sufficient height left above the stow for another unit. The space in the hold not occupied by actual cargo—i.e., amongst, between and around the cargo—is referred to as broken stowage. On regular trades, the actual stowage factor is often fairly accurately known by the terminal operator. The records of cargo plans on board may be a useful source of actual stowage factors when such cargoes have been carried in similar compartments in the past.

In the timber trades, it is common for the cargo quantity to be expressed in 'Milles' which equal 1,000 board feet. A board-foot is a volumetric measurement, which equals one square foot of timber, one foot thick. There are often problems establishing the weight of timber; this varies with the type of wood, and its moisture content, which depends upon the time of year the tree was felled, how long it has been in storage, and the method of transport to the port (e.g., floats of logs). A draft survey (see below) should be carried out on completion of loading the underdeck cargo, in order to establish its weight. A calculation is then made to determine how much cargo can be safely loaded on deck, ensuring that the vessel retains sufficient positive stability throughout the voyage. An allowance should be made for the weight of moisture which may be absorbed by the deck cargo.

13.8 Calibration tables

With liquid cargoes, the volume occupied by the cargo in the ship's tanks is found from the ship's tank calibration tables. A sounding or ullage is taken, and corrections are applied for any trim and list of the vessel. The volume obtained from these tables is then corrected for the temperature of the cargo, to obtain the true volume at a standard temperature. If it is required, the weight of the cargo is calculated by multiplying the observed density of the cargo by this true volume. The measurement of liquid cargoes, and the associated precautions, is discussed in chapter 9.18.

13.9 Draft surveys

In the majority of bulk trades, and for certain other shipments, the quantity of cargo on board is established by a draft survey, which is usually performed by an independent surveyor. This means that he has no commercial interest in the transaction, so should produce an impartial result. Even if such an independent surveyor is not appointed, **it is good practice for the ship to conduct a draft survey for every load and discharge operation in order to verify the weight of cargo as provided by the shore.** This may be a requirement of the charterers.

The calculations involved are usually performed by the Chief Officer, but the OOW should understand the principles involved, and be able to undertake this calculation himself. With careful observations, accuracies of within 0.5% are possible.

It is most important that the data required for these surveys be obtained by personal observation, and NOT by verbal agreement.

13.9.1 Principle of draft surveys

WT OF SHIP FULL − WT OF SHIP EMPTY
= WEIGHT OF CARGO.

Weight of the ship is its displacement, calculated from drafts read before and after loading or discharging. Any weights on board which change between the full and empty surveys will effect the results, so the weights of known variables are deducted from these displacements at both of the above surveys. These variables, sometimes called the 'deductibles', are BALLAST, FRESH WATER and FUEL. If there is a change in other weights—for example if stores are taken, lubricating oils replenished, or dunnage or sludge/slops landed ashore—then a correction is applied for these at the final survey—see section 13.9.6.

13.9.2 Reading the draft

1. When reading the draft, nothing should be moving on the ship—cargo, ballast, stores, fuel transfers, hatchcovers.

2. Read the draft marks from as close to the waterline as possible, in order to avoid errors due to parallax. Those read from a boat at rest with no wash are likely to be the most accurate.

3. If access to sight the draft marks directly is difficult, measure the distance from the waterline to the deck, and deduct this from the deck height obtained from the ship's plans. This practice is to be recommended midships, where the freeboard is given accurately in the ships documents. Measure the actual freeboard from the top of the statutory deck line cut into the hull midships. A tape with a float plate at the zero mark is very useful for this purpose.

   Draft = (summer freeboard + summer draft) [the 'freeboard constant'] − observed freeboard.

4. If practical, take the readings at slack water, because in shallow water, the ship may squat due to a strong tide or current. The ship is sucked down towards the seabed, thus the draft as read does not reflect the true free-floating draft, which is the one required for establishing the ship's displacement.

5. There are several appliances available to smooth out the rising and falling swell, to produce a more accurate draft reading. They work on the principle that surface disturbance does not extend to any great depth. An open-ended tube is lowered well below the surface, and a float inside this tube is aligned with the draft marks. Any movement of this float is minimal compared to the swell. Without such equipment, the OOW should take the highest and lowest readings of a series of swells, (a total of 12 is recommended) and then calculate an average. If the inboard draft is sheltered, and the outboard draft difficult to read, the OOW can obtain an accurate outboard figure using a simple U-tube manometer. A long length of clear plastic pipe is laid across the main deck amidships, each end is secured to the ship's rail at each side of the main deck, and the pipe is nearly filled with water. On each side, the height above the deck of the water-level in the tube is measured. The difference between these two heights is applied to the inshore draft to give an accurate offshore draft.

6. A hand lamp or torch with a powerful beam and a pair of binoculars, are useful equipment to assist in obtaining accurate drafts.

7. Any draft gauges are useful as a check, but must not be used to replace visual observations of the marks cut into the hull. They are helpful to verify that there has been no inadvertent alteration of the draft markings. It is useful to read the draft gauges at the same time as visual observations in order to establish any errors in these gauges. Such errors can be applied to correct any draft gauge readings taken as checks during various stages of the loading or discharging operation. The OOW should be familiar with the accuracy of the gauges under varying conditions.

13.9.3 Taking the density sample

1. The density sample should be taken as close as possible to the time when the draft is read.
2. Obtain several samples of water, from all around the ship, and at several depths between the waterline and the deepest draft.
3. Avoid areas around the vessel where there are engineroom cooling water discharges, ballast discharges, rivers, streams, or piped water outflows from the shore.
4. If there are marked differences in the densities of the samples, it could be that the ship is floating in water which is layered—for example, fresh river water floating on top of denser seawater. In such cases, a large number of samples from different depths will be required in order to establish the most accurate mean possible.

There are several patent 'density buckets' available to assist in obtaining suitable samples, but unfortunately very few are supplied to ships. If a draft surveyor is in attendance, he may have such a device. In their absence the OOW should take several samples using an ordinary metal bucket, weighted with scrap metal if necessary, and ensure that it is lowered well below the water line. The average of the densities from each sample is used for the draft survey calculations.

13.9.4 Obtaining the correct density

The load-line hydrometer measures specific gravity, or relative density, which is used to calculate the dock water allowance (DWA) from the ship's fresh water allowance (FWA). These hydrometers are usually made of metal. The dock water allowance is the main factor which determines by how much the loadline can be submerged in the water in which the ship is floating. The draft survey hydrometer measures the apparent density in air, and is usually made of glass. It is used to calculate the weight of water displaced by the ship.

If only a loadline hydrometer is available, then a correction must be applied to obtain the correct density for use in draft surveys.

A useful rule-of-thumb is:
- If the hydrometer is graduated at 60°F/60°F, then deduct 0.002.
- If the hydrometer is graduated at 15°C/4°C, then deduct 0.001.

Rinse out the sample jar with part of the water sample. The sample jar should be a glass jar with a minimum diameter of 50mm. and deep enough for the hydrometer to float at least 25mm. clear of the bottom. The jar should be nearly full, and the observer's eye should be level with the top of the jar to avoid parallax errors. Hold the hydrometer vertically by the top of the stem and gently lower it into the sample jar until it floats freely. Take the hydrometer reading where the water surface meets the stem, avoiding the meniscus. Some officers like to spin the hydrometer to verify it is floating free and as an aid to taking the reading.

> It is important to remember that the loadline must not be submerged at any stage of the voyage.

The junior officer should be quite clear that the density in vacuo (relative density) is used for loadline calculations, whilst the density in air (apparent density) is used for draft survey calculations. Once the midships draft corrected for relative density reaches the relevant loadline draft, then no more cargo can be loaded, even if a draft survey indicates that the displacement is less than the maximum for that loadline. A vessel which is sagged, as is common with loaded bulk carriers, will always carry less cargo than her loadline displacement would indicate—see chapter 11.9.

13.9.5 Consequences of inaccurate readings

The OOW is often requested to take the density, and he should always do this carefully, taking the above factors into account. As an example of the possible consequences of inaccurate density readings, a bulk carrier was loading for a voyage involving transit of the Panama Canal. The cargo quantity was determined by the Chief Officer by calculating the maximum cargo to guarantee the ship was at the maximum draft permitted by the canal authorities—39ft 06in tropical fresh water. As the shore loader could give only approximate figures, he calculated a maximum sailing draft, taking into account fuel and water to be used en route, and the density observed at the loading berth. On completion of loading, it can be shown that the actual density was three points more than that observed. This could have been caused by fresh water from a nearby river floating on top of denser seawater—i.e., the sample taken was from the surface water and did not represent the average density of the water in which the ship was floating. This resulted in the ship being a few centimetres overdraft at the canal. At this time Panama was suffering from low rainfall, so the canal level was lower than normal, and the maximum permitted draft was strictly enforced. The vessel had to debunker in order to transit the canal, and the total cost to the owner, including offhire and retransit fees was over $100,000.

13.9.6 The constant

The so-called draft survey 'constant' varies with the weight of stores and other variables over the long term, but is assumed to be fixed for the duration of the loading or discharge period. If the figure is recorded for each survey, as recommended by the UN *Draft Survey Code*,[55] then it will be apparent if the figure calculated on any occasion shows a major discrepancy. Experienced draft surveyors will have some idea of what figure to expect for this constant for each size and type of ship.

Inaccuracies in either the ship's hydrostatic data or tank calibration tables may be highlighted by unusually high or low constants for a ship of its size. A record of constants will show that such unusual constants are to be expected on the vessel in question, and are not a result of errors in that particular draft survey.

13.9.7 Draft survey calculation

1. Calculate the mean draft forward, midships and aft from the port and starboard drafts observed. Correct the fore and aft means to obtain the drafts at the forward and after perpendiculars, which are used for compiling displacement scales. The distance from the draft marks to the perpendiculars is given in the ship's stability manual. If not, it can be estimated from the quay. (The after perpendicular is in line with the rudder stock, and the forward perpendicular is where the summer waterline intersects the bow.)

2. Calculate the 'mean of means' draft to allow for hull deformation, or deflection due to hog or sag. This is the accepted international method, though it is known that the ship's form is quite complex, and does not follow a single smooth curve as this 'mean' assumes.

3. Obtain the displacement for the mean of means draft from the ship's hydrostatic particulars, which may be tables or graphs. There is a possibility of errors here because the tables supplied by the shipbuilder may not always be totally reliable. In most cases, graphs are not able to provide the degree of accuracy required.

4. Correct this displacement for trim. There are two corrections: The first is to correct the draft amidships as calculated above, to the true mean draft, which is the draft at the centre of floatation. It is sometimes known as the 'layer' correction. The second is to allow for the shift in the centre of floatation caused by the vessel's trim.

5. Apply a correction for any list.

6. Apply a correction for the observed density, to obtain the true displacement of the vessel.

7. Deduct the weight of known variables (or 'deductibles'): ballast, fresh water, fuel oil, diesel oil, to obtain the corrected (or net) displacement of the vessel. It is *vital* that the density of the ballast water is measured, and taken into account when calculating the weight of ballast from the soundings of the ballast tanks.

8. **NET DISPLACEMENT LOADED – NET DISPLACEMENT LIGHT = WEIGHT OF CARGO.**

9. A check on the accuracy of the figures can be obtained by calculating the ship's constant: **NET DISPLACEMENT LIGHT – LIGHTSHIP WEIGHT = CONSTANT** (see section 13.9.6).

10. A correction should be made for the weight of any ship's stores, including lubricating oil, loaded during the cargo operation.
    - If loading cargo, deduct this from the weight of cargo calculated.
    - If discharging cargo, add this to the weight of cargo calculated.
    - Vice-versa if known weights are discharged from the vessel, for example, sludge pumped ashore, lashings or dunnage landed.

11. Errors in the true drafts caused by differences between the temperature of the air and water are ignored.

For those readers who want to perform such calculations, a pro-forma is provided in appendix III, including the relevant formulae.

13.9.8 Determining deductibles

The involvement of the OOW in the draft survey will often include determining the quantity of ballast and fresh water on board at the time. The reader will have learned in chapter 10 that all ballast tanks should be sounded by hand, and that overflowing the tanks does not produce accurate figures due to the presence of air pockets. Care should be taken to ensure that the bob of the sounding line just touches the striker plate, and the reading on the line at the top of the sounding pipe (the full ullage) should be checked against the figure from the ship's tables. This is done to check that there is no blockage or obstruction in the sounding pipe, which would give a false reading. One should remember that the length of the sounding pipe may not be the same as the vertical height of the tank, due to the curvature of the ship's structure and/or sounding pipe. The readings on any remote tank reading gauges should be noted for comparison against the manual soundings, both as a check, and as a means of establishing any calibration errors in the gauges.

The density of the ballast water must be taken into account when calculating the weight of ballast from the ship's calibration tables. Special sampling dippers are available for this purpose, but the OOW can always obtain a sample by lowering a plastic tube down the sounding pipe and then sealing the top end with a bung, or his thumb! When obtaining this density, the same careful procedure as outlined in section 13.9.4 should be observed.

For fuel and other oils, it may be acceptable to use normal consumption rates to determine the difference in their weights at the initial and final draft survey. This is because the difference in these two sets of figures is usually quite small, and will probably be smaller than any errors from sounding the tanks and applying the relevant corrections, to determine the actual tonnage on board at each survey—i.e., it is more accurate to estimate the fuel used rather than to measure the quantities of fuel on board twice.

The anchor and cable must be in the same position as the initial and final survey, or a correction should be applied as in section 13.9.6.10 to allow for their weight. Similarly, the contents of the swimming pool must not be overlooked.

13.9.9 Further information

The reader who requires more detailed information on draft surveys is recommended to read the UN *Draft Survey Code*[55], *Bulk Carrier Practice*[3], or *Draught Surveys—a guide to good practice*[32].

13.10 Cargo distribution

Although the ship's draft is the final reference for total weight of cargo on board, with bulk cargoes it is difficult to estimate how the weight is distributed around the ship. This can be very important for the stress calculations, so there are two methods which are used to determine the distribution of the cargo.

13.10.1 Distribution by draft

One method of estimating the distribution is for the OOW to read the draft at the end of each stage of the cargo operation. For example, at the end of each pour on a bulker. By knowing the distribution of variable weights like the ballast, he will be able to calculate a good approximation of the weight of cargo loaded during the last stage/pour.

13.10.2 Distribution by space

Another method is to measure, or estimate, the space occupied by the cargo, or the space remaining empty. The known total weight can be proportioned between all the space occupied throughout the ship. This method was traditionally used by liner operators during multi-port loadings, to enable bookings to be updated at the next ports. It still has a valid place on break-bulk ships, where extra cargo can be booked at a subsequent port should there be extra space available from a previous port.

When requested to measure the space remaining, the OOW will need a long tape measure, a torch, and an assistant. When he enters each hold, he tries to visualise the empty space as a series of rectangular blocks. He measures the length, width and height of each of these blocks, then adds their volumes together to give the total space remaining. The common sense use of such features as the spacing of container fittings may assist the OOW to assess accurately the space in the short time that may be available. Some vessels have detailed capacity plans showing the volume of numerous small sections of each compartment, which can be used to assist such assessments.

Some bulkers have height marks on the fore and aft bulkheads which can be used to provide a rough estimate of space, when used in conjunction with ullage tables in the grain stability book. Timber ships often have height marks on the outboard timber retaining stanchions and crane pedestals which assist in stowing the deck cargo to the correct height.

13.11 Deadfreight

When a shipper has contracted to supply a full cargo and the freight is to be paid per tonne of cargo loaded, then any shortfall in the quantity loaded represents a loss of freight to the carrier. In these cases, the carrier will claim freight on the difference between the actual quantity loaded and the quantity which the Master declared on arrival that the ship could load. This is known as deadfreight.

Some charter parties contain a clause which makes it imperative that the correct quantity of cargo is loaded—for example: *If the vessel does not load the charterparty minimum (provided sufficient cargo is available) or loads in excess of the charterparty maximum, then any or all consequences, losses and damages are to be for the vessel's/owners' account.*

All produce contains moisture. On longer passages, inadequate ventilation can lead to mould growth. Bags which are damp-stained or mouldy on loading should be rejected by the OOW. See chapter 12.7.2. Photograph: courtesy of UK P&I Club.

Chapter 14

SHIP'S SERVICES

OBJECT

On completion of this chapter you will have an appreciation of some of the other activities that take place onboard a ship in port, which may involve you in a supervisory role, or to assist as required.

14.1 Role of the OOW

The OOW has a key role to ensure that the shipowner is not charged for goods and services he does not receive. Also, those which are supplied should match the quantity and quality shown on the bill. The OOW is often the first contact for those supplying goods or services to the ship. He should be able to direct the supplier to the appropriate part of the ship, and introduce him to the relevant officer.

14.2 Fresh water

Although some ships make sufficient fresh water whilst at sea for all their requirements, using their evaporators, most ships have to take on extra supplies of fresh water in port at some time. The OOW should locate the filling pipe and sounding pipe (or remote gauge) for each fresh water tank. He must be able to use their capacity tables, and know where these are kept.

Usually a shore filling line is used, but most ships also carry their own line. In either case, the first few minutes of flow should be allowed to wash overboard to ensure that the hose is clean, and free of debris, before allowing the water into the tank. The hose used to supply fresh water should be used for no other purpose, and the open ends should never be allowed to drop into the dock water, or pools of water lying on the quay or on deck. The OOW should supervise the people handling the hoses to ensure that hygienic standards are maintained, and that there is no contamination of the ship's fresh water.

Sometimes there can be problems when the connections are not compatible, and it is best if arrangements are made to have the delivery into the ship's tanks made via an open ended line. The OOW should check that the air pipe of the tank to be filled is clear and free, so that the air in the tank can readily ventilate to the atmosphere as the tank is filled with water. He should be aware of the quantity of water required to be loaded, and ensure that the supply is switched off when this figure is reached. If the tank is to be filled, he should monitor the operation to ensure that water is not wasted by overflowing onto the deck.

The OOW must check the shore gauge reading before and after taking water, and check the supplied quantity against tank soundings before he signs the waterman's receipt. He should also verify any times given, either of duration of supply, or attendance of the waterman, to avoid excess charges.

14.3 Receiving stores and spares

The suppliers of some smaller items will bring them on board themselves, and seek out the relevant officer. The OOW should be able to guide them to the correct recipient on board.

Large amounts of stores will be loaded by the crew, but the OOW should verify that the Chief Officer has checked with the foreman stevedore that there are no local restrictions on the timing or organisation of this activity.

The Chief Officer may require the OOW to check those items being delivered for the deck department. He should check every item on the list, both to ensure it is on board, and also that it is the correct item as described. He may need to check with the Chief Officer if he is unsure as to the suitability of some items. If there is any doubt as to the quantity or quality of the stores, it is essential that the delivery note is claused, and the Chief Officer informed, so that the Master can advise the owners before they settle this account.

It is important that any manuals, data or instruction sheets, and in particular test certificates which accompany the stores are retrieved and passed on to the Chief Officer for filing in the records. The same precautionary checks must be made to the stores handling crane/derricks as were outlined for the cargo handling equipment in chapter 4.5. Failure to inspect a topping lift wire resulted in the death of two seamen recently and damages of more than $1 million.[22]

The OOW should organise the crew to stow all items in their appropriate locker or storage place as soon as possible after they are loaded. Goods left lying around are a temptation to thieves.

14.4 Repairs and servicing

The maintenance of much of the ship's equipment must be done in port as often specialised technical assistance is required. The OOW should be able to direct the technicians to the appropriate officer. He may be called upon to assist with bridge or deck equipment by:
1. Providing data or equipment for the technicians.
2. Explaining the faults.
3. Organising assistance.
4. Testing the equipment is operating correctly after the repairs have been completed.

If he is directly involved, the OOW must always check the technician's sheet before signing it, to make sure:
1. The listed parts have been fitted or supplied.
2. That the action taken and results are correctly described.
3. That the time attended is correct.

Major repairs and structural alterations are usually left to drydock. However, some more urgent or immediate requirements may be undertaken during a normal port call. The OOW should ensure that all operations on deck are carried out in a safe manner, and arrange for extra fire patrols if required. Where burning or welding is being carried out, he must check the other side of the steelwork, for both fire risks and breakdown of coatings. The OOW should remember that he is responsible for the safety of all operations and all personnel on board the ship, and that this includes workers from ashore engaged in repairs and servicing.

Modifications to the ship's structure and fittings may be required for particular cargoes. The OOW should ensure that the modification is safe, and produces the desired effect. If they are temporary, the ship must be restored to a safe and watertight condition. All exposed steelwork should be given a protective coating. Some examples include: Extra padeyes for lashings; Supplementary handrails or guards; Holes cut in the top of hatches to load dusty cargoes such as cement by pneumatic means.

14.5 Crew changes

Besides the social nature of saying farewell to old shipmates, and welcoming new arrivals, the OOW may need to co-ordinate the baggage handling, direct new people to their accommodation, ensure that the crew leaving all timely catch the relevant transportation, and assist any accompanying officials.

It should be remembered that new crew members may not be familiar with the layout of the vessel, the location and operation of equipment, and the system of work on board. The OOW must make allowances, and anticipate that some duties may take a longer time than normal to accomplish, or may require closer supervision than usual. He should pay particular attention to the safety aspects discussed in chapters 3 and 4.

14.6 Statutory surveys

The following surveys regularly take place in port.
- Loadline.
- Safety equipment.
- Safety construction.
- Safety radio.
- Deratting or deratting exemption.
- MARPOL / IOPP.
- Classification society (continuous or special survey).

- Port State—see table below.
- Flag State annual inspections.
- Charterers (condition).
- P&I Club (condition).
- Liferaft, SCBA bottles, CO_2 bottles, fire-fighting equipment, etc.

The OOW should be able to direct the surveyor to the appropriate officer. In addition, he may be involved in accompanying the surveyor around the ship, and in assisting him with the locating and testing of equipment. All surveyors should be treated courteously, and it should be remembered that first impressions count for so much.

The OOW should ask the Chief Officer beforehand what is required for each survey, and what will be his involvement. Some organisations, such as Lloyd's Register, issue checklists to assist the officers in their preparations for surveys—see appendix XIV. On a well managed ship, the junior officer will be informed well in advance of those surveys which directly concern his areas of responsibility on board, and hopefully he will have fully prepared all the items for survey. An officer who is well informed and able to display a good working knowledge of his subject to a surveyor will greatly assist in the speedy and favourable conclusion to the survey.

14.7 Crew activities

The OOW should take an active supervisory role in any routine work being done by the crew whilst the ship is in port, to ensure their safety is not compromised. He should stop any nonessential crew activities which interfere with the cargo operations, or which place the crew too close to operations where there is any risk of personal injury. The Chief Officer should be informed. Besides the safety matters discussed in chapter 4, the OOW should also watch to ensure that:

1. No damage is done to property on the quay—for example paint blown on to a car.
2. No obstructions are caused—for example blocking an access.
3. No ship's equipment is left where it can damage shore equipment—for example, close to rail lines or where vehicles may collide with it.
4. No shore equipment is borrowed for ship's use, unless permission has been clearly granted.

Major categories of deficiencies as noted by European Port State Control Inspectors in 1993.[98]

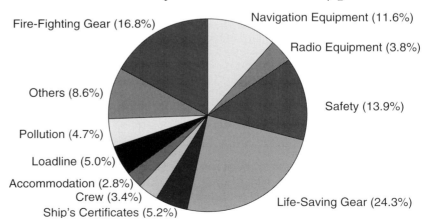

Fire-Fighting Gear (16.8%)
Navigation Equipment (11.6%)
Radio Equipment (3.8%)
Others (8.6%)
Safety (13.9%)
Pollution (4.7%)
Loadline (5.0%)
Accommodation (2.8%)
Crew (3.4%)
Ship's Certificates (5.2%)
Life-Saving Gear (24.3%)

Chapter 15
POLLUTION PREVENTION
OBJECT

On completion of this chapter you will be able to describe the precautions to take to avoid pollution of the environment by spillage of bunkers, cargo or garbage, emissions of smoke and pumping contaminated ballast.

15.1 Bunkering

Whenever a vessel takes on bunkers, the operation must be carefully planned and executed by persons who are familiar with the valve and pipeline systems. The penalties for even a small spillage of oil into an environmentally sensitive area can be substantial, and the clean up costs can be enormous—$15 million for a spill of 283 barrels in Los Angeles.[28] The average claim for bunker spills is $1 million.[21]

15.1.1 Responsibilities of the OOW

The Chief Engineer will be in charge of the bunkering operation. The OOW should keep in close contact with the bunkering team throughout; his principal duties are to ensure that:

1. All scuppers are plugged.
2. All moorings remain taut, to restrict the movement of the ship, and/or the bunker barge.
3. Cargo and ballast operations keep the ship upright.
4. The Chief Engineer is informed of any planned large change of trim due to cargo and ballast operations, **before** it occurs.
5. Appropriate signals are shown—red 'B' flag or all-round red light.
6. All crew are informed, so that the ship's emergency response plan can be activated without delay if required.
7. Ship's containment equipment is ready for immediate use.
8. Oil absorbent materials are placed at relevant points.
9. All save-alls are emptied and replugged.
10. If bunkers are delivered by barge, crew are standing-by to make fast the barge, arrange access (**not** the pilot ladder), and provide adequate fenders if required.
11. Firewires are rigged fore and aft if required by local regulations
12. The Chief Engineer will complete the ship's bunkering check list with a representative from the suppliers. The OOW may have to sign this to verify that he has completed the above listed procedures.
13. If it rains during bunkering, OOW must ensure that accumulations of water on deck, and in the save-alls, are drained away regularly, and the drains resealed.
14. If there is an oil spill, the OOW must make all efforts to contain it as quickly as possible. A floating mooring rope is an excellent emergency containment boom if there is not already one in place. He must immediately instigate the ship's emergency response plan.

15.1.2 Bunkering checklist

The Nautical Institute recommends that a bunkering checklist is completed before every bunkering operation. Some of these lists also include checks to be made during and after completion of the operation. The junior deck officer should make himself familiar with this checklist, and make sure that he understands what is involved for each item, and not just for those items which are his immediate responsibility. An example of a bunkering checklist is reproduced in appendix VII.

15.1.3 Shipboard oil pollution emergency response plan (Sopep)

The junior deck officer should study this plan when he first joins a ship, and ensure that he understands its aims and how to implement it. Although all plans contain similar information, and there may be a set pattern to the plans within one operator's fleet, each ship has to have its own individual plan, approved by the flag State, under Regulation 26 of Annex I to Marpol 73/78. He should ask the Master to explain any points in the plan which he does not understand. The OOW should check with the Master and Chief Engineer that the plan is updated with the relevant local information before commencing each bunkering operation, so that he may amend any related shipboard notices as required—e.g., contact numbers of the shore anti-pollution authorities.

The plan is designed to set in motion the necessary actions to stop or minimise any unexpected discharge of oil and to mitigate its effects. Usually it comprises of a series of flow-charts or checklists, arranged in logical sequence, to reduce oversight and error. Effective planning ensures that the necessary actions are taken in a structured, logical and timely manner. Reporting requirements are detailed, with checklists of the information required, and a list of contacts is included which are local, national, international and company orientated.

Guidance is offered on operational spills, such as pipe leakage, tank overflow, and hull leakage, in addition to catastrophe spills resulting from casualties such as collision, grounding, fire, explosion, excess list and hull failure. The plan also contains an inventory of ship's response equipment, with quantities, stowage positions and instructions for its use, with details of personnel responsible for its deployment and maintenance. The OOW may be also involved with the plan's provisions on testing and record keeping.

For more detailed information, the OOW should consult the bibliography in appendix I.[57-69]

15.1.4 Oil record book

The OOW should be familiar with the entries made in this book.

They should show the date, time and place, the quantity and description of liquids involved, and details of their origin and destination tank on board own ship, on another ship or ashore. Operations which should be recorded are:

I. MACHINERY SPACE OPERATIONS ON ALL SHIPS:
1. Ballasting or cleaning of fuel oil tanks—including disposal of water from these operations.
2. Disposal of oily residues, such as sludge.
3. Discharge of bilge water from machinery spaces and pump rooms.
4. Any occasion when oil or an oily mixture is discovered escaping from a ship due to leakage or damage.

II. CARGO/BALLAST OPERATIONS ON TANKERS:
1. Loading, internal transfer and discharge of oil cargoes.
2. Ballasting/deballasting of cargo and segregated ballast tanks.
3. Cleaning of cargo tanks, including crude oil washing (COW).
4. Discharge of water from slop tanks.
5. Disposal of all residues.
6. Closing of valves to slop tank and segregated ballast tanks.

15.1.5 Other problems with bunkers

Besides pollution, problems with bunkering occur due to the fuel supplied being unsuitable, off specification, or of incorrect quantity. Such problems mainly concern the Chief Engineer, and are beyond the scope of this book.

15.2 Cargo spills

The serious pollution which can result from a spillage of oil cargo means the OOW must pay close attention when he is operating the cargo valves on tankers. These precautions are described in chapter 9. Identical precautions apply to all ships carrying potentially dangerous or polluting cargo in a bulk liquid form, particularly gas and chemicals.

However, in these days when protection of the environment is being given top priority in many places, the OOW must be on guard for all forms of pollution which may originate from the cargo. This could be spills from insecure packaging, or leaks from packages damaged during loading or discharging. Packages already stowed on board, particularly those on deck, may begin to leak due to deterioration or damage. All such leaks and spills should be contained and recovered as soon as practicable. It is particularly important to take prompt action to deal with spills of dangerous cargoes (see chapter 7.12.1).

Bulk cargo which spills on deck should be swept up and, if not damaged, should be returned to the hold. The OOW must beware of allowing anyone to throw spilt cargo on the quay, or into the water, as this can be interpreted as polluting the port. It has been reported that coal dust washed overboard from the main deck by overflowing ballast in Pohang, Korea, resulted in one ship being fined Won 10 million (about US\$13,000).[27]

Dunnage, packing and lashing equipment should not be disposed of by throwing them overside or dumping them on the quay, as this can also be interpreted as polluting the port. All such unwanted items must always be collected and stored until they can be disposed of in an environmentally friendly way. Cargo spills which are not recovered are cargo loss, and may lead to claims for shortage, as discussed in chapter 13.

15.3 Ballast

Ballast may cause pollution because it has become contaminated as it flows through a polluted pipeline, or because it contains harmful organisms.

15.3.1 Polluted pipelines

Whenever deballasting for the first time after a sea passage, the OOW should always check the initial outflow of ballast water from the ship by physically sighting the overboard discharge. This will verify that the lines have not become contaminated—for example, by someone pumping the contents of oily bilges through a section of the line, or using the ballast pump to transfer other polluted liquids. It is not unknown for oil to appear in the deck service or fire line—an impossibility in theory! If he sees any pollution in the ballast discharge, the OOW must stop the deballasting operation, and inform the Chief Officer or Master immediately. They will decide on what action to take, but if the pollution is serious, the OOW should instigate the ship's oil pollution emergency response plan—see section 15.1.3.

In Canada, the Port Warden requires to sight this initial outflow for this very reason. He will then issue a permit to deballast. The OOW must never start deballasting before he checks that this permission has been granted. Other countries are likely to follow suit in the next few years.

15.3.2 Contaminated ballast water

There is increasing concern in certain countries that unwanted marine organisms are being introduced into new areas as a result of ships discharging ballast water containing organisms which are alien to the local environment and may be harmful to it. There have been claims that a large variety of fish, molluscs, crustaceans, worms and seaweeds have been transferred from one region of the world to another in this way.

In Australia, toxic dinoflagellates from ballast have been digested by shellfish. When these are eaten by humans, serious illness and even death has resulted. It has been found that these organisms are more prevalent in sediment, so it is recommended that ballast should be free from sediment when it is taken on board. The quarantine inspectors may require a sample of any sediment in the ballast tank, so this can be analysed to detect the presence of these organisms.

Canada and the USA are concerned about new species which they have found in the Great Lakes. The US Ballast Water Act of 1992 requires a minimum salinity of 30 parts per thousand. It is reported that a vessel which had ballasted upriver in Europe was sent back to sea from the Upper Lakes to reballast. This resulted in a week offhire and a large amount of extra expenses for the shipowner.[22]

The method used to control this influx at the moment is for ships to exchange their ballast water for clean sea water whilst they are mid-ocean. The junior deck officer may be involved in this process whilst the ship is at sea. There is a concern that some ships may not be able to exchange fully their ballast at sea safely—that is, keeping within seagoing maximum bending moments and shear forces. It is reported that new Argentinean sanitary regulations require the chlorination of ballast tanks; penalties for breach of these regulations can be as high as $1 million.[22]

There are investigations under way at the present time to try to discover a viable and efficient method for treating ballast water on board ships to eliminate these unwanted organisms. Chemical additives and heat treatment has been researched, but no positive conclusion has been reached. In view of the inability of ports to provide reception facilities for other forms of pollutants and waste materials, it is unlikely that suggestions to pump water ballast into reception facilities ashore will meet with much enthusiasm. For the foreseeable future, it seems likely that the exchange of ballast water at sea will be the only available solution.

For further information, the reader should study the IMO *Guidelines for Preventing the introduction of unwanted aquatic organisms and pathogens from ships' ballast water and sediment discharge.*[36]

15.4 Garbage

All garbage should be kept in covered containers, and foodstuffs in particular must not be permitted to litter the decks. The OOW must be alert for newly dumped garbage, as large fines can result from small infringements of local rules. For example, a ship was fined $1,000 for orange peel found on deck in New Orleans—this had been dropped by a shore worker, as there were no oranges in the ship's store at the time!

A well run ship will have a strict system of garbage disposal, in order to comply with Marpol Annexe IV[61] when she is at sea. It is good practice always to keep garbage contained in sealed bags. These can be disposed of when facilities are available, but increasingly ships are fitted with incinerators of sufficient capacity to make garbage disposal easy, cheap and legal. The OOW must not forget that hold sweepings and used dunnage may be classed as garbage.

To prove the ship complies with MARPOL regulations, it is recommended that a *Garbage Disposal Log* is maintained, showing when, where and how all the ship's garbage was processed.

15.5 Sewage

The discharge of raw sewage is prohibited in most ports, and the OOW should verify with the Chief Engineer that any such overboard discharges are locked closed. Shore officials sometimes need to sight the valves to verify that they are securely locked in the closed position. Some vessels have holding tanks which can store several days or weeks output.

Modern ships usually have equipment on board which treats sewage and produces only a clean water discharge. Even this discharge may be prohibited in certain ports, and the above precautions apply. Further information can be obtained from the IMO publication *Recommendations on International Effluent Standards and Guidelines for performance tests for sewage treatment plants.*[59]

15.6 Air pollution

The OOW should be alert for heavy emissions of smoke from the ship's funnel. Not only is this a sign that some machinery may be improperly adjusted, so he should inform the duty engineer, but also this may result in the ship being fined for air pollution.

Another source of air pollution is dust blown from the cargo. Several ports have local regulations which prohibit loading or discharge of dusty cargoes in winds above a certain force, or from a certain direction, particularly where there are residential properties downwind. The dust from dry bulk cargoes such as coal, grain, fertiliser, sulphur, and a whole range of 'light' commodities may cause annoyance to local residents. This can lead to protests, and other actions which adversely affect the ship's operation. It may also lead to fines. The OOW must always try to encourage the stevedores to handle the cargo in such a way as to minimise dust clouds. Not overfilling the grabs, nor swinging them whilst cargo is still spilling from them, are useful constraints.

A source of pollution which is giving increasing concern in some countries is vapours from tanks. When a tank is filled, the atmosphere inside the tank, which may contain such pollutants as evaporated cargo or inert gases, may be displaced through the ventilators into the local atmosphere. Control of these vapours can only be achieved by collection and recycling systems which will require modifications of vessels and terminals. Air pollution may be caused by noxious fumes or vapours emanating from cargoes as the result of damaged packaging.[77]

15.7 Miscellaneous pollution

In some ports regulations on pollution from any source are strictly enforced. Some examples to which the OOW should remain alert include:
1. Noise pollution from chipping machines.
2. Paint or scale chippings, and drips of paint in the dock water.
   It is always good practice to obtain permission of the port authority, preferably in writing, before undertaking any overside maintenance in port.
3. Hold bilges, even if all they contain is dirty water, should not be pumped overside in port if practicable.

4. Minor leaks of hydraulic oil from deck machinery can be considered as oil pollution, and should be contained accordingly.
5. When taking the after draft, the OOW should look out for any leak of oil from the stern gland.
6. Engine room bilges must never be pumped overside in port, as there is a strong possibility that they contain some oil. If they become full, and/or a high level alarm is activated, their contents should be transferred to a slop tank, or other holding tank, as available.

15.8 Pollution from other origins

During his regular patrols of the deck, the OOW should be alert for pollution in the area around the vessel, which has come from somewhere else other than his own ship. All such incidents should be logged, and immediately reported to the appropriate authorities ashore. It is important formally to establish the innocence of one's own ship, particularly with oil pollution. This may prevent the ship from being falsely accused as the originator of such pollution. It is not unknown for authorities in some ports to blame an easy target such as the only foreign ship in port, a ship owned by a large company, or even a ship where inefficiency or lack of supervision has been noted earlier. It may be useful to take photographs if these can show the true origin of the pollution—see chapter 18.9.

Cargo is spilt when grabs used to handle bulk cargo do not close properly. This can lead to claims for cargo shortage, and may also result in pollution claims. See chapters 13.4, 13.5, 13.7 and 15.2.
Photograph: courtesy of Brookes, Bell & Co.

Chapter 16
SHIP'S SECURITY
PURPOSE

On completion of this chapter you will be able to explain the importance of making the ship secure in port, and list the precautions to take against thieves, pirates, stowaways, drug-traffickers and other unwelcome visitors.

16.1 Importance of maintaining security

If the OOW does not ensure that the ship's security is maintained at all times in port, then the ship is likely to be visited by persons with criminal intent. Besides the adverse effect on the profitable operation of the ship resulting from theft of cargo or ship's stores, the planting of illegal drugs, and the boarding of stowaways, these unwelcome visitors may subject the crew to violence in pursuit of their activities. Other unwelcome visitors include those seeking to obtain evidence which may be used against the shipowner's interests.

> **THE GOLDEN RULE** must always be that no unauthorised persons should be permitted access to the vessel.

16.1.1 Security pass[6]

One of the simplest methods of controlling access to the ship is to have the gangway manned at all times by a responsible member of the crew. He should be given clear orders that no-one is to be allowed on board the ship unless they are identified and authorised. This can be achieved by a system of issuing security passes, preferably organised by shore authorities, to control access to the entire port area. These should show the name and occupation of the bearer, and ideally contain a photograph and also an expiry date/time. The ship's operator can help by insisting that all stevedores carry an identity card issued by their employers.

Even a simple ship's pass can be quite effective where no shore system is available. A card marked with the ship's official stamp is issued to anyone who has legitimate business on board the ship. It is useful if this pass is exchanged for a valuable personal document, which then is returned to the visitor when he disembarks and surrenders the ship's pass. If someone arrives at the gangway without a pass, the crew watchman must be instructed to call the OOW, who can then issue temporary passes to bona-fide visitors.

In order to protect the ship's personnel, no-one should be permitted to enter the accommodation block unless they are accompanied by a member of the crew, or have been granted special permission which can be readily verified by the gangway watchman.

16.1.2 Discipline of locking[6]

Every space on board ship which is kept locked in port reduces the places which can be used to hide stowaways, contraband or drugs, and from which goods can be stolen. It limits the scope for sabotage. Though a lock is not an absolute barrier against a determined assault, it is effective against most criminal visitors who would not like their actions to be detected immediately.

There is often a natural reluctance to keep locking doors on a ship, and unless there is firm supervision by the OOW on his regular patrols, they will be left open. The standard of locking on a ship is directly related to the standards of discipline on board the ship.

16.1.3 IMO guidelines to prevent unlawful acts[38]

Whilst the measures contained in this IMO document are intended for application to passenger ships, certain measures may be appropriate to other ships. The shipowner has to appoint a security officer, who will develop and maintain a ship security plan. This is implemented on board by a ship security officer, who is usually a nominated senior officer. The system is to be checked by annual ship security surveys.

The guidelines recognise that security in port is principally the responsibility of the port authority, who has to appoint a port security officer and implement a port security plan.

The guidelines recommend that access to certain areas of the ship is denied to unauthorised persons; this can normally be achieved by the careful and methodical use of door locks. The restricted areas are the bridge, radio room, engine control room and steering flat.

16.1.4 Use of firearms

The Nautical Institute strongly opposes the use of firearms by the OOW in order to protect the ship and its personnel. First, it is inevitable that if the ship uses firearms, then others will too, greatly increasing the risk of injury or death of ships staff. Secondly, if a local citizen is injured or killed by ship's staff, the ship and the person responsible may be arrested. This may lead to great expenses for the shipowner, and imprisonment or maybe execution of the seafarer involved.

16.1.5 Further guidance

If the reader serves on passenger ships, or seeks further detailed information on security measures, he should consult The Nautical Institute publication *Security at Sea.*[6]

16.2 Commercial security

Some unwelcome visitors are not criminals, but persons seeking information from the ship, which may well be to the detriment of the shipowner. Surveyors and other officials may be representing cargo owners, charterers or private individuals—for example lawyers engaged by an injured party. Such visitors should be treated courteously, and taken to the Master or Chief Officer. If a senior officer is not available, then the OOW must deny access to the vessel for such visitors.

<u>It is essential the OOW must not allow them to wander around the ship, take photographs or interview any of the ship's crew.</u>

The OOW should always be careful what he says to unidentified visitors, as many an innocent remark has later been quoted in Court, much to his embarrassment! He must never make statements to the Press. He should be cautious of surveyors who claim to be acting for the ship, but who have not first been to see the Master or Chief Officer; it is likely that such visitors are not being entirely truthful. Surveyors taking photographs for other parties must always be accompanied by a surveyor acting for the shipowner, who can ensure that photographs are taken which are representative of the entire stow, or area, and such evidence is not limited to compositions which exaggerate any damage, are unrepresentative, or otherwise present a biased or blinkered picture.

16.3 Unauthorised visitors

Unauthorised visitors such as persistent casual traders and opportunist businessmen are generally no more than a nuisance. However, some visitors with innocent purposes may engage in other activities which will lead to problems for the ship's staff, and financial loss to the ship's operator. They may turn to theft, drug planting, sabotage or stowaway. Also they can provide information to others on ship's security arrangements, the layout of accommodation, stores and hold accesses, and the location of keys, valuable items, and suitable hiding or storage places. Hawkers and traders should be told to set up their shops ashore.

Those 'businessmen' wanting to make purchases from the ship, and others offering to exchange money at black-market rates, should not be permitted on board. They are likely to bring problems to both the ship and its crew, and sometimes they operate in association with Customs officers, who subsequently board the ship to arrest the participants in the illegal trade. There have been cases of prostitutes planting drugs on board the ship, which are then found when a team of Customs 'suddenly' appear. The same could apply to a whole range of goods banned by certain countries. One Master was even taken before a court and fined for 'running a place of ill repute' when police found prostitutes on board his ship. With the prevalence of sexually transmitted diseases in many ports, the OOW should not allow these people on board in the interests of protecting the health of the crew.

16.4 Thieves

If the ship's security is lax, then opportunists may steal cargo, ship's stores and equipment, or crew personal effects. This may be undertaken by people who have some other legitimate reason for being on board, for example stevedores, in addition to those casual visitors discussed previously.

16.4.1 Preventive action

1. Restrict access to the ship to authorised persons.
2. Restrict access to the accommodation to one door close to the gangway, and under the supervision of the crew watchman.
3. Keep all doors locked whilst they are not being used—for example, stores, workshops, cabins, public rooms, stair wells, hold accesses, etc., including external doors to the steering flat and engineroom.
4. Keep all nonworking hatches closed, with their accesses securely locked and any side ports closed.
5. Lock away easily stolen items such as lifeboat equipment, and avoid tempting a thief by leaving items on display and/or unattended, which can be removed from the vessel with little effort.
6. Employ security personnel in the cargo holds if necessary. Crew can be used if numbers permit and shore security is suspect.
7. If thieving is rampant, employ the anti-piracy measures in section 16.5.1

16.4.2 Insurance advice

The OOW should consider taking out his own insurance for his personal effects with a reliable company. He should ensure that the terms of the policy cover all the risks associated with his position, taking into account he will be travelling around the world for an extended period, and recognise the practical problems of passing on relevant documentation and the difficulty of reporting to the police.

16.5 Piracy

The term piracy has been used to mean a concerted attack by a team of robbers, who may be armed, to differentiate this from 'thefts' from the ship by individuals who may have some other legitimate presence on board.

These attacks may occur anywhere in the world, and the OOW should remain alert wherever the ship is trading, not just in those regions which the press reports are the current hot-spots. They may occur whilst the ship is at sea, at anchor off a port, or at an anchorage or berthed within the port. Some owners encourage their ships not to anchor off ports known for piracy, but to drift well offshore, possibly blacked out, to discourage detection. For this publication, advice is limited to the inport situation. Pirate attacks are normally, but not always, made at night.

16.5.1 Preventive action

1. Ship's crew should be informed of the risks, and placed on alert. All the antitheft measures detailed in section 16.4.1 should be employed.

2. A full live officer watch must be maintained when cargo is not being worked. 'Live' means awake, available, appropriately dressed and equipped, closely supervising the crew patrols and ensuring that all the other precautions outlined in this section are efficiently maintained.

3. The crew should patrol all areas of the vessel in pairs, if numbers permit, and remain in radio contact with the OOW. They should make random rather than predictable patrols. This should be done with a high profile, making lots of noise, using long-range beam torches or lamps at night, to show potential pirates that this vessel is alert and vigilant. Hopefully they may move on to an easier target. Close attention should be paid to the ship's side when it is level with the quay—potential criminals could simply step on board anywhere on deck.

4. The gangway must be manned at all times by ship's personnel in radio contact with the OOW, whenever cargo is being worked.

5. It is recommended that the gangway, and any ramps, are raised level whenever cargo is not being worked, and lowered ONLY under the authority of the OOW for bona-fide reasons.

6. All decks and both quay and offshore sides of the vessel must be well illuminated at night. Searchlights should be used to sweep the water surrounding the ship, both to identify small boats and warn of the vessel's alertness. The aldis lamp is useful for this.

7. Remove all portable equipment from the deck when not in use.

8. Stow containers door-to-door whenever possible. Stow containers of valuable cargo in the most inaccessible positions.

9. All external accommodation doors should be kept locked, except for the one next to the manned gangway. Keys should be provided either on internal hooks, or preferably issued to all ship's staff, for safety reasons to aid escape in case of fire or other emergency.

10. All means of access to the ship should be sealed off—hawse pipes covered, large ratguards securely fitted to mooring lines, no ladders left dangling overside, no windows or portholes left open.

11. Deck hoses should be rigged to ward off pirates approaching in boats. They should be located at key points, though their number is restricted by the capacity of the fire pump to provide adequate pressure to several hoses.

12. The Master will have considered employing extra shore watchmen after discussing their value with the ship's agent. Sometimes these guards can identify known attackers before they board. In some ports, employing local security may help prevent attack, as this appears to 'buy' protection. In other ports, shore security personnel may aid the attackers.

13. Prohibit all unnecessary and unauthorised visitors to the ship. Traders and prostitutes can give information to pirates.

14. Have signalling equipment available for immediate use. This includes the ship's foghorns—air, electric and hand, aldis lamps, and personal police thunder-ball type whistles. These can be used both to raise the alarm, and scare off the attackers.

15. Practice antipiracy drills.

16. Log details of all preventative measures taken.

16.5.2 Action if attacked

1. Sound the ship's general alarm, to rouse all crew, and maybe frighten off the pirates. Training the aldis lamp on any pirate boats lets them know they have been spotted, and may discourage them from continuing with their attack.

2. Activate any other alarms and sirens, including the ship's whistle.

3. Turn on fire pump to pressurise the fire hoses, and use these to try to prevent pirates from boarding the ship from boats, or the shore.

4. If this discouragement is not successful, then the attempt should be abandoned in sufficient time to enable all ship's staff to retire to the accommodation in safety, and secure all accesses. (Preferably retire to an area which can be completely sealed)

5. Once they have boarded the ship, DO NOT CONFRONT PIRATES, as this may lead to physical attack. Ship's crews have been murdered by pirates in regions of the world where little value is placed on human life. There is absolutely no case for risking life to protect property. In general pirates will not resort to violence unless provoked. *Survive with honour.*

6. Call for assistance from ashore by VHF, or telephone if available.

7. Try to remember any distinguishing features of the assailants, to assist police ashore with identification.

8. The Master should report all incidents to the owners, the flag State and the International Maritime Bureau in addition to the local authorities.

16.6 Stowaways

Most people stow away on board ship in order to escape from their country of origin for political or, more usually in recent years, economic reasons. They become illegal immigrants and economic migrants, or asylum seekers and refugees. Often such stowaways do not have any means of identification, and pose a substantial problem in finding a country willing to accept them.

Occasionally stowaways are looking for free transport to a place they wish to visit or to be reunited with family or friends. There have been rare incidents of people stowing away just for the adventure, or even to accompany a 'loved' member of the crew! Such stowaways usually have full identification and pose little trouble to repatriate. Another danger is that stowaways are accompanying a consignment of illegal drugs—see chapter 16.7.

16.6.1 Increase in stowaways

The number of stowaways has increased rapidly in recent years, mainly due to advances in communications. People in poor countries have their aspirations increased by coming face to face with the lifestyles of people in the more developed countries on worldwide television. Also, the growing number of conflicts around the world is producing a growing number of refugees.

Many countries who were once sympathetic to immigrants are now imposing strict controls, and ships with stowaways are facing increasing problems with landing these people, the costs of which are escalating. It has been estimated that the total cost of stowaways to the industry is in excess of $5 million per annum.[7]

16.6.2 Costs of stowaways

1. Feeding and looking after the welfare of the stowaway, including medical expenses and perhaps providing adequate clothing.
2. Crew overtime for extra security duties.
3. Communications expenses.
4. Security costs, high in ports which require a round the clock armed shore guard to prevent the stowaway from slipping ashore.
5. Accommodation expenses, particularly ashore with extra security.
6. Legal costs of establishing the identity, nationality, etc., of a stowaway who has no papers.
7. Employment of translators.
8. Extra safety equipment purchased, if the number of stowaways plus crew exceeds the limits of current equipment or certification.
9. Fines in future ports of call.
10. Repatriation costs, including accompanying security escorts.
11. Port expenses if a special call has to be made for disembarkation.
12. Administration of all of the above.

There are even higher costs should the stowaways seek political asylum in countries such as the USA. There the immigration service has held the shipowner liable for hotel, medical and food expenses, as well as the costs of employing armed guards and interpreters. This can continue for a prolonged period due to the length of appeals in the asylum process. A recent case cost the shipowner $125,000.[28] Fourteen stowaways from Zaire were repatriated from Portugal recently at a cost to the shipowner of $126,000.[22]

16.6.3 Preventive measures

1. Employ all relevant antipiracy measures listed in section 16.5.1, particularly in ports known for a high risk of stowaways.
2. Remain alert for stowaways posing as bona-fide visitors, or even these visitors becoming stowaways (e.g., stevedores).
3. Issuing a ship's pass in exchange for some valuable document, such as a driving licence, credit card or employment papers, which are returned when disembarking, may be fairly simple but very effective.
4. It is useful for the OOW or gangway watchman to count heads on and off, particularly at the change of shift. The OOW should ask the foreman stevedore how many men are working on board, and check this figure against the gangway tally.
5. In some ports, any crew from the region may be able to recognise the nationality of those boarding the vessel; anyone not a national of the country in which the ship is berthed should be denied access unless they possess clear identification.
6. OOW should thoroughly search each cargo compartment upon completion of cargo operations, and then seal or lock the exit. If numbers permit, he should be assisted by another crew member, and keep in radio contact with the Chief Officer. He must have a suitably bright handlamp.
7. Keep everywhere locked or sealed. The more places which are secured the fewer places there are available in which a stowaway can hide.
8. Use false destination boards, advertising that the ship will be sailing to a port considered unattractive to potential stowaways. Some Masters advise not displaying a destination port at all, to prevent unnecessary discussions amongst the locals.
9. Offer incentives in high risk ports:
   - A bonus to the crew if they find a stowaway.
   - Reward the crew, agent, or local security if no stowaways appear.
10. It is not unknown for the ship's crew to assist stowaways, hence a detailed search of the accommodation should be made prior to departure from each port. This may need to be carried out sensitively, with each crew member, or an appropriate representative, present when his cabin is inspected. Lockers and recreational spaces should not be overlooked.
11. Log details of all extra stowaway preventive measures.

16.6.4 Stowaway searches

A full search of all parts of the vessel should be made before the ship leaves port. This is in addition to the routine searches of cargo compartments as they are completed. Time limitations may mean that a number of search teams each led by an officer take part in this search. A checklist should be used to ensure that no parts of the ship are overlooked, including all the accommodation, even areas which have apparently remained locked throughout the vessel's stay in port. The stowaway search should always be logged.

If cargo operations, or other activities, continue right up to the moment of departure, the vessel can be held up at standby whilst the search is undertaken. If the shore authorities do not permit this, then the search must be undertaken as soon as the vessel clears the quay. This will give sufficient time for any stowaways found to be landed before the ship leaves the port limits.

The OOW conducting the search should bear in mind that stowaways may be desperate to escape, and hence should be on guard against attack. They are often very cunning, and have been found in such places as bilges (under the water level), under bedboards, inside ventilators, at the top of masts, as well as the more usual hiding places inside covered lifeboats, funnels, stores, holds, chain lockers and hawsepipes, buried amidst the cargo and, ever increasingly, inside containers. In some ports where stowaways are a known major problem, the owner or charterer may employ special squads of searchers to assist the ship with the stowaway search just prior to departure. When such assistance is employed, each squad should be accompanied by a ship's officer.

Container security is a problem best tackled ashore, by increased patrols, extra sealing of containers, and preloading examination of all empty containers. This cannot eradicate the problem of complicity of shore officials, or stowaways entering containers before reaching port. The OOW can usefully supplement this security by checking the seals are intact on all loaded containers. Open-top or soft-top containers, or unsealed (empty) containers should be internally examined. It is reported that a carbon dioxide detector is very effective in detecting human presence.

16.6.5 Flushing out stowaways

The ship should consider ways to flush out stowaways at known high risk ports, or if intelligence reveals their presence.
1. Hammering steel, shrill whistles or other annoyingly loud noise.
2. High pressure water hoses.
3. Non-toxic smoke bombs, compressed air from CO_2 lines, and other 'frighteners'. It must be stressed that the stowaways must not be injured by such methods, otherwise the ship's staff involved may be prosecuted.
4. Use of psychology:
   - Calling to a 'known' stowaway,
   - Shouting that the compartment is about to be fumigated,
   - Announcing a fire, and ringing fire-alarms.
   - Offering asylum, cash and other 'bluff' inducements.

16.6.6 Action on finding a stowaway

1. If he has boarded in the present port, chase him ashore.
2. Search the area again for any accomplices—merely asking the stowaway if he is alone may not produce a truthful response.
3. Act firmly, but humanely. There have been cases of stowaways seeking compensation for poor treatment. Adverse treatment may also attract adverse publicity, to the detriment of the shipowner.
4. Hold him in a secure place, and remove all papers, valuables, cash, and anything that could be used to inflict injury. Ensure that any furnishings and fittings in the lockup cannot be misused for breaking out or injuring visiting personnel.
5. Separate numerous stowaways if possible.
6. Establish his identity, he may be reluctant to divulge details. Search his clothing, possessions and the area where he was found. The golden rule

is to retain all documentation.
7. Inform Master, who will then inform the owner and their P&I Club.

16.6.7 Further information

The Nautical Institute publication *Stowaways by Sea* provides a wealth of background information on the problems of stowaways.[7] It describes the reasons for the large increase in international migration in recent years, the organisation of stowaway rings by criminals, and the changes in both international immigration laws and attitudes. The position of those seeking political asylum is explained, and the relevance of human rights conventions to stowaways is discussed. There are plenty of case-study examples, and there is a questionnaire which would be useful in establishing a stowaway's identity.

16.7 Drugs

Ships are frequently used by criminals to transport drugs from suppliers to users. On most occasions the ship's staff have no knowledge that this is being done, but sometimes they take an active or a passive role. The OOW must always be on the lookout for suspicious behaviour, unauthorised visitors, unexpected activities and packages in unusual locations.

16.7.1 Risk of drug trafficking

There are no 'safe' trade routes. The risk of drugs being brought on board exists in all ports, as increasingly drugs are moving around the world from suppliers to users via some very roundabout and circuitous routes.

Drugs can be hidden in any number of places on board ship, and some very ingenious locations have been used in the past. General areas include:
(a) Inside tanks, cargo holds, void spaces, store rooms and cabins.
(b) Within parts of the ship's structure (behind panels, etc.).
(c) Inside machinery, inside individual items of stores, spares or victuals, and inside units of cargo or its packaging.
(d) In false compartments of the ship and containers of cargo or stores.
(e) Areas unlikely to be searched due to danger or difficult access, or even respect (the Master's pillow was used on one ship!).
(f) Where they may not appear out of place—e.g., stored with medicines.

16.7.2 Port security

Adequate security is essential for both discouragement and detection. Unauthorised personnel should be denied access to the ship, and all legitimate personnel should carry identification. Every package arriving on board should be scrutinised, including stores, spares, personal effects and items being returned after servicing or repair. *Security measures inevitably become a compromise between what is desirable and what is practicable.*[80]

Drug traffickers will generally carry out a reconnaissance of potential smuggling opportunities. An insecure vessel or cargo compound is more likely to be targeted than an obviously protected one, and smugglers will be deterred by visible security arrangements. It is therefore of great importance that security precautions are seen to be effective at all times. **The greatest deterrent to a potential smuggler is the obvious awareness of the threat by shorebased and seagoing staff.**[80]

In high risk areas, all the security measures outlined in section 16.6.3 should be taken, and additionally the OOW and duty seaman should be on the lookout for small craft, divers and swimmers approaching the ship. It is becoming increasingly common for major consignments of drugs to be attached to the underwater sections of the ship's hull. The OOW should be aware that the high street value of drugs ($200,000 per kilo for heroin and cocaine) attracts the attention of major international professional criminals, who may use instant and extremely violent tactics to avoid being discovered. Due precautions should always be taken.

There is a duty on shipowners to behave responsibly and to take all possible steps to prevent the smuggling of drugs on board their ships.[26] Under the US Anti-Drug Abuse Act enormous penalties may be imposed on the shipowner if prohibited drugs are found on board or in the cargo. Recently, a fine of over $100 million was imposed for drugs found inside a container.[25] The act also gives the authorities powers to seize the vessel.

16.7.3 Sea Carrier Initiative Agreement (SCIA)

Many shipowners have signed the *Sea Carrier Initiative Agreement*[81] with the US Customs. Besides the natural desire to discourage the use of their ships for the transportation of illegal drugs, the full implementation of the agreement by the shipowner should influence the authorities favourably when determining the level of fines if ever any drugs are found on board their ships.

Clause 8 of this agreement states that: *the Master and officers will:*

(a) *Take all reasonable measures to enhance security and control procedures in order to make it more difficult for unauthorised persons to gain access to vessels.*

(b) *Permit only persons displaying proper identity access to the ship.*

(c) *Regularly search vessels for illegal drugs prior to departure for, and en route to the USA, (and by implication, all destinations).*

(d) *Lock or seal specific compartments on board ship which may be used to conceal illegal drugs where such locking will not interfere with normal vessel operations or pose a possible safety hazard.*

(e) *For those areas which cannot be sealed or locked, limit access to those persons with legitimate business in such areas.*

P&I cover may be withheld if the SCIA is not followed.[26]

In addition, the International Chamber of Shipping (ICS), representing most shipowners, and the Customs Co-operation Council (CCC) have signed a *Memorandum of Understanding** to promote

awareness, increase co-operation and encourage security measures (including access control within the port and on board ship) without imposing excessive restrictions on legitimate trade.

* The full text is reproduced in *Drug Trafficking and Drug Abuse.*[80]

16.7.4 Contribution of the OOW[80]

It is recommended that all officers should have adequate knowledge of:
1. Ship security plans and related emergency procedures.
2. Detailed layout of the ship, and internal and external accesses.
3. The assessment of risk, threat and vulnerability.
4. Methods of conducting security inspections and physical searches.
5. Techniques used to circumvent security measures.
6. Recognition of characteristics and behavioural patterns of persons who may be likely to commit unlawful acts.
7. Techniques for detecting and recognising illicit substances.

16.7.5 Suspicious circumstances[9,80]

The OOW should seek an explanation if he notices:
1. Unauthorised visitors anywhere on board.
2. Unauthorised activities or unnecessary work by shore people.
3. Shore personnel or crew in unusual places without reason.
4. Items stowed in unusual locations.
5. Unnecessary structural alterations or new additions.
6. Evidence of tampering—tank tops, manholes, covers, doors, etc.
7. Minor damage such as chipped or disturbed paintwork, especially on the heads of screws or bolts. (Clean screws or bolts on an otherwise dirty or greasy fitting should also be treated suspiciously.)
8. Missing keys, or security arrangements violated.
9. Unexplained failure of machinery.
10. Strange odours—many drugs have characteristic smells.

16.7.6 Crew problems

In some parts of the world, taking drugs is as common as taking an alcoholic drink in other countries. Although the OOW may have some understanding of crew who have drugs for personal use, he must remember that they can cause problems for the ship in ports where the penalties for possession of even the smallest amount of drugs are severe.

It is more serious when the crew become engaged as couriers for drug traffickers. It is not unusual for a courier to be protected by one or two 'minders', whose identity is not always known to the courier. Their job is to ensure the courier delivers the consignment. If the OOW suspects crew involvement with drugs, he should never tackle the people concerned directly, but must always report his suspicions directly to the Master.

Some signs to look out for include:

(a) Nervous behaviour or acting suspiciously.
(b) Possessing large amounts of cash or expensive new purchases.
(c) Bulky and/or unusual clothing, particularly when going ashore or returning to the vessel.
(d) Unusual interest in a particular area of the ship.
(e) Possession of tools or equipment not connected with their job.

All officers should be thoroughly familiar with the drug and alcohol policy in force on board their ship.

16.7.7 Action if drugs are found[80]

1. Get another officer to witness the find.
2. Take photographs of the goods and the area.
3. Do not open suspicious packages.
4. Do not handle unknown substances—some drugs can be absorbed through the skin with severe or even fatal consequences.
5. Do not inhale powders, fumes or vapours.
6. Do not taste, eat or drink any suspect substances.
7. Do not smoke, or expose the goods to heat.
8. If possible, avoid handling the package or other parts of the area, in order to preserve any fingerprints or other evidence.
9. Establish a security guard, only move the goods to a secure place as a last resort in exceptional circumstances.
10. Inform the Master, or other senior officer, who will notify the proper authorities ashore.
11. Do not allow anyone to leave the vessel until these authorities arrive. However, the ICS/CCC Memorandum states that *shipping companies should not be asked to act as law enforcement entities nor their employees asked to exercise police powers.*[80]
12. Always wash hands and clean clothing of any contamination as soon as possible.
13. Write a report as soon as possible, and also make an entry in the log.

16.7.8 Further information

Full guidance on methods and procedures to be employed in preventing the vessel being used for the transportation of illegal drugs are contained in the *Sea Carrier Security Manual*[81] which should be on board every ship covered by the SCIA. This document has sections which deal with drug smuggling aboard vessels, in break-bulk cargo, and in containers. Advice is given on how to conduct searches, with tips on common areas of drug concealment, and behaviour patterns of both drug smugglers and drug users. The OOW should ensure that he is fully familiar with the contents of this manual.

Drug Trafficking and Drug Abuse[80] issued by the International Chamber of Shipping describes the specific properties of the various drugs including how to identify the drugs and detect their users. It contains much useful information on drug addiction and the characteristics and identification of common drugs. There is practical advice on security measures and the organisation of detection searches. Anti-drug smuggling protection measures are discussed in The Nautical Institute publication *Security at Sea.*[6]

16.8 Terrorists

If the vessel is subjected to a terrorist attack, the assailants are likely to be politically motivated, highly strung and charged up with adrenaline. Once the OOW has determined that an incident is a terrorist attack, and not a ruse by a drunken or drugged individual, it makes overwhelmingly good sense to fully comply with the orders given by the terrorists. **They MUST NEVER be resisted**, no matter how strong is the natural reaction of the OOW to prevent these people from taking over his ship. The OOW who identifies such an attack must consider carefully the consequences of his natural instinct to raise the alarm in case this action is misinterpreted by the assailants.[6]

Some terrorist organisations may seek publicity for their causes by planting bombs on ships they determine to be 'hostile'; such reasons may be quite remote and obscure. During periods of international tension, the OOW should be on the alert for suspicious parcels, and if he notices some unexplained 'cargo' he should inform the Chief Officer or Master immediately. Under no circumstances should he move or even touch any suspicious item. Advice on action to be taken if the ship is taken over by force, and information relating to sabotage, and bomb scares is contained in The Nautical Institute publication *Security at Sea.*[6]

16.9 Corruption

In some ports, poorly paid officials may take the opportunity to boost their income from fines and other penalties imposed on the ship. On a lower level, this can take the form of requesting presents to overlook certain 'infringements'; on a higher level, the officials may receive a percentage of huge fines imposed for breach of often quite obscure regulations.

Some examples of these are:

1. The presence on board of undeclared 'banned' goods. The ship's agent may be able to help in identifying those items which may be common in the ship's stores but can cause problems with officials.
2. Local flag etiquette not followed to the letter, for example if the courtesy ensign is allowed to touch the deck, or any flags are left up or not hoisted at exactly the appropriate hour. The OOW should ask the Chief Officer if the port is known for such practices, and ensure that the duty seaman raises and lowers the flags at the appropriate time.
3. Miscellaneous unsafe practices—for example if the gangway net is taken in just too soon before stand-by (five minutes in one report).
4. Breach of local rules—for example, no female visitors permitted on board foreign ships.
5. A drug dealer came on board a ship and left some 'free samples' for the crew. A police officer boarded shortly after, and 'found' the drugs.[22]
6. There have been cases where traders and prostitutes have hidden drugs on board a ship, which were found during a Customs raid later. It is known that the person planting the drugs received a percentage of the subsequent fine on the ship.

7. Traders who purchase scrap, alcohol and pornography may work in association with Customs officials, who impose large fines on the ship when the participants are 'caught'.

The OOW must remain alert to goods being removed from the ship, and he should instruct the gangway watchman that nothing must be removed from the ship unless an official pass has been issued. On some ships the issuing of such passes is controlled by a senior officer, on others this is delegated to the OOW. In such cases, the OOW must be very sure of the legality of the removal before he issues a pass. Where these are personal property of the crew, he should verify that taking these goods ashore could not be construed as smuggling. Where such goods are ship's property, such as scrap, items for repair or stores being landed, he should verify with a senior officer that permission has been granted for this disposal/removal.

The OOW should ensure that any official boarding the ship is sent straight to the Master, or another officer if appropriate, and must NEVER be allowed to wander around the ship unaccompanied. In ports where corruption is endemic, he should be alert when dealing with even minor officials. There have been incidents where an official has boarded the vessel and pointed out some minor infringement to the OOW. The official has intimated that a small 'present' will enable him to 'forget' the incident, instead of imposing a huge fine. The well-meaning OOW who complies with this request may be subsequently charged with attempted bribery! Also, there is a general understanding that piracy is an activity practised in poor countries where there is corruption and where the forces of law and order do not exist or are corrupt as well.[6]

16.10 Future of security

As ship's crews become increasingly small in number, it will be extremely difficult to undertake many of the security measures discussed in this chapter. The ship should rightly be able to rely on the port security measures—if no unauthorised people are permitted into the port area, there is much less risk of the ship being boarded by people with criminal intent as discussed in this chapter. However, there will always be ports where security is not tight, and the ship will still have to rely on her own measures. There is a whole range of high-tech equipment available to assist the OOW, and it is to be hoped that the prudent shipowner will install some of these devices on new tonnage. Some examples are:

1. Electronic barriers/fences. An alarm is raised whenever anyone crosses the ship's side, or strays into an unauthorised area or deck.
2. Surveillance systems. High sensitivity cameras, preferably linked to a video recorder.
3. Detection systems. Infra red, acoustic, pressure and movement detectors. An alarm is raised whenever someone attempts to enter an unauthorised area, selective switching enables the relevant parts of the ship to be protected whilst permitting access to working areas.
4. Smart keys. Doors and accesses will open and close automatically when a person wearing an identity card approaches. More advanced systems can recognise an authorised person's finger, palm or eyeball patterns. Less advanced systems require a code to be keyed in for access.
5. Improved design. Ships can be made more secure at the design stage. A useful innovation is to have the gangway leading directly onto the main deck, with the only access to the accommodation block being through a common office. Lockable gates may be installed adjacent to the gangway to prevent unauthorised persons gaining access to the accommodation block by directing them straight onto the main deck and cargo hatches.

In all circumstances, prevention is better than cure, and one cannot over-emphasise strict adherence to the golden rule:

NO UNAUTHORISED VISITORS PERMITTED ON BOARD.

If cargo is insufficiently secured, the stow may collapse during adverse weather on the voyage, as these containers illustrate. See chapter 17.
Photograph: author.

Chapter 17

SECURING THE CARGO

PURPOSE

On completion of this chapter you will be able to list the methods used to secure the cargo, and understand why this is necessary. You will be capable of supervising the lashing operation and checking the adequacy of the arrangements made for securing the cargo.

17.1 Importance of securing the cargo

Cargo is loaded into a ship whilst it is floating steady in the water, and upright, with a reasonable trim. When the ship puts to sea, it is subjected to external forces which result in six modes of motion—see section 17.3. Cargo stowed on deck is also exposed to the forces of wind, and of seas breaking on deck. If the cargo is insufficiently secured, it may move. This may cause it to be damaged, or cause damage to other cargo or to the ship's structure and fittings. Cargo stowed on deck with insufficient lashings may be lost overside in adverse weather. All cargo which moves could endanger the ship; if it pierces the hull, the ship may founder.

17.2 Causes of loss or damage[5]

1. Severe adverse weather conditions.
2. Lack of appreciation of the various forces involved.
3. Ignorance of relevant rules and guiding recommendations.
4. Cost limitation pressures.
5. Insufficient time and personnel to complete the securing of all cargo before departure.
6. Dunnage not utilised in an effective manner.
7. Inadequate strength, balance and/or number of lashings.
8. Wire loops and eyes made up wrongly, incorrect use of bulldog grips.*
9. Lack of strength continuity between the various securing components.
10. Taking lashing material round sharp edges, which causes them to part.
11. Incorrect or unbalanced stowage and inadequate weight distribution.
12. Perversity of shore labour when required to do the job properly!

*Bulldog grips must be fitted with the bridge applied to the working part of the rope, and the U-bolt round the standing part or tail, as shown in the diagrams. They should be adequately greased, and tightened so that the standing part of the wire is visibly compressed.[54] Grips should be placed a distance apart equal to six times the diameter of the wire used, and the minimum number of grips to use is: three for wires up to 20 mm. diameter, four for wires up to 32 mm. diameter, five for wires up to 38 mm. diameter.

17.3 Ship's motion in a seaway

Ships move through the water propelled by their engines. They are also moved by the action of the sea in the following ways:

Transverse motion	Longitudinal motion	Vertical motion
(a) Roll.	(a) Pitch.	(a) Heave.
(b) Yaw.	(b) Surge.	(b) Pitch.
(c) Sway.	(c) Yaw.	(c) Roll.

Roll, pitch and yaw are rotational motions. Surge, sway and pitch are linear motions.

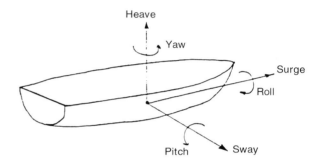

17.4 IMO Guidelines

The general principles from the IMO *Code of Safe Practice for Cargo Stowage and Securing*[54] are listed in chapter 7.8.1.

17.4.1 Criteria for estimating the risk of cargo shifting

Clause 1.5 states *When estimating the risk of cargo shifting, the following should be considered:*
1. *Dimensional and physical properties of the cargo.*
2. *Location of the cargo and its stowage on board.*
3. *Suitability of the ship for the particular cargo.*
4. *Suitability of the securing arrangements for the particular cargo.*
5. *Expected seasonal weather and sea conditions.*
6. *Expected ship behaviour during the intended voyage.*
7. *Stability of the ship.*
8. *Geographical area of the voyage.*
9. *Duration of the voyage.*

These criteria should be taken into account when selecting suitable stowage and securing methods and whenever reviewing the forces to be absorbed by the securing equipment. Bearing in mind the above criteria, the Master should accept the cargo on board his ship only if he is satisfied that it can be safely transported.

17.4.2 Cargo securing manual

Clause 1.6 states that all ships carrying cargo in units, which includes a container, flat, pallet, vehicle,

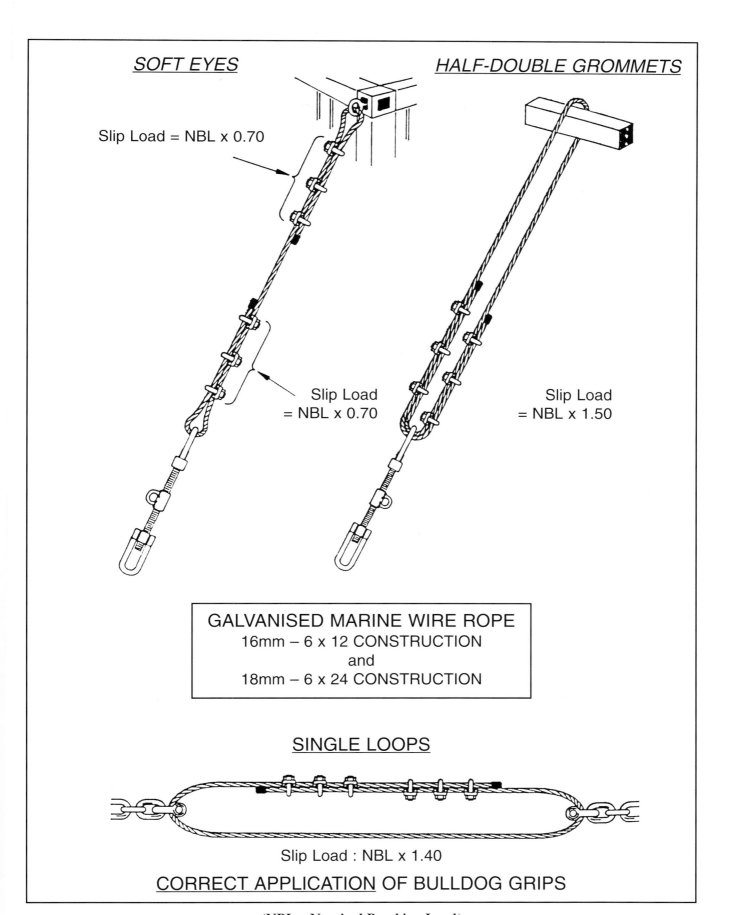

SOFT EYES

Slip Load = NBL x 0.70

Slip Load
= NBL x 0.70

HALF-DOUBLE GROMMETS

Slip Load
= NBL x 1.50

GALVANISED MARINE WIRE ROPE
16mm – 6 x 12 CONSTRUCTION
and
18mm – 6 x 24 CONSTRUCTION

SINGLE LOOPS

Slip Load : NBL x 1.40

CORRECT APPLICATION OF BULLDOG GRIPS

(NBL = Nominal Breaking Load)

Reproduced from The Nautical Institute publication
The Lashing and Securing of Deck Cargoes.[2]

portable tank, packaged unit or any other entity, should carry a cargo securing manual.

The preamble to the rules states: *it is important that the officers on board are fully aware of the correct application, use and limitations* (of the securing gear), *and the order of the forces involved. The crew and other persons employed for the securing of cargoes should also be instructed in the correct application and use of the cargo securing gear on board the ship.*

The cargo securing manual specifies the securing gear provided on board and its correct application. A sufficient reserve quantity has to be provided. Information on the safe working load of each item is given, with details of any maintenance required. The contents of each chapter of the manual is listed to ensure international uniformity:

CHAPTER 1: DETAILS OF FIXED CARGO SECURING ARRANGEMENTS AND THEIR LOCATION, including their type and strength.
(1) On bulkheads and frames (e.g., padeyes, eyebolts).
(2) On decks (e.g., elephants feet, container fittings.)
(3) On deckheads (e.g., padeyes).

CHAPTER 2: LOCATION AND STOWAGE OF PORTABLE CARGO SECURING GEAR.

CHAPTER 3: DETAILS OF PORTABLE CARGO SECURING GEAR, inventory of items provided, including their strength and use.
(1) Container stacking and interlocking fittings, bridge-fittings.
(2) Chains, wire ropes, rods.
(3) Tensioners, turnbuckles.
(4) Securing gear for cars and other vehicles.
(5) Trestles and jacks, for vehicle trailers.
(6) Anti-skid material.

CHAPTER 4: CORRECT APPLICATION OF PORTABLE SECURING GEAR ON VARIOUS CARGO UNITS, VEHICLES AND OTHER ENTITIES.

The text should be supplemented by suitable drawings and sketches to facilitate the correct understanding and proper application of the gear to various types of cargo and units.

CHAPTER 5: INDICATION OF THE MAGNITUDE OF FORCES EXPECTED TO ACT ON CARGO UNITS IN VARIOUS POSITIONS ONBOARD THE SHIP.
(1) Tables or diagrams giving a broad outline of the accelerations which can be experienced in various positions on board the ship in adverse sea conditions.
(2) Examples of the forces acting on typical cargo units when subjected to these accelerations.
(3) Examples of the number and strength of portable securings required to counteract these forces.

17.4.3 Cargo securing equipment

Clause 1.7 states *The ship's cargo securing equipment should be: available in sufficient quantity; suitable for its intended purpose; of adequate strength; easy to use; well maintained.*

17.4.4 Cargo securing arrangements

Clause 2.3 states *Particular care should be taken to distribute the forces as evenly as practicable between the cargo securing devices. If this is not feasible, the arrangements should be upgraded. If, due to the complex structure of a securing arrangement or other circumstances, the person in charge is unable to assess the suitability of the arrangement from experience and knowledge of good seamanship, the arrangement should be verified by using an acceptable calculation method.*

Specific guidance is given in the annexes of the code for the stowage and securing of :-

Annex 1	Containers on deck.
Annex 2	Portable tanks.
Annex 3	Portable receptacles.
Annex 4	Wheel based cargoes.
Annex 5	Heavy items.
Annex 6	Coiled steel sheet.
Annex 7	Heavy metal products.
Annex 8	Anchor chains.
Annex 9	Metal scrap in bulk.
Annex 10	Flexible intermediate bulk containers (FIBC) ('Jumbo bags').
Annex 11	Underdeck stowage of logs.
Annex 12	Unit loads.

The OOW should read any annex which is applicable to the cargo carried on a particular voyage, and ensure that the relevant lashing requirements are undertaken. If he does not understand any of the requirements, he should seek the advice of the Chief Officer or Master.

17.5 Types of cargo securing arrangements

1. **Lashing.** Rope, wire, webbing, banding, strapping or chain. Tightened with bottlescrews, or other patent tensioning devices. (Lashing is often used to describe all securing arrangements.)
2. **Tomming.** Constructing a framework of square-section softwood, to chock off the cargo against ship's structure or other cargo.
3. **Filling.** Use of air bags, empty pallets, old tyres, etc. to fill the voids between items of cargo, and between cargo and the ship's structure.
4. **Anti-skid.** Flat boards used to increase friction.
5. **Binding.** Stabilise a stow with dunnage to make several units into one block, also stowing bags or cartons in different directions in each layer to form a self-locking block (a 'brick wall' effect).
6. **Structural alterations.** Very heavy and/or awkwardly shaped cargo may be secured by welding the unit directly to the ship's structure, or by fabricating a steel framework or other support or chock which is permanently attached to the ship's structure.

17.6 Basics of securing cargo

1. A good tight stowage may avoid the need to secure, provided the cargo is adequately packaged, and there are no heavy units.
2. Heavy units may still require securing even if the space around them is filled with other cargo. Particular attention should be paid to the likelihood of such units slipping or tipping.

3. An exposed face, or one which may become exposed on the voyage, may need to be backlashed.

4. A number of units can be secured together into one block.

5. Fixed securing points on the cargo should always be used, but it must be remembered that securing points designed for inland transport may not be suitable for securing items on board ship.

6. Independent lashings must only be secured to suitably strong points of the ships structure, preferably designated lashing points.
The total load on such points must not exceed their designed limit.

7. Lashings should be as short as possible.

8. Whenever possible, the multiple lashings to one item of cargo should be kept under equal tension. The mixing of devices with different strengths and elasticities should be avoided.

9. Lashings must be capable of being checked and tightened on passage.

10. Lashings should be sufficient to prevent the load from moving when the ship rolls through 30 degrees with 13 second roll periods.[5]

11. Cargo will lift before it shifts—so tie it down well.

12. Wire lashings to tanks and cylinders with no lashing points should pass around the cargo from both sides, with the two ends of the wire tightened and secured on the same side—see diagrams.[54]

13. If there are insufficient lashing points on the ship for the cargo, additional securing points may have to be welded to strong points of the ship's structure. The OOW should check with the Chief Officer that this is permitted before allowing anyone to start welding. All the usual welding precautions should be taken, and the OOW must monitor the other side of the steelwork. In particular, any damaged coatings must be repaired. Some charterparties permit such additions provided they are removed at the end of the charter. Often the removal process causes more damage; it may be preferable to allow them to remain as they may prove useful on another voyage.

It will often be prudent to lay out the securing system before the cargo is loaded. Bundles can best be secured by loading them on top of wire rope lashing which has previously been laid on the deck. This is then tightened and secured above the stow. Cross wires for a timber deck cargo must be secured at the ship's side before that area is blocked off by the cargo.

When he checks the lashings, the OOW should visualise a large green mid-ocean swell breaking on board just as the ship rolls heavily into it, and ensure that the lashings are adequate to cope. There is no second chance at sea, so the lashings must be suitable before departure.[5]

17.7 Strength of lashings[5]

A good rule of thumb is that the holding power of the lashings (the sum of the breaking strains of all the components of the lashing system) should be twice the weight of the unit of cargo below decks.

For cargo on deck, the holding power of the lashings holding the cargo vertically downwards should be three times the weight of the unit. The holding power of the lashings preventing athwartships movement should be 70% of the unit's weight, and those preventing fore-and-aft movement should be 30% of the unit's weight. A full treatise on how to establish the strengths of lashings is given in The Nautical Institute's publication *Lashing and Securing of Deck Cargoes.*[5]

17.8 Timber deck cargoes

The stowage of cargo on deck is considered in 7.8.3. The OOW serving on a ship carrying a cargo of timber on deck must make himself thoroughly familiar with the contents of the IMO *Code of safe practice for ships carrying timber deck cargoes.*[52] The following notes are a summary of its main recommendations.

Packaged timber should be stowed fore and aft, and only bundles which have both ends squared off should be stowed on deck, in order to facilitate a compact stow. Bundles with only one end squared off may be stowed on deck if they are not at the perimeter, and every effort should be made to avoid broken stowage. Each tier must be equally firm. The stow must not impair visibility from the bridge, and the forward face must not have overhanging shoulders which could be caught by a head sea. If the ship is to pass through a winter zone, the height of the cargo above the deck must not exceed one third of the ship's breadth.

The cargo must be secured throughout its length by independent transverse lashings not more than 3 metres apart for cargo heights up to 4 metres above the weather deck, and not more than 1.5 metres apart for cargo heights over 6 metres. The spacing of lashings for cargoes between these two heights is calculated by interpolation. The breaking strain of the lashings must be at least 13.6 tonnes. Uprights can be used as additions to, but NOT instead of, these lashings whenever necessary to ensure a compact and secure stow. Lashings must be provided with a method of adjusting their tension on passage, and a means of jettisoning the cargo, though the value of this latter point in practice is open to scepticism.

A suitable walkway must be provided on top of the stow to ensure safe crew access, with ladders to the deck where appropriate. Safety lifelines should be rigged where necessary

17.8.1 Extra lashings for logs

In addition to independent lashings not more than 3 metres apart, a 'hog' wire is rove between port and starboard uprights when the logs reach a height of three-quarters the upright. As other logs are stowed on top of this wire, it is tightened and the uprights are pulled inboard. Further, a dual continuous 'wiggle' wire is passed from side to side

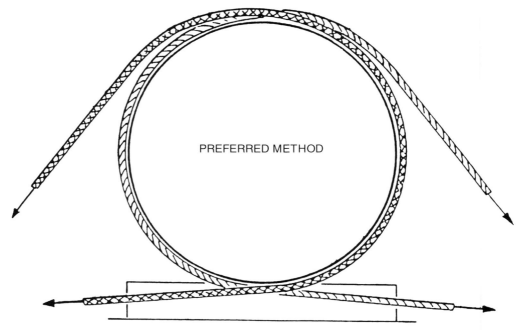

PREFERRED METHOD

*Principle of securing heavy items having
no suitable securing point*

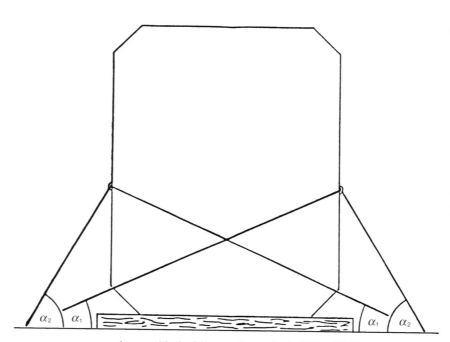

α_1: favourable lashing angle against sliding (25°)
α_2: favourable lashing angle against tipping (45°–60°)

Principles of securing heavy items against sliding and tipping

Reproduced from the IMO publication
Code of Safe Practice for Cargo Stowage and Securing.[54]

over the top of the cargo, through snatch blocks held in place by foot wires to the deck edge, and tensioned by leading the wire to a winch.

17.8.2 Timber loadlines

Timber loadlines permit the vessel to load to a deeper draft than the normal loadlines. They are applicable no matter what cargo is stowed below decks, but the deck cargo must be a solid stow of timber to at least the height of the superstructure, filling the entire well from fore to aft and side to side with no gaps or omissions. There are also special stability requirements. For further details, study the IMO publication *Code of Safe Practice for Ships Carrying Timber Deck Cargoes*.[52]

17.9 Container lashings

Every ship designed to carry containers should have plans on board which show how containers can be arranged on board, and a cargo securing manual. They will show the maximum permissible total weight for each stack, and how each stack should be lashed and secured. The OOW must check that these stack limits are not exceeded, and that the containers are properly lashed according to the plans.

Occasionally, although the total stack weight may be correct, there may be an incorrect distribution of weights within the stack. The lashing system is designed for certain vertical weight distributions, and may not be sufficient if the weight distribution is different. Recently, several stacks collapsed on a ship because the top containers in each stack were heavier than permitted for the designed lashings, although the total stack weight was within limits. When the ship encountered heavy weather and began to roll, the rolling motion built up a pendulum effect in the top heavy containers which broke the lashings and caused the stacks to collapse.[28]

The OOW should be familiar with the correct use of the various components of the container lashing system—twistlocks (left and right hand), turn-buckles, interlayer stackers or cones (single and double), bridge fittings, tensioners, locators, side stays, penguin hooks, chains, lashing rods (of various lengths) and deck connections. If any of these terms are unfamiliar, he should ask the Chief Officer to explain.

17.9.1 Containers on non-purpose built ships

The standard principles for lashing cargo should be followed, bearing in mind that the weight of an ISO container is concentrated at the four corner castings. These should sit on substantial dunnage to spread the weight, taking into account the deck strength (found in the ship's stability book). On no account should the skirts of the bottom rails be in contact with the dunnage bed, as these are not strength members, and will buckle and collapse if placed on dunnage.

If the weight of the container is unknown, it is reasonable to assume 20 tonnes for a 20ft unit, and 30 tonnes for a 40ft unit. It is useful to remember that the point loading on each corner casting for a heavy 20ft' unit can be as high as nearly 200 tonnes per sq.metre.

On deck, containers should be stowed fore and aft, only one tier high, and chocked off against sliding athwartships. They should not extend over the ship's side, and adequate supports should be provided when they overhang hatches or deck structures.[54] They must be lashed independently; the strength of the lashings should be three times their weight. If the vessel is fitted with permanent foot locks or restraints for the lower corner castings, then two or more tiers may be stowed on deck. Twist-locks should be used between each tier, and bridge fittings or tension clamps used to lock the upper corner castings of adjacent containers in the top tier.

Below decks, it is important to check that the tanktop and structure beneath is sufficient to take the weight of the stack of containers. The bottom tier should be locked into tanktop fittings, and the entire stow should form one inter-locked block, which is adequately secured to the ship's structure. If the stow becomes slack, the containers may collapse. One ship which hit a freak wave off the coast of Virginia had 36 containers severely damaged and the tanktop was ruptured in 11 places around inadequate container fittings. The tanktop took over a week to repair owing to having to clean and gas-free the oil tanks beneath. (See photograph on page 152).

17.9.2 Securing cargo inside containers

One major problem with pre-stuffed containers is that the OOW does not have any control over the methods by which they are packed and secured. Increasingly, those who stuff containers at factories well removed from the marine environment are being educated into the forces likely to be applied to the container during transit. However, it has been found that the securing arrangements are often inadequate. If this cargo breaks adrift, the safety of many other containers, and of the ship itself could be at risk. If the containers are being stuffed on the quayside, or on board, the OOW should apply the same theories to stowage and securing of the cargo inside the container as he would do with the same cargo being stowed conventionally in the hold.

The OOW should examine the securing arrangements of cargo in any containers which are open, such as flat racks and open top. Some container ship operators have a system of random checks on all containers. *Thomas's Stowage* quotes the classic case of tin ingots breaking loose within a container stowed on deck and bursting through the door. As a result the lashings parted, and subsequently 43 adjacent containers were lost overside.[70]

The stowage of cargo inside containers was discussed in chapter 8.2.4.

17.10 Further information

More detailed information is provided in the IMO *Code of Safe Practice for Cargo Stowage and Securing*[54] and in The Nautical Institute's *Lashing and Securing of Deck Cargoes*.[5]

Chapter 18
KEEPING RECORDS
PURPOSE

On completion of this chapter you will be able to list the entries which you should make in the deck logbook, explain how they should be made, and when to make them. You will appreciate why certain entries are so important when the logbook is used as evidence, and be aware of other records which are maintained and retained onboard ship.

18.1 Importance of keeping records

If there is a dispute or a claim in the future, the shipowner will want to have as much evidence as possible in order to pursue his case. When the relevant information and clear documents are readily available, claims can usually be resolved quickly, avoiding lengthy legal wrangles with their associated substantial costs. If the claim does reach the Courts, judges place great weight upon documentation from the vessel. Hence it is essential for the OOW to keep records of everything that happens whilst he is on duty.

A large number of detailed log entries emphasise to a surveyor, or a lawyer, that the vessel's watchkeepers have been paying attention to their duties, and verify that the vessel was operated in a seamanlike manner. This will probably lead to judgements being made which are favourable to the shipowner. Further, a small number of entries has been interpreted as indicating that no-one was paying any attention to the operation of the vessel.

18.2 Deck logbook as evidence

Entries made in the logbook at the time of any incident or event are extremely valuable evidence.

Sometimes a claim may take several years to reach Court, so even if the OOW has forgotten what happened by this time, and he is called as a witness, he can reread his entries in the logbook to refresh his memory.

There could be problems for an officer called as a witness if he has no records to rely upon, and only a vague recollection of the events which occurred so long beforehand. Also, the Court will rarely accept the evidence of a witness if his evidence is inconsistent with a document which came into existence at the time.[13] If the OOW is more aware of the type of evidence required to defend a claim, then he is more likely to make better entries in the log book. This may lead to an increased awareness of potential problems which could arise on board, and hopefully lead to greater care being taken by the watchkeeper.[1,2]

In order to avoid liability if cargo is lost or damaged, the carrier will have to demonstrate that he has fully and properly cared for the cargo. Hence, all cargo handling operations must be accurately recorded and fully documented so that the carrier will be able to produce the evidence necessary to defend a claim.[1] For further guidance, the reader should consult The Nautical Institute publication *The Masters Role in Collecting Evidence* which contains useful advice on observation and record keeping.[1]

18.3 Recording all the facts

When writing up the deck logbook for his watch in port, the OOW should always try to record as many relevant facts as possible. Unfortunately, the design of some printed logbooks does not allow enough space for more than a short statement every hour. The best logbooks have all the fixed column entries on one side of the sheet, and a completely blank lined page for remarks, each day. If the logbook does not have sufficient space, the OOW can write his entries on a separate sheet of paper which is then permanently attached to the relevant daily page. However, he must always first consult the Chief Officer or the Master before adopting such practices.

One method employed by some operators to overcome this shortage of space for descriptive entries is to list common, regular and routine log entries on an index page at the beginning of the log book, each being given a reference number. On the daily pages, the relevant items are recorded by referring to these numbers: *Items 2,5,7,12,16.... observed*. Again, the OOW must consult his seniors before adopting such a practice himself.

It is always better to write too much than too little. The entries should enable the reader to reconstruct a clear and complete picture of the events exactly as they happened. Opinions should never be recorded, only pure facts and observations. All entries should be clear and precise, leaving no room for misinterpretation. It should be remembered that many people who read logbooks do not have a seafaring background. The author does not support the view that *least said, soonest mended*, whereby some people claim that the OOW should make as few entries as possible in the logbook. Their argument is that fewer entries lead to fewer mistakes, and that fewer entries make it unlikely that the OOW may make an entry in the logbook which is to the detriment of the shipowner. If the OOW is careful, accurate and honest, and checks all entries he makes, the deck logbook should be extremely valuable evidence in favour of the shipowner.

As with all the other advice contained in this guide, the OOW must always be guided by the practices in force on his ship. He must always comply with the system adopted by his employers, and he must always obey the orders of the Master. Whilst it should do no harm to point out the advice contained in this guide, the OOW must never adopt this advice if it is in conflict with that of the Master or the shipowner.

18.4 Cargo and port logbooks

Some ships use a separate cargo logbook which is kept in the deck office or cargo control room. The OOW enters all relevant times and data into this working document, and the major entries are transferred to the deck logbook, sometimes by the Chief Officer. This rough logbook should be retained and filed, for reasons which are outlined in sections 18.5 and 18.6.

It is the practice on some vessels to keep a detailed port logbook, which is given the same status as the deck logbook. In this case, where this chapter advises an entry should be made in the deck logbook, the OOW should make the appropriate entry in the port logbook. Consequently, very few entries are made in the deck logbook on such vessels whilst they are in port. However, practices vary, and the OOW serving on ships which keep both logbooks should seek the advice of a senior officer as to what particular entries are to be made in each of these two books.

18.5 Retaining records

If there is insufficient evidence from the ship, there is a serious risk that the cargo owners or charterers will win a claim against the shipowner on some occasions when really they ought to lose. The ship which keeps careful records and produces them will always find favour with the Courts.[13] Since handling a claim may take a long time, even years, it is not sufficient merely to maintain good records, it is essential to retain them, and to be able to retrieve them with ease. The OOW should learn the paperwork filing system on board, so that he may place documents in their proper place.

18.6 OOW's rough notebook

The deck logbook is accepted as the contemporary record of the voyage. In law, original records made at the time are more valuable evidence than those subsequently composed. This means that the first recorded note of any event is more useful than documents which have been written up later. It has been stated in Court that the rough notebook which the OOW carries around with him is that first record, and so should be preserved, just in case. One lawyer, when he heard that this rough notebook became so dirty after a few day's use on deck that it was thrown overside and replaced with a new one, stated to the Court: *Let the Court note that this shipowner was in the habit of jettisoning first-hand evidence at sea.* Entries which the officer makes in the logbook subsequently, have been held to be 'selective' with the truth! It is essential that these rough notebooks are filed away on board in case they are ever needed.

For similar reasons, it is important that the OOW makes all the entries in the logbook in his own handwriting for his period of watch, and The Nautical Institute recommends that he signs his name at the end of each watch after the last of the entries he makes in the logbook.

18.6.1 Rough reports

Sometimes an incident will occur on board that requires the OOW to write a report on the events. In the case of a serious incident, the OOW, and indeed his seniors, may be reluctant to write such a report before consulting the owners. The legal view is that such consultations may affect the contents of the report, and this must be avoided if the report is to be believed as truthful evidence from an unbiased witness. So it is best to write a rough report as soon after the incident as possible.[13] Such rough reports must be retained as original evidence in case they are required to be produced.

Some authorities recommend that these reports are headed *For the sole attention of the company's solicitors only.* This is to ensure that the document receives 'legal privilege', which is an attempt to retain privacy and prevent the document being requested by any opposition lawyer. Such privilege is not permitted in some circumstances.

The OOW should always be truthful in reports, especially those which may come before a Court of law. However, he should bear in mind that the opposing lawyer may study this document closely, and may cross-examine the OOW on its contents. Some experts recommend that the author of a report makes no comments which could embarrass him, or place his employer at a disadvantage, if the report became public knowledge. Although an omission may be forgiven, an untruth cannot be forgiven.

18.7 Minor claims

Many minor incidents occur during the course of a voyage which may not develop into a claim. Those that do can cost more to investigate than the amount of the claim. Hence the shipowner may be tempted to pay the claim rather than face the costs of disputing it. A series of minor claims can add up to substantial sums. So if the logbook entries contain sufficient information to enable the shipowner justifiably to refute the claim, he can make substantial savings. Hence the regular routine logging of all relevant information is a very valuable habit for the OOW to acquire.

18.8 Other records kept on board

Besides the deck logbook, other records which may concern the OOW and which should be retained and suitably filed include:
- Any cargo workbooks, including cargo calculations.
- Stability calculations.
- Draft surveys, including associated calculations.
- Cargo plans.
- Ballast plans, and any ballast books (see chapter 10.21).
- Cargo equipment records.
- Maintenance records of all deck equipment, including hatches.
- Movement (bell) books.
- Sounding books. (The Nautical Institute recommends that actual readings are recorded in preference to *'full'* and *'empty'*).
- Records of bilge pumping, and acidity of bilge water.
- Ventilation records.

- Cargo or hold temperatures, and any gas detector readings.
- Weather observation logs.
- Weather faxes, and weather reports received.
- Tank order books or operation chits.
- Cargo tally books.
- Records of all prearrival/preloading tests (see chapter 2.3).
- Reefer container settings (advice sheets and monitor records).
- Print-outs of all automatic recorders on board.
- Any specific recommendations for handling and/or stowage provided by the shipper and/or charterer.

In addition, the Chief Engineer will retain all technical records, and the Master will retain all commercial records.

18.9 Photographic records

It has been pointed out in several places earlier in this manual that photographs of damage, injuries, poor systems, etc., are very useful evidence. To quote a popular cliche: *A photograph is worth a thousand words*. The same can be said of videos. It is essential that all such records are properly labelled with the time and date, preferably using an automatic recording facility on the camera, and are identified with a brief note of what they are intended to depict. Again, these records must be efficiently filed to enable them to be quickly retrieved if required at some time in the future.

However, the OOW must always check that photography is permitted in that port, as there are severe penalties for taking photographs within some port areas, even on board one's own ship. It must be borne in mind that photographs, like written evidence, may be used by the opposition to support their case. It is inadvisable to take photographs which show obvious deficiencies on board.[25]

Photographs should be seen as complementing documentary evidence, and not as a replacement for proper written records. **It is important to remember that taking a photograph is <u>not</u> a substitute for taking action to avoid an incident or damage.**

18.9.1 Examples of the use of photographic evidence

The OOW may take a photograph to establish:
1. The condition of the ship's accesses—see chapter 4.2.5. (and provide proof of vigilance over safe conditions on board.)
2. The condition of the holds prior to loading.
3. Stevedore negligence—poor handling techniques, use of incorrect equipment, overloading slings, damage to cargo or ship, etc.
4. The preshipment condition of the cargo, including weakness of packing.
5. The state of the stow, and lashings, at the time of final closing and/or first opening of the hatches.
6. Cargo losses—for example spills from handling equipment or shore transportation, bulk cargo blown by the wind, or rampant thieving.
7. Swell conditions during draft surveys, which may render the results inaccurate.

8. The extent of oil pollution, by recording the size of any slicks. It is useful to take photographs of oil slicks from other origins, if such photographs can show that the oil did not come from one's own ship.
9. The conditions surrounding any accidents, and records of damage incurred, broken parts, faulty equipment and personal injuries.
10. The identity of stowaways.

This list is by no means exhaustive, but it should give the OOW an idea of the usefulness of photographic evidence in varying circumstances and hopefully encourage him to use this means of establishing records when other incidents occur.

18.10 Erasures

Entries in the logbooks should always be written neatly, in ink. If a mistake is made, the OOW should draw a single line through the relevant words, and initial this correction. Words should never be erased either by rubbing out or painting over with a correcting fluid. Erasures appear suspicious when log books are examined by the opposing party in a dispute. Further, those examining a logbook which contains many erasures may draw adverse inferences about the way the vessel is being operated.[1]

18.11 Falsifications

Experience suggests that ship's staff, sometimes aided and abetted by shipowners, occasionally think that their case could be improved if the entries in the log book were altered in some way. This is a risky strategy, which is not recommended. Scientific techniques are available which can detect all alterations, and decipher the original. The fact that an alteration has been made will make the Court suspicious of the officers concerned.[13] This could mean that other parts of their evidence, which may be genuine and essential to the shipowner's case, are not entirely believed, or even dismissed.

18.12 Accurate timings

It is essential that the time recorded for each log entry is accurate. The Master will want to use the logbook entries to check the *statement of facts* which the agent presents to him shortly before sailing. Some statements of facts are very detailed, so it is important that the logbook records are written in sufficient detail to enable him to check each entry on the statement of facts.

It is most important that stoppages to cargo operations are both accurately timed, and the reasons for them are discovered and recorded. The OOW should check regularly with the head stevedore, checker or shore timekeeper, to verify that the times recorded by the ship and shore agree. Any discrepancies are much easier to sort out at the time of occurrence rather than in that busy period just before the ship sails when the Master is inundated with paperwork. In particular, it is important to establish who was responsible for the stoppage, as delays caused by the ship could lead to financial penalties (e.g., offhire) for the shipowner.

18.13 Logging drafts

The vessel's drafts should be recorded at least twice daily; this is an absolute minimum. It is good practice to record the draft at each change of watch. During very quick loading/discharging operations on ships such as bulk carriers, the draft should be read at the end of each pour, and compared with the precomputed value. The readings on any draft gauges will be sufficiently accurate for this purpose, which is to monitor that the correct quantities are being loaded, and that the ballast and cargo operations are progressing together in sequence as planned, so that bending moments and shear forces are not exceeded inadvertently. The density should be recorded with each draft.

18.14 Logging the weather

The Nautical Institute recommends that the weather is logged every four hours, at the usual end of sea-watch times. Some companies permit fewer entries than this, and the OOW should be guided by the Chief Officer's or Master's standing orders. In any case, it is good practice to ALWAYS record the times when rain, or other forms of precipitation, starts and stops. Often the period allowed for cargo operations will be so many weather-working-days— see chapter 6.4.2—so it is essential that the OOW maintains records of such periods, so that the Master can check the statement of facts accurately.

Even when cargo is not being worked, including periods at anchor awaiting a berth, this information must be recorded, because this period may be part of the laytime permitted for cargo operations. Only by maintaining full and accurate weather records can the Master readily check the laytime calculations. It is useful to record precautions taken against damage by adverse weather to delicate cargoes—for example, radar watch for approaching rain and measures to enable the hatches to be closed rapidly—see chapter 7.7.6

18.15 Logging damage

The OOW should pay special attention to ALL damage he sees occur. This includes damage to the ship, its fittings, the cargo, and equipment not belonging to the vessel. Remember that it is a requirement of most charterparties that such damage is reported in writing within 24 hours, or else any claim may be invalid. Hence the OOW should keep a constant lookout for new damage, and report it to the Chief Officer immediately, even if he doesn't actually see it happen. It is usual to record the details of damage on forms specially printed for this purpose, which may be supplied by the shipowner, operator or charterer, an example of which is reproduced in appendix XII -see chapter 6.8. Even so, a brief summary of the incident should be entered into the log book. Whenever possible, the OOW should take photographs of all such damage— see section 18.9. It is good practice for the OOW to investigate every loud bang, and rocking of the vessel—also see chapter 7.10.

18.16 Hold inspections

As each hold is completed, the watchkeeper should record the fact that he has inspected the hold, noting in particular as appropriate:
1. All cargo for that port has been discharged—i.e., no over-carriage.
2. The securing arrangements for the cargo have been checked, and the stow is secured sufficiently for the next intended sea passage.
3. A search has been made for stowaways, and that afterwards all the hold accesses have been locked.

If the hatchcovers and hold accesses are sealed, which may be required by a charterer, or the practice of the particular trade, then this fact should be recorded in the logbook, together with the numbers and locations of the seals, and the names of the people performing this operation. On reefers, this may include battery space accesses.

18.17 Miscellaneous entries

The OOW should also record the times and full details of:
1. All officials, surveyors, inspectors, contractors, stevedores, etc. boarding and leaving the vessel. The NAMES of important visitors should be recorded, along with the type of work they perform.
   e.g., *0915-1645: Captain R. Smith (Hong Kong Government) attended for Annual Safety Equipment survey.*
   *0830-1100: Mr P. Jones (Lloyd's Register) attended for CSH/CSM * items 1025, 1640, 2305 and 2310. [*Continuous survey of hull/machinery]*
   The numbers of such visitors should be noted, including the number of stevedore gangs (and securing gangs) in each hold, and in total.
   e.g., *0800: Four stevedore gangs on board, two at No.3, one at Nos.1 & 4.*
   1300: Two lashing gangs on board, working on deck as required.
2. Opening and closing of each hatch, valve, ramp or cargo door.
3. Commence work, complete work, at EACH cargo compartment.
   Note that these terms indicate the first and last occasion when cargo was worked at this compartment in this port.
   It is good practice to record brief details of the equipment used—e.g., two shore grabs, one conveyor, ship's cranes, four spouts,etc.
4. Resume work, cease work, at EACH cargo compartment.
   Note that these terms indicate that work has already taken place at this compartment on a previous occasion, or that work will continue at this compartment on a future occasion, in this port. (Compare with point 3 above.)
5. Commence and complete each ballast tank.
   When deballasting, it is useful to record the final tonnage remaining in the tank on completion.
   On some vessels, it is the practice to record ballast pump readings—see chapter 10.

6. All delays to cargo operations, for example due to:
   (a) Machinery breakdowns ashore.
   (b) Ship's handling equipment failure.
   (c) Adverse weather.
   (d) No cargo available
   (e) Shore transportation problems.
   (f) Strikes and other labour disputes, etc.
   The OOW should be as detailed as he can, and bring these facts to the attention of the Chief Officer as soon as possible—see section 18.12.
7. On reefers, the times of starting and stopping of the refrigeration machinery, and the reason.
8. Taking bunkers, fresh water, stores, etc. (see chapter 14).
   Also record the TONNAGES or QUANTITIES received.
9. Samples of cargo, bunkers, etc., taken.
   Include the names and positions of any witnesses to these procedures, and details of the sampling methods employed.
10. Other craft arriving alongside, and departing.
    Their NAMES and purpose of visit should also be recorded.
11. Commencement and completion of repairs, with brief details of the work undertaken.
12. All accidents to the ship and personnel.
    The OOW should be guided by the Chief Officer or Master as to how much detail of these incidents is required. They will be compiling separate reports, and may want to verify intended log entries before they are made permanent in the logbook (see chapter 4.11).
13. Any fumigation undertaken, with the names of operators and the type and quantity of fumigant used.
14. Any protest made by, or to the ship.

15. Shifting ship, either along the quay, or to another berth.
    The OOW should record the same details as are usually recorded for port arrival and departure entries.
16. Any pollution observed which has not originated from own vessel (as discussed in chapter 15.8).
17. All extra security measures undertaken, including all searches conducted for stowaways, drugs and contraband (see chapter 16).
18. All extra safety measures undertaken, including rigging of safety lines, cleaning spills and restriction of access (see chapter 4).
19. All extra precautions taken on the advice of shore authorities, charterers, agents, shippers of the cargo, etc.

Entries under 17–19 can be used to show that the ship took all necessary precautions as were reasonably practicable to avoid an incident, and such evidence may be essential if the ship's staff has to defend a charge of violating local laws and regulations—for example, under Health and Safety Regulations. These and the other logbook entries discussed earlier may be useful evidence for the shipowner to prove that he complies with his contractual obligations with insurance underwriters, P&I Clubs, and cargo shippers, and with any relevant classification society, flag State, local, national or international rules and regulations. Officers serving on tankers are reminded of the extra logbook entries which are suggested in chapter 9.

It is appreciated that the OOW may have considered that keeping records was a tedious and repetitive task. After completing this chapter it is hoped that he will appreciate the significance of his entries, and avoid approaching this task with an attitude of complacency.

Chapter 19

DEPARTURE FROM PORT

PURPOSE

On completion of this chapter you will be able to supervise the closing and securing of the hatches, and assist with predeparture procedures.

19.1 Predeparture procedures

The time between the completion of cargo and departure will represent one of the most busy periods of the vessel's stay in port. Not only does the vessel have to make physical preparations for the forthcoming sea passage, but also commercial preparations have to be made. The Master has to ensure that various documents are completed, and the Chief Officer's attention will be in demand from numerous officials, such as stevedores or loading masters, port and terminal representatives, and perhaps numerous surveyors.

During this busy period, the well-organised and well prepared junior officer can be a valuable asset to the ship. He should consult the checklist in appendix XVIII, and make sure that he knows exactly what is to be done in order to complete each item successfully. He should organise the relevant officers and crew so that all these preparations are completed to a satisfactory standard, well before the time of departure. This will ensure that there are no financial losses due to delays. It is of immense assistance to the Master and Chief Officer to be able to concentrate on their paperwork, knowing they can rely on an efficient OOW to supervise properly all the other preparations for departure.

19.2 Predeparture surveys

The OOW may be required to assist with the following surveys which may be undertaken before the ship leaves port:

1. **Draft survey,** on completion of cargo operations— see chapter 13.9.

2. **On or off-hire surveys,** if a new charter commences upon departure. It is common for charters to commence/end on 'DLOSP', which means dropping last outward sea pilot—see chapter 2.6.2.

3. **Cargo survey,** to check satisfactory completion of stowage and lashing. Hold and hatch accesses may be sealed by an independent surveyor.

19.3 Still water rolling tests

Sometimes the ship will perform a rolling test, to check the ship's metacentric height. This is done by slackening the moorings, and inducing a roll by lifting a weight off the quay. Sometimes this is done on ships loading a timber deck cargo before completion of loading, when the weight of the deck cargo is not known accurately, in order to ascertain how much additional cargo can be loaded on deck.

REMINDER: Roll period (seconds) = $\dfrac{2 \times \pi \times K}{\sqrt{(g \times GM)}}$

where K = Radius of gyration.
This is related to the ship's beam, but one may increase its value by 'winging-out' weights,
i.e. loading away from the centreline.

π = Pi, a constant (3.14159)

g = Force of gravity (9.81 cm/sec)

GM = Ship's metacentric height.

For larger vessels, this formula may be simplified to:

Roll period = $0.7 \times$ beam $\div \sqrt{GM}$

19.4 Inspecting empty holds for damage

On completion of discharge of each hold, the OOW should inspect the hold to see if any part of the structure is damaged. This includes both damage due to physical contact, as discussed earlier, and gradual deterioration of parts of the structure caused by stress or corrosion. He should report any defects he finds to a senior officer, some things he should look out for include:

● cracks in plating, frames, webs and other strengtheners;

● excessive corrosion in any of these items;

● decay and breakdown of welds;

● buckling or deformation of structural members;

● structural defects;

● missing fittings;

● breakdown of paint coatings.

For those officers serving in bulk carriers, detailed advice on what to look out for is given in the International Association of Classification Societies (IACS) publication *Guidelines for Surveys, Assessment and Repair of Hull Structure*[73]. This booklet contains excellent diagrams to guide the officer to those areas of the structure where defects are most likely to occur. This may also provide useful guidance for officers serving in other types of ships, and some examples are reproduced in appendix V.

19.5 Hatchcovers

The hatchcovers must be secured before the ship puts to sea; the sealing arrangements must be in perfect order to prevent the entry of water into the cargo holds.

These covers have to withstand the weight of any deck cargo, and of many tonnes of seawater which may break over the deck during adverse weather. Hence they are strong, rigid structures. However, the ship flexes or works in a seaway, and so the joint between the flexible ship and the rigid hatchcover must be capable of absorbing this movement, in addition to providing a watertight seal. This is usually achieved by having a steel compression bar bearing against a rubber (neoprene) gasket. These components must be pressed firmly and evenly together over their entire length. **Cleats are used to restrict the movement of the hatchcovers—not to increase the compression of the hatch rubbers.** There are various designs, and the OOW must ensure that he is totally familiar with the system on his ship.

Leaks can occur even when all the components are in good condition and the hatch cover is properly secured. Usually this occurs when the freeboard is low, as with loaded bulk carriers, the seas and swells are high, as during northern ocean winters, and the vessel is carrying high density cargo, so the GM is high, causing the ship to rack or twist. Drains are provided to ensure that this leakage is returned to deck, and not onto the cargo.

With sensitive cargoes, it is good practice to test the hatchcovers are watertight before loading commences. Such tests can be made using high-pressure hoses, chalk, or ultrasonic equipment. These tests should be logged. It is good practice for the OOW to examine the hatch covers for physical damage each time they are operated, so that faults can be spotted quickly, and there is time to correct them before sailing. Hatch cover failure is the cause of 12% of the major cargo claims settled by the UK P&I Club.

19.5.1 Physical damage

1. The OOW must watch for any damage to the compression bars, which may be caused by heavy cargo, or grabs, landing on them, or by wires of cargo-handling equipment wearing grooves in them.
   There should be no excessive build-up of scale on the compression bars as this prevents the making of a good seal.
2. Locators, which guide the panels into their correct position, may be damaged, worn away, or built up with scale. Consequently the panels may not make proper contact with each other or with the hatch coaming.
3. The OOW should be on the lookout for any mechanical damage to the hatch coamings and covers, for example if heavy cargo or grabs collide with them, which may result in water entering the holds through cracks or through the distortion of the sealing arrangements.
4. If the drainage system is damaged, or blocked, then any water which does enter will not be able to drain back to deck, and so will run into the hold and on to the cargo. These must be properly cleaned and proved clear before the hatches are closed for the final departure.
   The OOW should verify that the nonreturn mechanism is functioning correctly. Compressed air is useful for this purpose.
5. The cleats and other securing devices must not be bent, their threads must be clean, and capable of being adjusted quickly, and any rubbers must be sufficiently elastic for proper compression. Cross cleats must not be slack, and their springs must be operating correctly.
6. Any connecting chains must be of the correct tension and length to permit smooth and proper operation.
7. Any operating wires must be in sound condition.
8. The operating system, whether electric, hydraulic or pneumatic, should be free of leaks, capable of supplying sufficient power and operate smoothly, with all controls working correctly.

19.5.2 Rubber seal

The rubber must be in good condition :-
1. There should be no gaps.
2. It should be seated firmly in its guide.
3. There should be no large build up of rust in the seating guide, which can cause distortion of the rubber, or create high spots.
4. It should be elastic, i.e. able to be compressed. There should be no large permanent indent or compression. Manufacturers recommend that the compression must not exceed 25% of the original thickness, when it approaches this figure the rubber should be replaced. It must not feel rock-hard, or be cracked.
5. It must not be covered with paint, nor ingrained with cargo.
6. Any repairs must be made using materials of the original specification. This is because the size, shape, compressibility, elasticity, hardness and construction is specific to each cover design, including the size and weight of individual covers.
7. The entire length of failed packing must be replaced, not just the offending section, as this may lead to distortion of the joint.

19.5.3 Consequences of leaking hatches

If seawater enters a hold through a hatchcover which is obviously in poor condition, the shipowner will be fully liable for all costs. He will not be able to rely on any clauses in the charterparty or bill of lading which limit his liability, because there has been a lack of due diligence to make the vessel seaworthy. Recently sea water penetrated the hatches of a vessel crossing the Atlantic during storms. A few small gaps were found in the rubber packing which resulted in a settlement of $93,000 for damaged cargo.[22]

P&I Clubs have become so concerned about the lack of maintenance of hatchcovers that they have considered not paying claims which can be shown to have originated from this cause. Such claims may be subject to enquiry as to the maintenance of the hatchcovers both generally, and specifically immediately prior to the voyage in question.[26]

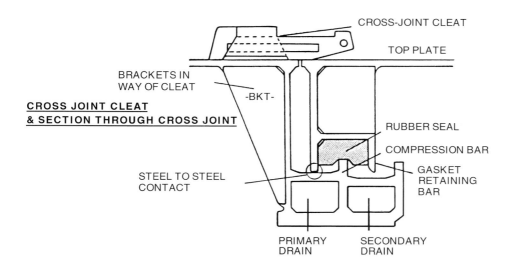

CROSS-JOINT CLEAT

TOP PLATE

BRACKETS IN
WAY OF CLEAT

-BKT-

**CROSS JOINT CLEAT
& SECTION THROUGH CROSS JOINT**

RUBBER SEAL

COMPRESSION BAR

GASKET
RETAINING
BAR

STEEL TO STEEL
CONTACT

PRIMARY
DRAIN

SECONDARY
DRAIN

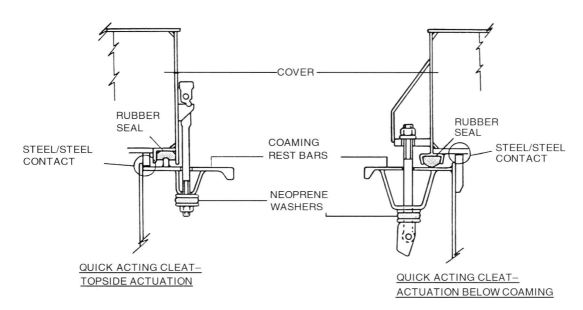

COVER

RUBBER
SEAL

STEEL/STEEL
CONTACT

COAMING
REST BARS

NEOPRENE
WASHERS

RUBBER
SEAL

STEEL/STEEL
CONTACT

QUICK ACTING CLEAT–
TOPSIDE ACTUATION

QUICK ACTING CLEAT–
ACTUATION BELOW COAMING

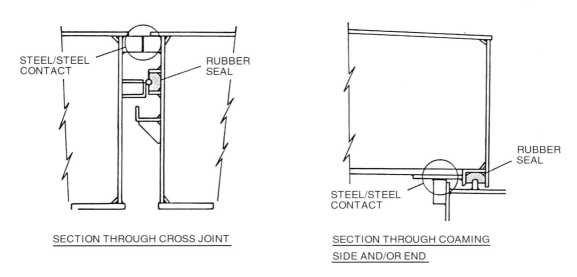

STEEL/STEEL
CONTACT

RUBBER
SEAL

RUBBER
SEAL

STEEL/STEEL
CONTACT

SECTION THROUGH CROSS JOINT

SECTION THROUGH COAMING
SIDE AND/OR END

Reproduced from The Nautical Institute publication *Bulk Carrier Practice*,
original material courtesy of MacGregor-Navire (GBR) Ltd.

19.5.4 Securing the hatches for sea

The OOW must ensure that all these steps are followed:

1. Any cargo spilt on the covers must be removed before they are moved.
2. Remove any plugs from the drain holes, and test the drain is free and the non-return valve is working (compressed air is useful).
3. Sweep the coaming, and ensure the compression bar is clean (use a shovel, a brush, then compressed air).
4. Check the rubber is clean, scrape off any cargo or dust.
5. Check the hatch structure for damage—see section 19.5.1.
6. Check the hatch rubbers—see section 19.5.2.
7. Examine the operating system. Check:
   (a) Wires or chains for damage and stretch.
   (b) All wheels and blocks rotate correctly.
   (c) Hydraulic system for leaks.
   (d) Nothing will obstruct the operation.
8. Remove securing devices, or unlash the covers, as appropriate.
9. Check all personnel are standing clear.
10. Ensure that the operator can see the entire operation, or else another person is employed to watch any areas which the operator cannot see.
11. Close the covers in the correct sequence. The OOW should ask the Chief Officer or read the manufacturer's handbook if he is unsure of the exact procedure.
12. Check that each panel of the covers is correctly positioned. Cleats should be correctly aligned, and the compression bar should be located centrally on the rubber gasket. (With single-pull covers, the trailing panel needs to be pulled tight to ensure that all the cross joints are properly compressed.)
13. Lower the covers into position on the coaming.
14. Recheck that all panels remain correctly positioned.
15. Fasten the cleats in the correct sequence. There are major differences in the sequence for similar looking covers, if he is unsure the OOW should check with the Chief Officer or read the manufacturer's handbook. It is essential that all aspects of the hatch securing mechanism are free, fully operational, and properly adjusted.
16. Apply sealing tape to joints if required.

The OOW should know the location of any emergency operating equipment for the hatch covers, and be familiar with its use.

19.5.5 Taping of cross-joints

1. Remove old tape.
2. Scrape off all loose rust, scale and paint.
3. Remove all dust, dirt, oil, grease, and cargo remains.
4. Dry the surface. (Gentle use of blow lamps may be useful—but only if the cargo in the hold is not flammable and there are no known inflammable gases in the vicinity.)
5. Apply the tape warm. Many tapes have poor adhesion when they are cold, placing them in the top of the engineroom a day before they are needed is a useful tip.

One problem is the lack of time to apply the tape properly. With limited personnel, and hatches open for loading and/or lashing until departure, preparation is often inadequate, and the entire operation is often undertaken under duress, and in a haphazard manner.

There is a danger that taping encourages deterioration in the hatch structure. This is because the space between the panels is unventilated and this creates an atmosphere which promotes corrosion.

It is sometimes stated that by applying tape, the ship is admitting that the hatches leak. The defence is that by taping, the ship is trying to care for the cargo to the best of its ability. On some ships tape is only applied in exceptional circumstances—for example when the GM is very high which may cause severe racking, or when particularly adverse weather is expected. The danger with such practices is that if the hatches leak on a voyage when no tape is applied, the readily visible evidence of previous taping may indicate a lack of care on the voyage in question. Hence the decision to apply tape to hatch covers is one which must be very carefully considered by the Master in consultation with the shipowners. This is because of the legal and commercial consequences of unseaworthiness. Some owners require a letter of instruction from a charterer who requests the ship to tape the hatches.

19.5.6 Further information

The reader who seeks further information on the operation, maintenance and securing of hatch covers should consult the manufacturer's literature, including all handbooks available onboard the ship. General principles and excellent practical advice is contained in The Nautical Institute's publication *Bulk Carrier Practice*.[3]

The OOW should arrange for any bulk cargo sticking between the frames to be removed while it is still accessible. This avoids having to use undesirable methods to loosen the cargo, such as hammering the frames. See chapters 8.1.9 and 8.1.11.
Photograph: courtesy UK P&I Club.

These coils have surface rust, possibly caused by being stowed in the open, in a salt-laden atmosphere close to the sea. The banding is loose, which may present difficulties during cargo handling, and may cause the stow to collapse. The bill of lading should be claused to indicate these facts. See chapters 12 and 7.7.7/3 and appendix II.
Photograph: courtesy Brookes, Bell & Co.

This rip in the tanktop into a fuel tank was caused by a container which 'jumped' from its footlock when the vessel hit a freak wave. See chapter 17.9.1.
Photograph: author.

All accesses should be fully secured before the vessel departs. This scene is the result of seawater entering the foc's'le store during storms in the North Pacific. See chapter 19 and 3.15.2/10.
Photograph: author.

Appendix I
Bibliography and references

The numbers shown thus [7] are references from the main text.

Nautical Institute Publications.

[1]   The Masters Role in Collecting Evidence.
[2]   Accident and Loss Prevention at Sea.
[3]   Bulk Carrier Practice.
[4]   Bridge Team Management.
[5]   Lashing and Securing of Deck Cargoes.
[6]   Security at Sea.
[7]   Stowaways by Sea.
[8]   Management of Safety in Shipping.
[9]   The Nautical Institute on Command.
[10] The Work of the Nautical Surveyor.
[11] The Mariner and the Law, 1 : Signing Bills of Lading.
[12]   2 : Unsafe berths and ports.
[13]   3 : Seaworthiness.
[14]   4 : Salvage.
[15] Bridge Watchkeeping—a practical guide.
[16] Command Seminars. 1984/86/88/90/92/95.
[17] Seaways—various issues 1980-1995.
[18] Crude Carrier Practice.
[19] Commercial Management for Shipmasters.

P & I Club Publications.

UK P&I Club.

[20] Carefully to Carry, editions 1–14.
[21] Analysis of Major Claims, 1991,1992,1993.
[22] Loss Prevention News.

West of England P&I Club.

[23] Annual Reviews. 1989–1993.
[24] Loss Prevention Bulletins.
[25] P&I Claims, some practical notes for ship's officers.

Britannia P&I Club.

[26] Selected Circulars.
[27] Risk Watch.
[28] Britannia News.
[29] P&I Checklists for Masters.

North of England P&I Club.

[30] Signals newsletters.
[31] Steel preshipment surveys. (Loss Prevention Guide).
[32] Draught Surveys. (Loss Prevention Guide).

Newcastle P&I Club.

[33] Full Ahead newsletters.

Gard P&I Club.

[34] Towards safer ships and cleaner seas—
      —a handbook for modern tankship operations.

IMO Publications.

The numbers shown IMO-xxx are the Sales Numbers for the English Edition.

(a) Operational.

[35] IMO Dangerous Goods Labels, Placards and mark.	
[36] Guidelines for preventing the introduction of unwanted aquatic organisms and pathogens from ship's ballast and sediment discharges.	
[37] International Convention on Standards of Training, Certification and Watchkeeping. (STCW)	IMO-938.
[38] MSC guidelines to prevent unlawful acts at sea.	
[39] International Safety Management (ISM) code.	IMO-186.
[40] International Convention for the Safety of Life at Sea. (SOLAS)	IMO-110.
[41] International Conference on Load Lines.	IMO-701.
[42] Convention on the facilitation of International Maritime Traffic. (FAL).	IMO-350.

(b) Cargo.

[43] International Code for the Construction and Equipment of ships carrying Liquified Gases in Bulk.	IMO-104.
[Ships built pre-1986 = IMO-782 ; Ships built pre-1976 = IMO-788]	
[44] International Code for the Construction and Equipment of ships carrying Liquid Dangerous Chemicals in Bulk.(IBC).	IMO-100.
[45] Code for the Construction and Equipment of ships carrying Dangerous Chemicals in Bulk. (BCH). [Ships built pre-1986]	IMO-772.
[46] International Convention for Safe Containers. (CSC).	IMO-282.
[47] Crude Oil Washing Systems.	IMO-617.
[48] Inert Gas Systems, guidelines.	IMO-860.
[49] International Maritime Dangerous Goods (IMDG) code.	IMO-200.
The consolidated Supplement contains:–	IMO-210.
Emergency Procedures (EmS).	IMO-254.
Medical First Aid Guide (MFAG).	IMO-251.
[50] Code of Safe Practice for Solid Bulk Cargoes.(BC).	IMO-260.
Reporting Procedures.	
Packing Guidelines.	
[51] Recommendations on the Safe Use of Pesticides in Ships.	IMO-267.
[52] Code of Safe Practice for ships carrying Timber Deck Cargoes.	IMO-275.
[53] Code of Safe Practice for ships carrying Grain in Bulk. (International Grain Code).	IMO-240.
[54] Code of Safe Practice for Cargo Stowage and Securing.	IMO-292.
[55] Code of Uniform Standards and Procedures for the Performance of Draught Surveys for Coal Cargoes. [UNESCO-ECE]	

(c) Pollution.

[56] Dedicated Clean Ballast Tanks.	IMO-619.
[57] International Convention on Oil Pollution Preparedness, Response and Co-operation. (OPRC).	IMO-550.
[58] Guidelines for the Development of Shipboard Oil Pollution Emergency Plans.	IMO-586.
[59] Recommendations on International Effluent Standards and Guidelines for Performance Tests for Sewage Treatment Plants.	IMO-592.
[60] Manual on Oil Pollution.	
[ ] I. Prevention.	IMO-000.
[ ] II. Contingency Planning.	IMO-560.
[ ] III. Salvage.	IMO-566.
[ ] IV. Combating Oil Spills.	IMO-569.
[61] International Convention for the Prevention of Pollution from Ships. (MARPOL). [consolidated].	IMO-520.
[62] Manual on Chemical Pollution.	IMO-630.
[63] International Convention for the Prevention of Pollution of the Sea by Oil. (OILPOL).	IMO-500.
[64] Oily Water Separators and Monitoring Equipment.	IMO-608.

Commercial Publications.

[65]   International Safety Guide for Oil Tankers and Terminals. (ISGOTT)
[66]   Shipboard Oil Pollution Emergency Plans. UK-DOT. M.Notice M1524.
[67]   Response to Marine Oil Spills. ITOPF.
[68]   Guidelines for the preparation of shipboard oil spill contingency plans.
       ITOPF / OCIMF.
[69]   Model Shipboard Oil Pollution Emergency Plan. ICS / ITOPF / OCIMF.
[70]   Thomas' Stowage.
[71]   Bulk Carriers, Guidance and Information to Ship Owners and Operators. IACS.
[72]   Bulk Carriers, Guidance to Operators on the Inspection of Cargo Holds. LR.
[73]   Guidelines for Surveys, Assessment and Repair of Hull Structure. IACS.
[74]   Steel carriage by sea. A.Sparks. LLP.
[75]   Tanker handbook for deck officers. Capt.C.Baptist. Brown,S & Ferguson.
[76]   Petroleum tanker safety. Southampton Institute - Warsash Campus.
[77]   Marine Claims. C.Luddeke. LLP.
[78]   The theory and practice of seamanship. G.L.Danton.
[79]   Admiralty Manuals of seamanship, Volumes I,II & III.   HMSO.
[80]   Drug trafficking and drug abuse.   ICS.
[81]   Sea Carrier Security Manual.   U.S.Customs.
[82]   Pirates and Armed Robbers, a Masters' Guide. ISF.
[83]   Shipping Law. Chorley & Giles. Pitman.
[84]   Carriage of Goods by sea. Payne.
[85]   Business and Law for the Shipmaster. F.N.Hopkins. Brown S.& Ferguson.
[86]   Money and Ships, Various Conference Proceedings. Seatrade.
[87]   Marine Cargo Operations. C.L.Sauerbier.   J.Wiley.
[88]   Ship Stability for Masters and Mates. D.R.Derrett.
[89]   Guidelines on the application of the ISM Code. ICS/ISF.
[90]   Think Safe.   Shell International Marine Ltd.
[91]   Code of Safe Working Practice for Merchant Seamen. UK-DOT.
[92]   Effective Mooring. Shell.
[93]   Stay Safe.   ISF/ICS/WoE.
[94]   Safety at Sea International journal, Various issues.
[95]   Safety in Oil Tankers. I.C.S.
[96]   Safety in Chemical Tankers. I.C.S.
[97]   Safety in Liquified Gas Tankers. I.C.S.
[98]   1993 Annual report of the Memorandum of Understanding
       on Port State Control.   Secretariat in the Netherlands.
[99]   Training Onboard   L.A.Holder.   Witherby/Videotel.

Examples of descriptive clauses on bills of lading for steel cargoes

Reference : chapter 12.3 and 12.4

1. Surface condition of steel cargo.

The following clauses have been recommended by the International Group of P&I Clubs to ensure consistency in describing 'rust' on steel cargo or its steel packaging.[31]

1. **Covered with snow.**
Surface covered with snow or ice or both.

2. **Galvanising affected by white oxidation marks.**
Zinc coating losing lustre and etched with white coloured oxidation marks.

3. **Galvanising affected by white rust.**
Zinc coating heavily oxidated and covered in voluminous white coloured rust.

4. **Galvanising dull.**
Zinc coating losing lustre as a result of early oxidation.

5. **Grease spots and oil patches apparent.**
Surface stained with drops of grease and oil from mechanical handling equipment, or other sources.

6. **Partly rust stained.**
Fine powdery rust covering less than 75% of the surface. Light tan to light brown in colour and easily removed by rubbing, scraping or wire-brushing to reveal a smooth steel surface. The remainder of the surface may still have mill scale attached.

7. **Partly rusty.**
Brown to heavy deep brown rust covering less than 75% of the surface. Slightly uneven and dull steel surface revealed when removed by wire-brushing. Remainder of the surface may be "partly rust stained".

8. **Rust on edges.**
Brown to heavy deep brown rust confined to the edges, otherwise same comments as "Partly rusty"

9. **Rust spots apparent.**
Localised very slight penetration of rust through mill scale, not bulbous and reveals a smooth steel surface when removed by wire-brushing.

10. **Rust spotting.**
Localised penetration of rust through mill scale, bulbous and reveals an uneven steel surface when removed by wire-brushing.

11. **Rust stained.**
Fine powdery rust over the whole surface, light tan to light brown in colour, and easily removed by rubbing, scraping or wire-brushing to reveal a smooth steel surface.

12. **Rust with pitting.**
Brown to heavy deep brown rust which when removed by wire-brushing reveals pitting of the steel surface.

13. **Rusty.**
Brown to heavy deep brown rust which when removed by wire-brushing reveals an uneven and dull steel surface.

14. **Stained by an unidentifiable powder.**
Surface coated (the extent should be indicated) with a powder which has not been identified (its colour should be stated) which could contain aggressive chemicals or be capable of holding moisture.

15. **Streaky rust indicated previous contact with water.**
Surface has rust streaks indicating that water has previously dripped down the cargo.

16. **Surface areas reacting to silver nitrate solution tests.**

Silver Nitrate tests prove that the surface has been in contact with salt water or other chlorides.

17. **Wet before shipment.**

Water visible on the surface, or dripping out of bundles.

2. Mechanical damage to steel cargo.

The following clauses are typical of those used to describe mechanical damage to steel cargo or its packaging.[31,74] They should accurately describe the apparent order and condition of the cargo and its packaging at the time of shipment. The following information should also be stated:–

—The number of places the stated damage occurs on one unit.

—The total number of units affected, giving the individual marks of the pieces affected if practicable.

—The location of the damage on the unit.

—The dimensions of the damage.

1. *Piece number —, inner and outer circumference edges of packing locally dented where marked by handling gear.*
2. *— packages have the top packing pierced and torn open in — places, and the plate is visibly scored.*
3. *Package number —, side packing torn in two places.*
4. *Edges of — plates gouged, in bundle number — .*
5. *Coil number —, edges dented / buckled where handling gear marked, affects — windings.*
6. *Coil number —, edges of — windings affected by deep score marks.*
7. *— coils inner turns telescoped out to — centimetres.*
8. *— coils loosely wound, and strapping bands slack.*
9. *— coils have — bands broken.*
10. *— coils distorted and ovalised.*
11. *— plates edges bent upwards in — places.*
12. *Plate number — permanently waved along its entire length.*
13. *Edges of plate waved/distorted.*
14. *Interlocking grooves dented / bent / distorted.*
15. *Machined surfaces scored / nicked / indented.*
16. *— beams bent, flanges and webs distorted.*
17. *Flanges of beams (in bundles) incorrectly overlapping for stowage purposes.*
18. *— bundles loosely secured.*
19. *All bundles insufficiently strapped.*
20. *Strapping bands missing / broken on — bundles.*
21. *— pipes dented at one end, pipes out of round.*
22. *— pipes locally dented in — places.*
23. *— pipes cement coating chipped / cracked / broken off.*
24. *Pipe number —, bevelled edge nicked / scored to a depth of — cm.*
25. *Protective coating chafed / scored / missing on — pieces.*
26. *— bundles loosely secured, wire slack, and leaning to one side.*
27. *— bundles, end windings pulled out, bent / twisted / mangled.*
28. *— pieces in the bundle bent along entire length.*
29. *Bundle pieces projecting on ends, — pieces bent.*
30. *Dented in — positions.*
    (For hollow sections, the reduction of internal diameter should be measured and stated.)

Displacement calculation for a draft survey

	ARRIVAL			DEPARTURE			LINE
DATE AND TIME							*1
	FORD	AFT	MID	FORD	AFT	MID	
OBSERVED DRAFT: PORT							*2
STBD							*3
MEAN							4
APPARENT TRIM							5
DISTANCE FROM PERPS.							+6
LENGTH BETWEEN MARKS							7
DRAFT MARK CORRECTION							8
TRUE DRAFT							9
TRUE TRIM							10
TRUE MEAN DRAFT (TMD)							11
OBSERVED DENSITY							*12
SCALE DENSITY							+13
T.P.C. AT MID.PORT							+14
T.P.C. AT MID.STDB.							+15
T.P.C. AT TRUE MEAN DRAFT							+16
L.C.F.							+17
L.B.P.							+18
M.T.C. @ TMD+50 cm.							+19
M.T.C. @ TMD-50 cm.							+20
DISPLACEMENT @ TMD							+21
1st. TRIM CORRECTION							22
2nd. TRIM CORRECTION							23
LIST CORRECTION							24
DISPLACEMENT @ EVENKEEL							25
TRUE DISPLACEMENT							26
BALLAST							*27
FUEL OIL							*28
DIESEL OIL							*29
LUB.OIL							*30
FRESH WATER							*31
STORES							*32
MISC							*33
MISC							*34
TOTAL DEDUCTABLES							35
NET DISPLACEMENT							36
CARGO LOADED/DISCHARGED							37

Explanation of lines.

*   Obtained by observation.
+   Obtained from ship's approved stability manual and
        from ship's approved calibration tables.
    Others obtained by calculations as follows:

L4 $= \dfrac{L2 + L3}{2}$

L5 $= L4 \text{ (aft)} - L4 \text{ (ford)}$ { STERN TRIM IS POSITIVE }

L6. If not in ship's tables, can be estimated from observation.
    Named NEGATIVE if the perpendicular is forward of the marks.

L7 $= L18 + L6 \text{ (aft)} - L6 \text{ (ford)}$ { REMEMBER a negative number multiplied by another
                                                          negative number results in a positive number }

L8 $= \dfrac{L5 \times L6}{L7}$

L9 $= L4 + L8$

L10 $= L9 \text{ (aft)} - L9 \text{ (ford)}$ { STERN TRIM IS POSITIVE }

L11 $= \dfrac{(6 \times L9 \text{ mid}) + (L9 \text{ aft}) + (L9 \text{ ford})}{8}$

L17. LCF is usually measured from Midships.
    It is usual to name LCF as NEGATIVE if it is FORWARD of Midships. However, on some
    ships, the data is listed with positive meaning forward of admidships. The officer should
    ensure he is familiar with the system used on his ship.
    { If it is given in the tables from the Aft Perpendicular,
    then apply LBP÷2 to obtain the required figure.}

L22 $= \dfrac{L16 \times L17 \times L10 \times 100}{L18}$

L23 $= \dfrac{(L19 \approx L20) \times L10 \times L10 \times 50}{L18}$ { THIS CORRECTION IS ALWAYS POSITIVE }

L24 $= (L9 \text{ port} \sim L9 \text{ stbd}) \times (L14 \sim L15) \times 6$

L25 $= L21 + L22 + L23 + L24$

L26 $= \dfrac{L25 \times L12}{L13}$

L35 $= L27 + L28 + L29 + L30 + L31 + L32 + L33 + L34$

L36 $= L26 - L35$

L37 $= L36 \text{ (arrival)} \sim L36 \text{ (departure)}$

SURVEY CHECKLIST

ANNUAL SURVEYS
INTERMEDIATE SURVEYS
DOCKING SURVEYS

IN ACCORDANCE WITH THE CLASSIFICATION REGULATIONS AND PROTOCOL 1988 RELATING TO SOLAS 1974 AND 1966 ILLC.
SURVEY REQUIREMENTS FOR CARGO SHIPS INCLUDING OIL TANKERS.
(See separate checklists for Chemical Tankers and Gas Carriers)

FOR ANNUAL OR INTERMEDIATE SURVEY MARK 'X' TO INDICATE 'YES' IN APPROPRIATE CIRCLE FOR EACH ITEM. IF AN ITEM IS NOT APPLICABLE MARK 'NA' IN APPROPRIATE CIRCLE. ALL REQUIRED DATES SHOULD BE RECORDED AT THESE SURVEYS.

FOR DOCKING SURVEY COMPLETE SECTION G ONLY.

ANNUAL SURVEY:	TO BE HELD WITHIN 3 MONTHS BEFORE OR AFTER THE ANNIVERSARY DATE.
INTERMEDIATE SURVEY:	INSTEAD OF THE 2ND OR 3RD ANNUAL SURVEY.
DOCKING SURVEY:	TO BE HELD AT APPROX. $2^1/_2$ YEAR INTERVALS.
IN-WATER SURVEY:	IN LIEU OF ANY ONE OF THE 2 DRYDOCKINGS REQUIRED IN A PERIOD OF 5 YEARS.

A.	**GENERAL (ANNUAL AND INTERMEDIATE SURVEYS)**	
A.1	Have modifications been made to the ship or equipment which would affect the validity of the Safcon or Loadline Certificates? (any modifications are to be reported)	Yes/No*
A.2	Are the periodical surveys required for boilers and other pressure vessels overdue?	Yes/No*
A.3	Are the CSM and CSH Cycles up to date in accordance with the current survey status?	Yes/No*
A.4	Is the Periodical Survey of the automation and/or remote controls for the main propulsion plant overdue? (see also section D)	Yes/No*
A.5	Is the Periodical Survey of the Inert Gas System overdue? (see also section F)	Yes/No*

B.	**DOCUMENTATION (ANNUAL AND INTERMEDIATE SURVEYS)**			
B.1	List the following:	*Expiry Date*	*A.S. or I.S.* *Endorsement Date*	*Certificate issued by*
	(a) Cargo Ship Safety Construction Certificate			
	(b) Cargo Ship Safety Equipment Certificate			
	(c) Cargo Ship Safety Radio Certificate			
	(d) International Load Line Certificate			
	(e) International Oil Pollution Prevention Certificate			
B.2	The Log entries record that the following have been checked or tested and found satisfactory within twelve (12) hours before departure from any port.			
	(a) Steering gear. (The tests included, where applicable, the operation of the main steering gear, the auxiliary steering gear, remote control systems, bridge steering position, emergency power supply, rudder angle indicators, steering gear system power unit failure alarms, automatic isolating arrangements and other alarms.)			◯
	(b) Communications system bridge to steering gear compartment.			◯
	(c) Full movement of the rudder.			◯
	(d) Visual inspection of steering linkage.			◯
B.3	The log entries record that emergency steering drills have been carried out every three (3) months.			◯
B.4	The change-over procedure diagrams of steering gear are posted.			◯
B.5	All Officers are reportedly familar with steering gear change-over procedures.			◯
B.6	The approved stability/loading information is on board.			◯
B.7	For ships assigned timber loadlines the approved timber deck cargo loading, and lashing plan is on board			◯

Name of Ship	LR Number	Report Number	Surveyor's Signature	Date	Page
					1

C. HULL SURVEY (ANNUAL AND INTERMEDIATE SURVEYS)

C.1	The condition of the hull and its closing appliances is satisfactory as far as could be seen. The following items should be included as applicable.	○
	Weather decks, hatchways, vents and air pipes; casings, fiddley openings, skylights, flush deck scuttles, deckhouses and companionways; superstructures, side, bow and stern doors; windows, sidescuttles and deadlights; chutes and other openings; scuppers, sanitary discharges and valves; guardrails and bulwarks; freeing ports, gangways, walkways and lifelines; and permanent fittings for timber deck cargoes.	
C.2	The condition of anchoring and mooring equipment is satisfactory, as far as could be seen.	○
C.3	The watertight doors in the watertight bulkheads have been examined, operationally tested (remotely and locally) and found satisfactory.	○
C.4	The condition of watertight bulkhead penetrations is satisfactory, as far as could be seen.	○
C.5	The structural fire protection arrangements remain unchanged. (Alterations are to be reported)	○
C.6	The manual and/or automatic fire doors have been operationally tested and found satisfactory	○
C.7	The operation of the loading instrument has been verified.	○
C.8	The freeboard marks have been verified. (Report summer freeboard ....m\m)	○
C.9	Hatch covers have been checked and tested where necessary and found weathertight.	○
C.10	*Dry Bulk Cargo Ships*	
	Two cargo holds examined and found satisfactory.	○
	Report holds examined:	
C.11	*Salt Water Ballast Tank Examinations (applicable to all ship types)*	○
	The tanks where protective coating was not applied at construction or the protection has deteriorated and not renewed have been examined and found satisfactory.	○
	Note: THOSE TANKS WHICH MAY REQUIRE TO BE EXAMINED ANNUALLY ARE INDICATED IN THE SHIPS SURVEY STATUS	
	Report the tanks examined:	
	Peak Tanks:	
	Topside Tanks:	
	Deep Tanks/Side Tanks:	
	Waterballast Tanks on Oil Tankers and Oil/Ore Carriers:	

D. MACHINERY AND ELECTRICAL INSTALLATION SURVEY (ANNUAL AND INTERMEDIATE SURVEYS)

D.1	The machinery and boiler spaces and essential machinery have been generally examined and found satisfactory.	○
D.2	The emergency escape routes from the machinery and boiler spaces are free of obstruction.	○
D.3	The machinery and boiler spaces are free of all visible fire and explosion hazards.	○
D.4	The main and auxiliary steering arrangements, including their associated equipment and control system, have been examined, operated and found satisfactory.	○
D.5	All the means of communication between navigating bridge, machinery and control and alternative steering positions have been tested and found satisfactory.	○
D.6	The bilge pumping systems, including bilge wells, reach rods, pumps and level alarms where fitted, have been examined and operated as far as practicable and all found satisfactory.	○
D.7	An external examination of boilers, pressure vessels, including safety devices, foundations, controls, relieving gear, insulation, gauges and piping has been carried out as far as practicable, and found satisfactory.	○
D.8	An examination of the electrical system together with an operational test has been carried out as far as practicable, and found satisfactory.	○
D.9	An examination and test, as far as practicable, of emergency sources of power, including control and change-over arrangements have been carried out and all found satisfactory.	○
D.10	A general examination of automation equipment has been carried out and operation considered satisfactory.	○

Name of Ship	LR Number	Report Number	Surveyor's Signature	Date	Page
					2

FORM 2100 (07/91) LLOYD'S REGISTER OF SHIPPING

E. FIRE FIGHTING EQUIPMENT SURVEY (ANNUAL AND INTERMEDIATE SURVEYS)

E.1	The fire control plan and duplicate have been examined and are properly posted.	◯
E.2	All fire and/or smoked detection systems have been examined and tested, as far as was practicable, and found satisfactory.	◯
E.3	An operative test of the fire main system and each fire pump, including the emergency fire pump, has been carried out separately, to demonstrate that the two required jets of water could be provided simultaneously from different hydrants.	◯
E.4	All fire hoses, nozzles, applicators and spanners are situated at their respective stations and in satisfactory condition.	◯
E.5	The fixed fire fighting system controls, piping, instructions and markings are properly maintained and serviced. Date of last reported system test:	◯
E6	All semi-portable and portable extinguishers are fully charged, in their stowed position and with valid service dates.	◯
E.7	The remote controls for stopping fans and machinery and shutting off fuel supplies in machinery spaces are in working order.	◯
E.8	The closing arrangements of ventilators, annular spaces, skylights, doorways and tunnel where applicable are satisfactory.	◯
E.9	The fireman's outfits are complete and in satisfactory condition.	◯

F. OIL TANKERS/OIL ORE CARRIERS (ANNUAL AND INTERMEDIATE SURVEYS)
(In addition to A, B, C, D & E)

F.1	**Weather Deck** Cargo tank openings including gaskets, covers, coamings, P/V valves and flame screens are all satisfactory as far as could be seen.	◯
F.2	Flame screens on vents at all bunker, oily ballast and oily slop tanks and void spaces are satisfactory as far as could be seen.	◯
F.3	An external examination of cargo, crude oil washing, bunker, ballast and vent piping systems including vent masts and headers has been carried out and all found in satisfactory condition.	◯
F.4	The condition of electrical of electrical equipment in dangerous zones is satisfactory as far as could be ascertained.	◯
F.5	**Cargo Pump Room** Potential sources of ignition (in or near the cargo pump room) such as loose gear, excessive product in bilges, excessive vapours, combustible materials, etc. have been elimated.	◯
F.6	The access ladders are in satisfactory condition.	◯
F.7	All electrical equipment is in satisfactory condition as far as could be ascertained.	◯
F.8	The pump room bulkheads are free of signs of oil leakage or fractures.	◯
F.9	The sealing arrangements of bulkhead penetrations are satisfactory.	◯
F.10	An external examination of piping systems has been carried out and all found in satisfactory condition.	◯
F.11	The cargo, bilge, ballast and stripping pumps examined as far as practicable and found satisfactory for:	
	(a) Excessive gland seal leakage	◯
	(b) Operation of electrical and mechanical remote operating and shutdown devices	◯
	(c) Integrity of pump room bilge system and pump foundations	◯
F.12	The pump room ventilation system is operational, and the ducting intact, the dampers are operable and the screens are clean.	◯
F.13	As far as could be seen, the installed pressure gauges on cargo discharge lines and level indicator systems are operational.	◯
F.14	**Inert Gas Systems (where fitted)** From external examination, all components and piping found free of signs of corrosion or gas/effluent leakage.	◯
F.15	Both inert gas blowers are operational.	◯

Name of Ship	LR Number	Report Number	Surveyor's Signature	Date	Page
					3

FORM 2100 (07/91) LLOYD'S REGISTER OF SHIPPING

F.	OIL TANKERS/OIL ORE CARRIERS CONTINUED (ANNUAL AND INTERMEDIATE SURVEYS) (In addition to A, B, C, D & E)	
	Intert Gas Systems (where fitted) – continued	
F.16	The scrubber room ventilation system is operational	◯
F.17	The deck water seal filling and draining system is operational and without evidence of water carry-over.	◯
F.18	The non-return valve is operational.	◯
F.19	The operation of all remotely operated or automatically controlled valves, in particular the flue gas isolating valve(s) found satisfactory.	◯
F.20	The interlocking feature of the soot blowers checked and found satisfactory.	◯
F.21	The gas pressure regulating valve automatically closes when the inert gas blowers are secured.	◯
F.22	The following safety devices of the inert gas system have been checked, as far as practicable, using simulated conditions where necessary and found satisfactory:	◯
	(a) High oxygen content of gas in the inert gas main	◯
	(b) Low gas pressure in the inert gas main	◯
	(c) Low pressure in the supply to the deck water seal	◯
	(d) High temperature of gas in the inert gas main	◯
	(e) Low water pressure to the scrubber	◯
	(f) Accuracy of portable and fixed oxygen measuring equipment by means of calibration gas	◯
	(g) Water level in the scrubber	◯
	(h) Failure of the inert gas blowers	◯
	(i) Failure of the power supply to the automatic control system for the gas regulating valve and to the instrumentation for continuous indication and permanent recording of pressure and oxygen content in the inert gas main	◯
	(j) High gas pressure in the inert gas main	◯
F.23	*Fire Extinguishing Arrangements* All isolating valves and piping of the cargo tank and cargo pump room fixed fire fighting system were externally examined as far as practicable and found satisfactory.	◯
F.24	The deck foam and deck sprinkler systems were found to be operable and in satisfactory condition.	◯

G.	DOCKING SURVEYS	
G.1	A satisfactory examination of the shell including bottom and bow plating, keel, stern, sternframe and rudder was carried out.	◯
G.2	The clearances of rudder bearings are satisfactory. Report clearances:	◯
G.3	The sea suctions and overboard discharge valves and their connections to the hull were generally examined and all found satisfactory.	◯
G.4	The propeller and fastenings, sternbush fastenings, and the gratings at the sea inlets were examined and found satisfactory.	◯
G.5	The propeller shaft seal(s) were found satisfactory and tight or the propeller shaft(s) clearance(s) were satisfactory. Report Clearances/Poker gauge readings:	◯
G.6	The anchoring and mooring equipment was examined as far as practicable, the anchors and cables partially raised and lowered using the windlass and found satisfactory.	◯
	Note: CONSIDERATION SHOULD BE GIVEN TO THE EXAMINATION OF ANCHORS, CHAIN CABLES CHAIN LOCKERS AND THICKNESS DETERMINATION REQUIREMENTS AT DOCKING SURVEYS PRIOR TO SPECIAL SURVEYS	

Name of Ship	LR Number	Report Number	Surveyor's Signature	Date	Page
					4

FORM 2100 (07/91) LLOYD'S REGISTER OF SHIPPING

H.	ADDITIONAL SURVEY REQUIREMENTS: INTERMEDIATE SURVEYS

H.1 The electrical generating sets have been examined under working conditions and found satisfactory. ○

H.2 *Salt Water Ballast Tanks (Ships 5-10 years old)*

An internal general examination of representative salt water ballast tanks has been satisfactorily carried out. ○

The following tanks were examined:

(a) Peak tanks
Report tanks examined ○

(b) Topside Tanks
Reported tanks examined: ○

(c) Deep Tanks and Side Tanks
Report tanks examined: ○

(d) Independent Double Bottom Tanks
Report tanks examined: ○

(e) Water Ballast Tanks on Oil Tankers and Oil/Ore Carriers (all tanks)
Report tanks examined: ○

H.3 *Salt Water Ballast Tanks (Ships over 10 years old)*

An internal general examination of *all* salt water ballast tanks has been satisfactorily carried out ○

The following tanks were examined:

(a) Fore and Aft Peak Tanks
Report tanks examined: ○

(b) Topside Tanks
Report tanks examined: ○

(c) Deep Tanks and Side Tanks
Report tanks examined: ○

(d) Independent Double Bottom Tanks
Report tanks examined: ○

(e) Water Ballast Tanks on Oil Tankers and Oil/Ore Carriers
Report tanks examined: ○

H.4 *Dry Cargo Ships over 15 years old*

A forward and aft cargo hold examined and found satisfactory
Report holds examined: ○

H.5 *Oil Tankers and Oil/Ore Carriers*

(a) A satisfactory examination of cargo, crude oil washing, bunker, ballast, steam and vent piping on the weather decks, including vent masts and headers was carried out. ○

(b) A satisfactory general examination of the electrical equipment and cables in dangerous zones such as cargo pump rooms and areas adjacent to cargo tanks was carried out. ○

(c) The insulation resistance of the circuits was satisfactorily tested or there is a recent record of insulation resistance testing that is considered acceptable. ○

H.6 *Oil Tanker and Oil/Ore Carries over 10 years old*

(a) The anchors and cables were satisfactorily partially raised and lowered using the windlass. ○

(b) At least two cargo tanks were examined internally and found satisfactory. ○
Report tanks examined.

(c) The machinery and boiler spaces, including tank tops, bilges and cofferdams, sea suctions and discharges were generally examined and found satisfactory. ○

Name of Ship	LR Number	Report Number	Surveyor's Signature	Date	Page
					5

L.R. GUIDANCE IN RESPECT OF PROCEDURE TO BE ADOPTED BY OWNERS FOR EXPEDITING SAFETY EQUIPMENT RENEWAL SURVEYS ON CARGO SHIPS AND ANNUAL AND INTERMEDIATE SURVEYS AS APPLICABLE

1. To avoid unnecessary delay to the ship, much of the following preparatory work can have been dealt with prior to the Surveyor's initial visit to the ship.

2. The Master to have readily available, for use by the attending surveyor, the Lloyd's Register Report S.E.1 "Record of Safety Equipment" together with the original and certified copy of the latest Cargo Ship Safety Equipment Certificate.

3. All lifeboats to be cleared of bottom boards, food and water containers, buoyancy tanks and equipment.

    3.1 The Master, or other responsible officer, could possibly ascertain by personal inspection, the condition of the buoyancy tanks and anticipate the surveyor requiring the repair or testing of the buoyancy tanks. These could then have been placed ashore in the hands of responsible repairers for attention where applicable.

    3.2 Masts and sails erected in pulling boats.

    3.3 The motor boat engine, or other mechanical means of propulsion, tried under working conditions, preferably in the water.

    3.4 External Water Spray System and Internal Self Contained Air Support Systems to be verified operational and fully charged.

4. The surveyor to be requested to attend when items 2 and 3 above are prepared and ready.

    4.1 Each boat will be examined internally and externally by the surveyor and any necessary repairs itemised.

    4.2 Means for illuminating the launching gear, lifeboats and rafts to be tested; source of power to be checked.

5. All boats to be swung out; at least 50 per cent lowered into the water; each painter end secured at the embarkation position.

    5.1 Davit span ropes and boarding ladders to be lowered.

    5.2 Fall release mechanism to be tested.

    5.3 Motor or other mechanically operated lifeboat to have a short trial afloat, to test ahead and astern manoeuvring.

6. All lifeboat equipment to be laid out for examination near the lifeboat stations. A responsible ship's officer can already have checked the loose equipment against the Report S.E.1 and any obvious deficiencies can be made good.

7. Liferaft certificates to be produced, indicating also the date of the last servicing. In addition, the list of equipment verified as being in accordance with Convention requirements.

8. Lifejackets and thermal protective aids and/or immersions suits to be collected at one position for examination; any obvious deficiencies or damage made good by responsible ship's officer.

9. Lifebuoys, lights, smoke floats and buoyant lines to be in their positions for examination.

10. Navigation lights, electric and oil, with spares, to be assembled at one place, so far as practicable, for examination.

    10.1 Masthead lights, sidelights and anchor light to be tested in position. Visual and/or audible failure warning devices on bridge to be verified operational.

11. Pilot ladder to be lowered overside at position, together with the accommodation ladder if this forms part of the pilot boarding arrangements.

    11.1 Electric light for same to be tested in position.

12. Fire hoses and nozzles to be ranged for examination and container boxes to be examined; any defective hoses to be replaced.

13. Breathing apparatus and firemen's equipment to be demonstrated as operating satisfactorily by a responsible ship's officer. Care to be taken that air cylinders are fully charged.

14. Main and emergency fire pumps to be tested with one hose rigged aft and one forward. It would be beneficial if ship's officers satisfy themselves, before the actual survey, that the emergency fire pump is operational.

15. All portable fire extinguishers will be examined, repaired, tested and recharged as necessary.

16. The CO_2, halon, foam, water spray, dry powder or steam smothering systems will be examined and tested, using the procedures set out in the operating manual.

16.1 Arrangements should be made to check the level of the charge in the CO_2 or halon system and for any deficiency to be made good.

16.2 Arrangements should be provided to blow through any CO_2 or halon system with compressed air and any steam smothering system with steam.

16.3 The operating mechanism and alarm systems will be examined and tested as necessary.

16.4 The foam concentrate of any foam system will be examined and tested and renewed if necessary. The system will be operated and afterwards flushed with water.

16.5 It may be necessary to engage the services of a specialised contractor to facilitate the survey of all fire appliances.

17. Audible fire warning systems, abandon ship warnings and ship's siren to be tested.

18. Stop switches outside the engine room for fans, etc., engine room discharge, remote control for valves, dampers and E.R. skylight closing devices to be operating satisfactorily.

19. Lifeboat and bridge pyrotechnics should be renewed when 3 years old, or as required by national regulations. Therefore, the necessary replacements can be made before the surveyor attends.

20. Before issuing the certificate, the Owner or his representative must afford the surveyor an opportunity to examine all completed repairs and replacements, as the responsibility for certification rest solely with the surveyor.

20.1 The surveyor can, however, only ensure that the safety equipment is in good condition at the time of survey and it is the responsibility of the Master to maintain it so. Maintenance of equipment between surveys is just as important as the survey itself.

20.2 It will be appreciated that any port authority, at any time, is entitled to examine the safety aspects of any ship, irrespective of flag, and therefore spot checks between surveys can be an embarrassment.

Structural defects—what to look out for[73]

1. Shell plating and frames.

1. Accelerated wastage and possible grooving.

2. Fractures in the webs of the frames and brackets.

3. Fractures in the shell plating.

4. Buckling of the side shell frames.

5. Detachment of frames from the side shell.

6. Detachment of end brackets from the wing tank structure.

7. Fatigue fractures, particularly at the ends of frames and brackets.

8. Deformations, especially the lower regions of the frames.

Damages to side shell frames

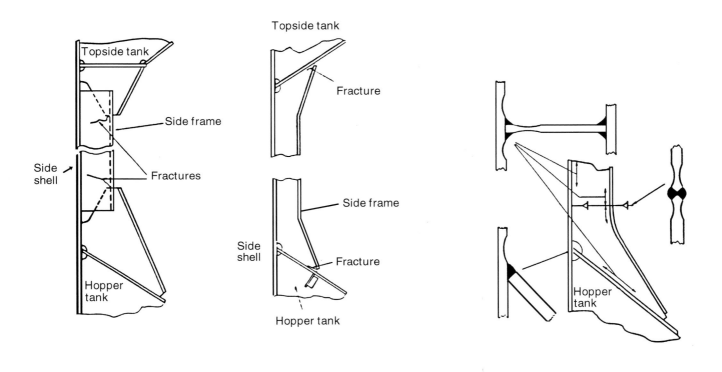

**Separate bracket
configuration** **Integral bracket
configuration** **Examples of
possible grooving**

The type of bracket configuration used will, to a large extent, dictate the location and extent of fracture. Where separate brackets are employed, the fracture location is normally at the bracket toe position on the frames, whereas with integral brackets the fracture location is at the toe position on the hopper and topside tank.

2.   The transverse bulkhead.

1.   Fractures at the boundaries of corrugations and bulkhead stools.

2.   Buckling of corrugations and plating.

3.   Excessive corrosion, especially in lower regions, paying particular attention to such areas as:−
    (a)   Bulkhead plating adjacent to the shell plating.
    (b)   Trunks between the topside and hopper tanks.
    (c)   Bulkhead plating and weld connections to the lower/upper stool shelf plates.
    (d)   Weld connections of stool plating to the lower/upper shelf plates and inner bottom.
    (e)   Weld connections to topside and hopper tanks.
    (f)   All areas where the coating has broken down.

Typical fracturing at the connection of transverse bulkhead structure

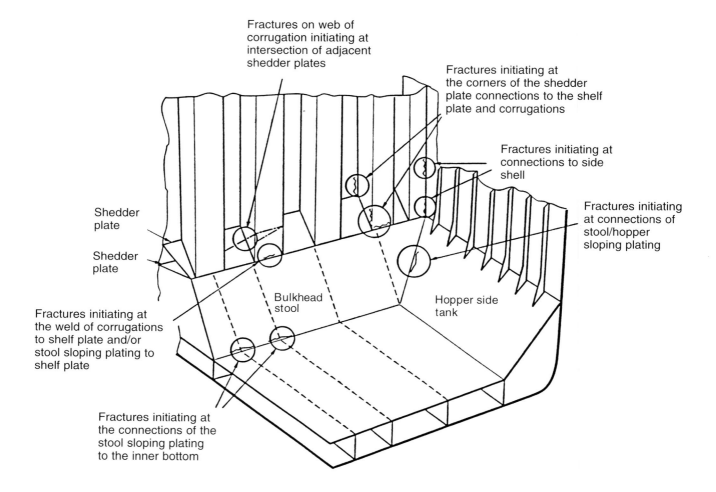

(Similar damages may occur at the upper connections of the bulkhead to the deck structure)

3.   The topside tank.

1.   Local corrosion due to breakdown of the coatings.

2.   Fractures or grooving in way of connections between longitudinals and web frames.

3.   Fractures at the connections in line with hold transverse bulkheads.

4.   Fractures at the connections in line with the transverse framing and end brackets.

5.   Wastage at edges of openings and slots.

6.   Wastage of the bottom plate, and connections to side plating.

4.   The double bottom structure, including the hopper tank.

1.   Fractures at the transition between the double bottom and the hopper tank.

2.   Fractures in the double bottom in way of the transverse bulkhead stool.

3.   Corrosion in ballast tanks close to heated fuel oil tanks.

4.   Wear of the shell plating below suction heads.

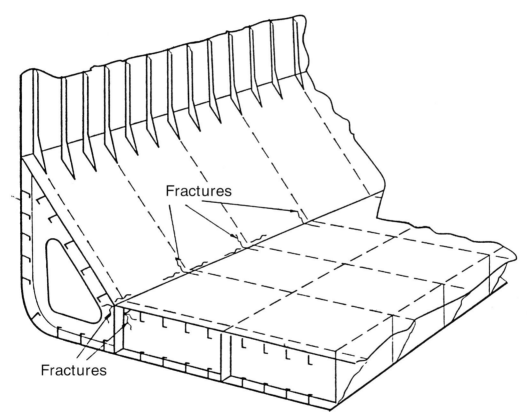

Typical fractures in the connection of hopper plating and tanktop/inner bottom

The illustrations in this appendix are reproduced from *Guidelines for Surveys, Assessment and Repair of Hull Structures* courtesy of the International Association of Classification Societies (IACS).

IMO dangerous goods labels and segregation[35]

General requirements for segregation in stowage between the various classes of dangerous goods.

Since the properties of substances or articles within each class may vary greatly, the individual schedules should always be consulted for particular requirements for segregation, as these take precedence over the general requirements indicated in the table below.

CLASS		1.1 1.2 1.5	1.3	1.4	2.1	2.2	2.3	3	4.1	4.2	4.3	5.1	5.2	6.1	6.2	7	8	9
Explosives	1.1, 1.2, 1.5	*	*	*	4	2	2	4	4	4	4	4	4	2	4	2	4	X
Explosives	1.3	*	*	*	4	2	2	4	3	3	4	4	4	2	4	2	4	X
Explosives	1.4	*	*	*	2	1	1	2	2	2	2	2	2	X	4	2	2	X
Flammable gases	2.1	4	4	2	X	X	X	2	1	2	X	2	2	X	4	2	1	X
Non-toxic, non-flammable gases	2.2	2	2	1	X	X	X	1	X	1	X	X	1	X	2	1	X	X
Poisonous gases	2.3	2	2	1	X	X	X	2	X	2	X	X	2	X	2	1	X	X
Flammable liquids	3	4	4	2	2	1	2	X	X	2	1	2	2	X	3	2	X	X
Flammable solids	4.1	4	3	2	1	X	X	X	X	1	X	1	2	X	3	2	1	X
Spontaneously combustible substances	4.2	4	3	2	2	1	2	2	1	X	1	2	2	1	3	2	1	X
Substances which are dangerous when wet	4.3	4	4	2	X	X	X	1	X	1	X	2	2	X	2	2	1	X
Oxidizing substances	5.1	4	4	2	2	X	X	2	1	2	2	X	2	1	3	1	2	X
Organic peroxides	5.2	4	4	2	2	1	2	2	2	2	2	2	X	1	3	2	2	X
Poisons	6.1	2	2	X	X	X	X	X	X	1	X	1	1	X	1	X	X	X
Infectious substances	6.2	4	4	4	4	2	2	3	3	3	2	3	3	1	X	3	3	X
Radioactive materials	7	2	2	2	2	1	1	2	2	2	2	1	2	X	3	X	2	X
Corrosives	8	4	2	2	1	X	X	X	1	1	1	2	2	X	3	2	X	X
Miscellaneous dangerous substances and articles	9	X	X	X	X	X	X	X	X	X	X	X	X	X	X	X	X	X

Segregation should also take account of a single subsidiary risk label.

KEY: 1 : "Away from"
      2 : "Separated from"
      3 : "Separated by a complete compartment or hold from"
      4 : "Separated longitudinally by an intervening complete compartment or hold from"
      X : No general segregation required, but any particular requirements are shown in the individual schedules.
      * : See subsection 6.4 of the introduction to Class 1.

The precise meanings of these terms are defined in Section 15 of the General Introduction to the IMDG Code.

IMO DANGEROUS GOODS
LABELS, PLACARDS AND MARK

PLACARDS

SCALE: 4:1
ACTUAL SIZE: 250 mm × 250 mm

Samples of display of the UN number on placards or the orange panel for cargo transport units

ALTERNATIVE 1

ALTERNATIVE 2

FOR CLASS 7

(See also subsection 6.5 of the introduction to class 7 in the IMDG Code.)

SOLAS CONVENTION

Packages containing dangerous goods should be durably marked with the correct technical name and be provided with distinctive labels, stencils of the labels, or placards, as appropriate. The method of marking the correct technical name and of affixing labels, applying stencils of labels, or affixing placards on packages should be such that this information will still be identifiable on packages surviving at least three months' immersion in the sea. *(1974 SOLAS Convention, as amended, regulation 4 of chapter VII)*

IMDG CODE

Labels and placards are assigned to each class of dangerous goods in the IMDG Code, and denote the hazards involved by means of colours and symbols. Colours and symbols should be as illustrated except that symbols, texts and numbers on green, red and blue labels and placards may be white.

The class number should appear in the bottom corner of the label or placard. The use of the texts shown on the illustrations and of further descriptive texts is optional. However, for class 7 the text should always appear on the labels and the special placard. If texts are used for the other classes, the texts shown on the illustrations are recommended for the purpose of uniformity.

Dangerous goods which possess subsidiary dangerous properties must also bear subsidiary risk labels or placards denoting these hazards. Subsidiary risk labels and placards should not bear the class number in the bottom corner.

Labels for packages should not be less than 100 mm × 100 mm except in the case of packages which, because of their size, can only bear smaller labels. Placards for cargo transport units should not be less than 250 mm × 250 mm, should correspond with respect to colour and symbols to the labels, and should display the class number in digits not less than 25 mm high.

Some consignments of dangerous goods should have the UN number of the goods displayed in black digits not less than 65 mm high either against a white background in the lower half of the placard or on a rectangular orange panel not less than 120 mm high and 300 mm wide, with a 10 mm black border, to be placed immediately adjacent to the placard.

All labels, placards, orange panels and marine pollutant marks should be removed from cargo transport units or masked as soon as the dangerous goods have been unpacked and any residue removed. Detailed requirements regarding marking, labelling and placarding are contained in the IMDG Code.

MARK

SCALE: 3:1
ACTUAL SIZE: 100 mm × 100 mm

MARINE POLLUTANT mark for harmful (environmentally hazardous) substances. The mark should be in a contrasting colour to the packaging or, when used as a sticker, coloured black and white. For packages the triangular mark should have sides of at least 100 mm except in the case of packages which, because of their size, can only bear smaller marks. For cargo transport units this dimension should be not less than 250 mm.
(Annex III of MARPOL 73/78, as amended)

LABELS

SCALE: 3:1
ACTUAL SIZE: 100 mm × 100 mm

Class 1

* The appropriate division number and compatibility group are to be placed in this location, e.g. 1.1 D.
** The appropriate compatibility group is to be placed in this location, e.g. G.

For goods of class 1 in division 1.4 compatibility group S, each package may alternatively be marked 1.4 S.

Explosive subsidiary risk label for self-reactive substances in class 4.1 and organic peroxides (class 5.2) with explosive properties (for requirements see IMDG Code).

Class 2

Class 3

Class 4

Class 5

Class 6

Class 7

Class 8

Class 9

Bunkering checklist[24]

- ☐ Inform all the ship's staff of the bunkering operation.
- ☐ Ensure all personnel are aware of the Emergency Response Procedures.
- ☐ Discuss the bunkering plan and tank sequence with officers involved.
- ☐ Close and secure all associated overboard discharge valves.
- ☐ Close and blank-off all unnecessary manifold valves/connections.
- ☐ Plug all deck scuppers and ensure they are oil- and water-tight.
- ☐ Empty out and plug all savealls.
- ☐ Place oil absorbent materials at key locations.
- ☐ Provide a means of draining off any accumulation of deck water.
- ☐ Establish and check a common communications link between
  (a) Bunkering Station. (b) Duty Officer. (c) Engineroom.
- ☐ Check all bunker tank air pipes are open and unblocked.
- ☐ Ensure all sounding caps are tight when not being used.
- ☐ Reconfirm space remaining in all bunker tanks.
- ☐ Check all bunker tank high level alarms are functioning.
- ☐ Ensure all fire precautions are observed.
- ☐ Check hose is of sufficient length.
- ☐ Inspect hose and couplings for damage.
- ☐ Check weight of hose is less than SWL of hose lifting gear.
- ☐ Place drip trays under hose couplings and flanges.
- ☐ Check delivery note quantity and specification are correct.
- ☐ Discuss bunkering plan with the supplier.
- ☐ Discuss vessel's emergency response procedures with supplier.
- ☐ Discuss supplier's emergency response procedures with ship's staff.
- ☐ Establish communication link between vessel and supplier.
  Agree distinct signals for:
  - ☐ Commence pumping.   ☐ Increase pumping rate.
    ☐ Reduce pumping rate.
  - ☐ Cease pumping.
  - ☐ Emergency Stop.
- ☐ Agree total quantity to be supplied. Specify:_____
- ☐ Agree units of measurement—tonnes, barrels, cubic metres, etc. Specify:_____
- ☐ Agree maximum pumping rate and pressure. Specify:_____
- ☐ Carry out spot analysis with vessel's fuel test kit.
- ☐ Conduct compatibility test, if necessary.
- ☐ Sight, agree and record shore/barge meter readings or tank soundings. (Record on facing page).
- ☐ Rig fire wires, if required.
- ☐ Ensure seamen are assigned to tend moorings.
- ☐ Ensure a designated overflow tank is prepared, and lined up.
- ☐ Prepare (line-up) the filling line—open all relevant valves.
- ☐ Commence bunkering at a reduced rate.
- ☐ Monitor supply line pressure.
- ☐ Examine hose connections for leakage.
- ☐ Check all valves on the system.

Bunker Plan

SEQUENCE	TANK	GRADE	QUANTITIES			REMARKS
			INITIAL	RECEIVE	FINAL	

Shore/Barge Readings

We confirm the above checks have been carried out.

Signed for vessel: _____ Chief Engineer   Master

Signed for supplier: _____ Name   Position

FURTHER CHECKS DURING AND AFTER BUNKERING

☐ Check oil is entering the correct tank.
☐ Reduce pumping rate and/or open next tank before topping off.
☐ Close valves as each tank is completed.
☐ Witness, seal, date, jointly countersign, and retain bunker samples.
☐ Ensure sufficient ullage in final tank for hose draining/line blowing.
☐ Notify supplier when final tank is reached.
☐ Give suppliers ample warning to reduce pumping rate.
☐ Give suppliers ample warning to stop pumping.
☐ On completion, close all filling valves.
☐ Ensure all hoses are fully drained.
☐ Close and blank off manifold connection.
☐ Blank off disconnected hose couplings.
☐ Reconfirm all bunker line and tank filling valves are secured.
☐ Reconfirm all bunker tank soundings.
☐ Sight, agree and record shore/barge meter readings or tank soundings.
☐ Verify all details on the bunker receipts are correct.
☐ Complete relevant entries in Oil Record Book and Log Books.

Bulk cargo operations control form[3]

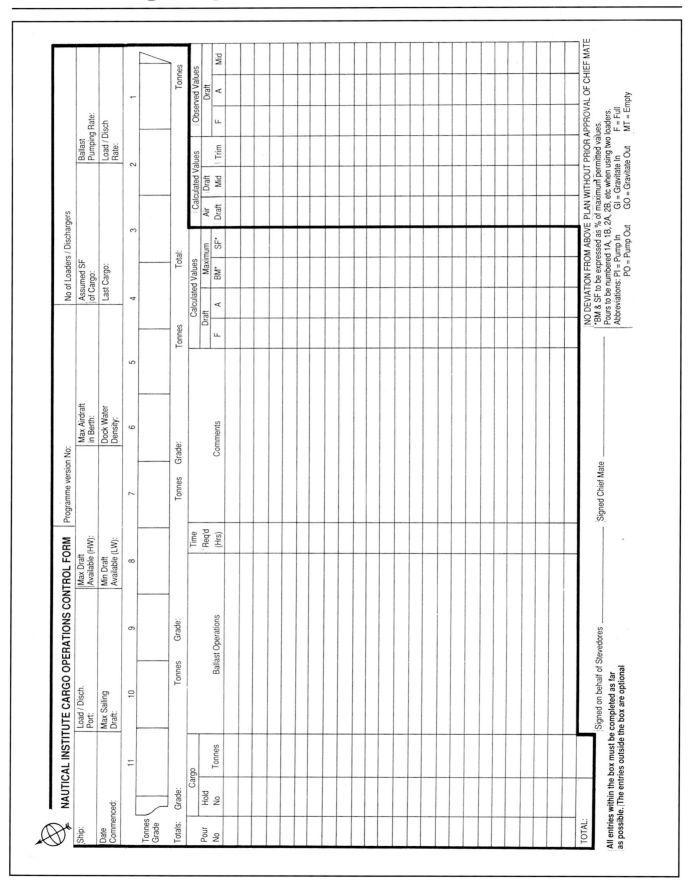

Examples of permits to work[65]

HOT WORK PERMIT

Relating to any work involving temperature conditions which are likely to be of sufficient intensity to cause ignition of combustible gases, vapours or liquids in or adjacent to the area involved.

General

This permit is valid   From ....Hrs   Date ....

To..Hrs   Date ....

Location of work..

....

Has enclosed space entry permit been issued?   Yes/No

Description of work ....

....

Personnel carrying out work ....

....

Responsible person in attendance ....

Section 1

1.1   Has the work area been checked with a combustible gas indicator for hydrocarbon vapours?   Yes/No

Time ....

1.2   Has the surrounding area been made safe?   Yes/No

Time ....

Section 2

2.1   Has the work area been checked with a combustible gas indicator for hydrocarbon vapours?   Yes/No

2.2   Has the equipment or pipeline been purged?   Yes/No

2.3   Has the equipment or pipeline been blanked?   Yes/No

2.4   Is this equipment or pipeline free of liquid?   Yes/No

2.5   Is the surrounding area safe?   Yes/No

2.6   Is additional fire protection available?   Yes/No

2.7   Is the equipment isolated electrically?   Yes/No

2.8   Special conditions/precautions

....

....

In the circumstances noted it is considered safe to proceed with this work.

Signed   ....Master/Responsible Officer

....Person in charge of work team

Section 3

The work has been completed and all persons under my supervision, materials and equipment have been withdrawn.

Authorised person in charge ....Time..Date ....

First copy for display at work area

Second copy for ships or terminal records.

To appear on reverse side of permit

HOT WORK PERMIT

GENERAL

(a) Starting/finishing time must not exceed the Authorized Signatories'/Responsible Officer's working hours.

(b) Specific location of work to be given.

(c) Description of work to include type of equipment to be used.

SECTION 1   Applies to all hazardous work not involving naked flame or continuous spark production, and would include use of electrical equipment, use of air driven rotary equipment, lifting equipment/materials over operating plant.

SECTION 2   Applies to all hot work involving high temperatures, open flame, arc or continuous source of sparks, etc. This type of work includes but is not limited to:

Welding or burning
Grinding
Sand or grit blasting
Metal chipping

Tests for combustible gas should be carried out immediately before commencement of hot work and at frequent intervals as long as the work is in progress.

COLD WORK PERMIT

Relating to any work involving temperature conditions which are likely to be of sufficient intensity to cause ignition of combustible gases, vapours or liquids in or adjacent to the area involved.

General

This permit is valid   From ....Hrs   Date ....

To ....Hrs   Date ....

Location of work...

....

Has enclosed space entry permit been issued?   Yes/No

Description of work ....

....

Personnel carrying out work ....

....

Responsible person in attendance ....

Section 1

Preparation and checks to be carried out by Officer in Charge of work to be performed.

1.1   The equipment/pipeline has been prepared as follows:

Vented to atmosphere:	Yes/No	Drained:	Yes/No
Washed:	Yes/No	Purged:	Yes/No
Other..			

1.2   The equipment/pipeline has been isolated as follows:

Lines Spaded:	Yes/No	Lines Disconnected:	Yes/No
Valves Closed:	Yes/No	Other	

1.3   Is equipment free from:

Oil: Yes/No   Gas: Yes/No H_2S: Yes/No   Steam: Yes/No
Pressure: Yes/No

1.4   Is surrounding area free from hazards?   Yes/No

1.5   If work is to be performed on electrical equipment has that equipment been isolated?   Yes/No

Section 2

Information and instructions to person carrying out work:

2.1   The following personal protection must be worn...

....

2.2   Equipment/Pipeline contained following material in service...

....

2.3   Equipment expected to contain the following hazardous material when opened ....

....

2.4   Special Conditions/Precautions ....

....

In the circumstances noted it is considered safe to proceed with this work.

Signed   ....Master/Responsible Officer

                 ....Person carrying out work task
                                                                 or in charge of work team

Section 3

The work has been completed and all persons under my supervision, materials and equipment have been withdrawn.

Authorized person in charge.....................................Time...Date ....

First copy for display at work area

Second copy for ships or terminal records.

To appear on reverse side of permit

COLD WORK PERMIT

GENERAL

    (a)   Starting/finishing time must not exceed the Authorized Signatories'/Responsible Officer's working hours.

    (b)   Specific location of work to be given.

    (c)   Description of work to include type of equipment to be used.

    (d)   This permit should be used for but not limited to the following cold work:

          1.   Blanking/deblanking.

          2.   Disconnecting and connecting pipework.

          3.   Removing and fitting of valves, blanks, spades or blinds.

          4.   Work on pumps, etc.

          5.   Clean up (oil spills).

This appendix is reproduced by permission of ICS/OCIMF from *ISGOTT Guide.*

Checklist for entry into enclosed spaces

Date: _____ **Period of validity:**_____

Location of space to be entered: _____

Names/ranks authorised to enter:_____

Description of work to be done: _____

_____

☐ Has the space been ventilated? **For how long?:** _____

☐ Has the oxygen meter been tested?

　OXYGEN CONTENT OF THE ENCLOSED SPACE: _____

☐ Has the explosimeter been tested ?

　EXPLOSIMETER READING OF THE SPACE: _____

☐ Has the toxic gas meter been tested?

　TOXICITY OF THE ENCLOSED SPACE: _____

☐ Is there a system for continuously monitoring the atmosphere?

☐ Is the space to be continuously ventilated?

☐ Will a responsible person remain at the entrance to the space?

　Is there an agreed communication system in place, and tested,

　☐　between the person at the entrance and those inside?

　☐　between the person at the entrance and the officer of the watch?

☐ Is rescue and resuscitation equipment ready at the entrance?

☐ Is fire-fighting equipment available at the entrance?

☐ Is access to the space adequate and safe?

☐ Is lighting in the space adequate and intrinsically safe?

☐ Is all equipment and tools in good condition and intrinsically safe?

☐ Has the officer of the watch been informed of the operation?

☐ Are the persons entering the space familiar with safety procedures?

☐ Have the persons entering the space been given detailed instructions on the work to be performed?

☐ Have precautions been taken to prevent the entry of injurious substances to the space, including relevant valves lashed and notices posted?

☐ Have all potential hazards been identified?

　Has any necessary extra safety equipment been checked and tested–

　☐　Safety harness and line　　　　☐　Suitable footwear.

　☐　Breathing apparatus.　　　　　☐　Safety Helmet or Bump Cap.

　☐　Light sticks.　　　　　　　　　☐　Suitable protective clothing.

Personnel accident report form

SHIP

Name:...Owner/Operator/: ....

Type: Cargo ☐   Passenger ☐   Tanker ☐   Container ☐   Bulk Carrier ☐   Other ☐

Gross Tonnage: .... Trade: Home ☐   Foreign ☐   Machinery: Steam ☐   Diesel ☐

SEAFARER

Name: ....   Rank/Rating:..

Address:..

Date of birth: ....   Sex: Male ☐   Female ☐

Dis A. No: ....   Nationality: ....

Port of Engagement: ....   Date of Employment: ....

ACCIDENT

Date of Accident: ....   Time:.....................   By Whom Reported:.........................

Date Reported:....................................   Time:.....................   To Whom Reported: ....

Place: On Board ☐   Ashore ☐   If on board, place on Ship: ....

If at sea, State Lat:.............. Long: .... If in Port, State Name: ....

Weather: Good ☐   Moderate ☐   Bad ☐   Shipping Seas/Spray ☐   Ice/Snow on Deck ☐

Was Seafarer at authorised place of work: Yes ☐   No ☐   Was Seafarer Sober: Yes ☐   No ☐

Was Seafarer on Duty: Yes ☐   No ☐   If on duty, hours worked continuously prior to Accident: ☐

Total number of hours worked by Seafarer in the 24 hours prior to the Accident

How was Seafarer employed at the time?: ....

Was the accident caused through negligence, default or misconduct of injured or other person: Yes ☐   No ☐

If Yes, give particulars: ....

Detailed description of accident:..

....

....

....

....

....

Cause of Accident: ....

What was the source of lighting?..

If rope involved was it: Natural Fibre ☐   Synthetic Fibre ☐   Wire Rope ☐   Combination Rope ☐

Names, addresses and Dis A. Nos. of witnesses: ....

....

....

INJURY

Nature: ....

Body location: ....

Has Injury incapacited Seafarer from work?   Yes ☐   No ☐

Period of Incapacity: Less than 1 day ☐   1 to 3 days ☐   4 to 7 days ☐   More than 7 days ☐

Date Injured Seafarer Ceased Work:..............................   Was a log entry made? ....Yes ☐   No ☐

If Yes, Copies of all relevant Log Entries must accompany this Report.

Was Seafarer Discharged through Injury: Yes ☐   No ☐

If Yes, State Name of Port and Date: ....

Particulars of Medical treatment on board/ashore (attach Medical Report): ....

....

....

Reproduced by courtesy of UK Chamber of Shipping.

Damage report form *(to Cargo or to the Ship)*

Ship's name : _____

Port and berth name : _____

Date/time of incident : _____

TO: _____

I regret to inform you that due to the negligence of your labour, the damages which are stated below have occurred, for which I hold you responsible.

(Attach supplementary sheets if there is insufficient space on this form.)

Description of incident:

Nature of damage:

(Give part numbers and/or cargo marks as appropriate)

Cause of damage:

(Give name of person causing damage)

Repairs required:

(Give details of any independent damage survey, and for ship, state any CLASS requirements)

You are hereby requested to repair these damages to your account prior to the vessel's departure. Costs of delays to count until the damages have been repaired to my satisfaction. Should you fail to effect proper repairs and should I decide to depart in order to mitigate losses, then you will remain responsible for the actual costs and times lost repairing these damages elsewhere.

Officer compiling this report : _____

Signed : _____ Date: _____

Countersigned Master : _____ Date: _____

* I HEREBY ACKNOWLEDGE RECEIPT OF THIS REPORT.
* I HEREBY AGREE THAT THE FACTS STATED IN THIS REPORT ARE CORRECT.
* I HEREBY ADMIT LIABILITY FOR THE DAMAGE AS STATED IN THIS REPORT.
* DELETE AS NECESSARY

Signed : _____ Date: _____

Position : _____

Company : _____

Stability Calculation

COMPARTMENT	WEIGHT	V.C.G.	MOMENT	L.C.G.	+ve L.M.	-ve L.M.	F.S.MOMENT
No.1 HOLD	3 507	8.24	28,898	-62.22	<><><><>	218,206	
No.2 HOLD	3,724	7.84	29,196	-43.09	<><><><>	160,467	
No.3 HOLD	4,067	7.75	31,519	-22.17	<><><><>	90,165	
No.4 HOLD	5,283	7.82	41,313	-0.95	<><><><>	5,019	
No.5 HOLD	4,162	7.75	32,255	20.30	84,489	<><><><>	
No.6 HOLD	4,402	7.78	34,248	41.68	183,475	<><><><>	
HOLD TOTAL	25,145		197,429		267,964	473,857	
No.1 T/S P&S		13.16		-62.42	<><><><>		
No.2 T/S P&S		12.99		-43.05	<><><><>		
No.3 T/S P&S		12.87		-21.82	<><><><>		
No.4 T/S P&S		10.57		-0.57	<><><><>		
No.5 T/S P&S		12.87		20.67		<><><><>	
No.6 T/S P&S		12.88		42.17		<><><><>	
CARGO TOTAL	25,145		197,429		267,964	473,857	
FORE PEAK		5.45		-77.06	<><><><>		
No.1 D/B P&S		1.24		-62.28	<><><><>		
No.2 D/B P&S		1.33		-42.60	<><><><>		
No.2 D/B CTR.		0.72		-42.64	<><><><>		
No.3 D/B P&S		1.29		-21.68	<><><><>		
No.4/5 D/B P&S		1.29		9.97		<><><><>	
AFT PEAK		10.00		80.85		<><><><>	
BALLAST TOTAL	0		0				
No.3 D/B CTR.	214	0.72	154	-21.82	<><><><>	4,669	
No.4 D/B CTR.	259	0.72	186	-0.57	<><><><>	147	
No.5 D/B CTR.	247	0.72	178	20.67	5,105	<><><><>	
No.6 D/B CTR.	197	0.75	148	42.50	8,373	<><><><>	
No.6 D/B P&S	353	1.46	515	41.47	14,637	<><><><>	
HFO TOTAL	1,270		1,181		28,117	4,816	
No.7 D/B P&S	136	1.35	184	57.90	3,252	<><><><>	
Upper DOT P&S	60	12.49	749	54.20	7,874	<><><><>	
MDO TOTAL	196		933		11,126	0	
F.W. P&S	57	13.44	766	79.04	4,505	<><><><>	
D.W. P&S	65	12.98	844	74.83	4,864	<><><><>	
F.W. TOTAL	122		1,610		9,369	0	
L.O. DRAIN	30	0.69	21	67.67	2,030	<><><><>	
COOL & FEED	24	-	69	-	1,797	<><><><>	
STORES	217	-	2,292	-	10,374	<><><><>	
LIGHTSHIP	6721	-	63,252	-	81,141	<><><><>	
SHIP TOTAL	8,580		69,358		143,954	4,816	
GRAND TOTAL	33,725		266,787		411,918	478,673	

V.M. =

KM =	9.42	LCG =	-1.98		
KG =	7.91	LCB =	-2.91	LCF =	0.92
GM =	1.51	MCT1cm=	392.7	LBP =	168
GG' =	0.25	TRIM =	0.80	DRAFT =	10.13	FORWARD
G'M =	1.26	DRAFT =	10.53	DRAFT =	10.93	AFT

SHEARING FORCE CHECK SHEET

VOY 14   29·03·95

Depart Vancouver, BC

25,145 M/T   to JAPAN

DISPLACEMENT △ = 33,725 t

TRIM = 0·80 m
(+: BY STERN, -: BY BOW)

BASIC DISPLACEMENT △b = 34,000 t
(TAKE THE NEAREST ONE TO △)

DIFFERENCE OF DISPLACEMENT

△ - △b = -275 t

LINE NO.	ITEM	WEIGHT (t)
1	FORE PEAK	–
2	NO.1 CARGO HOLD	3,507
3	NO.1 TOPSIDE P&S	–
4	NO.1 D.B. P&S	–
5	SUM (1) (LINE 1~4)	3,507
6	NO.2 CARGO HOLD	3,724
7	NO.2 TOPSIDE P&S	–
8	NO.2 D.B. CTR.	–
9	NO.2 D.B. P&S	–
10	SUM (2) (LINE 5~9)	7,231
11	NO.3 CARGO HOLD	4,067
12	NO.3 TOPSIDE P&S	–
13	NO.3 D.B. CTR.	214
14	NO.3 D.B. P&S	–
15	SUM (3) (LINE 10~14)	11,512
16	NO.4 CARGO HOLD	5,283
17	NO.4 TOPSIDE & WING P&S	–
18	NO.4 D.B. CTR.	259
19	1/2 OF NO.4/5 D.B. P&S	–
20	SUM (4) (LINE 15~19)	17,054
21	1/2 OF NO.4/5 D.B. P&S	–
22	NO.5 CARGO HOLD	4,162
23	NO.5 TOPSIDE P&S	–
24	NO.5 D.B. CTR.	247
25	SUM (5) (LINE 20~24)	21,463

	CHECKING POSITION	FR.70	FR.95	FR.120	FR.145	FR.170
26	ENTER EACH SUM OF WEIGHT IN RIGHT COLUMN RESPECTIVELY	SUM(5) 21,463	SUM(4) 17,054	SUM(3) 11,512	SUM(2) 7,231	SUM(1) 3,507
27	LIGHT SHIP & CONSTANT WEIGHT	3781	3014	2242	1476	834
28	WEIGHT TOTAL (LINE 26 + 27) (t)	25,244	20,068	13,754	8,707	4,341
29	BUOYANCY CORRESPONDINGS TO △b	25,503	20,253	14,995	9,743	4,620
30	MULTIPLIER FOR (△-△b) CORRECT. *	⟨0·706⟩	⟨0·563⟩	⟨0·419⟩	⟨0·276⟩	⟨0·135⟩
31	(△-△b) CORRECT.: (△-△b) x LINE 30	-194	-154	-115	-76	-37
32	MULTIPLIER FOR TRIM CORRECTION *	⟨325⟩	⟨383⟩	⟨378⟩	⟨311⟩	⟨182⟩
33	TRIM CORRECTION: TRIM x LINE 32	-260	-306	-302	-249	-146
34	BUOYANCY (LINE 29 + 31 + 33) (t)	25,049	19,793	14,578	9,418	4,437
35	SHEARING FORCE (LINE 28 - 34) (t)	+195	+275	-824	-711	+96
36	ALLOWABLE SHEARING FORCE (t)	±2633	±2975	±2983	±2797	±2418

* TAKE THE NUMERAL FROM THE TABLE BELOW APPROPRIATELY TO △b

BUOYANCY DATA	BASIC DISPT. △b (t)	CHECKING POSITION				
		FR.70	FR.95	FR.120	FR.145	FR.170
BUOYANCY CORRESPONDING TO △b (t)	34000	25503	20253	14995	9743	4620
	31000	23372	18556	13732	8913	4216
	28000	21215	16839	12455	8077	3812
	25000	19030	15101	11164	7231	3404
	22000	16812	13337	9853	6374	2992
MULTIPLIER FOR (△-△b) CORRECTION	34000	0.706	0.563	0.419	0.276	0.135
	31000	0.715	0.569	0.424	0.278	0.135
	28000	0.725	0.577	0.429	0.281	0.136
	25000	0.734	0.584	0.434	0.284	0.137
	22000	0.742	0.590	0.439	0.287	0.138
MULTIPLIER FOR TRIM CORRECTION	34000	-325	-383	-378	-311	-182
	31000	-309	-370	-368	-303	-176
	28000	-293	-357	-357	-295	-172
	25000	-279	-346	-349	-289	-169
	22000	-269	-337	-343	-286	-167

BENDING MOMENT CHECK SHEET

(handwritten, top right) Voy 14 29-03-95 — Depart Vancouver BC — 25.145 m/t — for Japan

DISPLACEMENT Δ = 33,725 t, TRIM = 0.80 m (+: BY STERN, -: BY BOW)

BASIC DISPLACEMENT Δb = 34,000 t (TAKE THE NEAREST ONE TO Δ)

DIFFERENCE OF DISPLACEMENT Δ - Δb = -275 t

LINE NO.	CHECKING POSITION ITEM		WEIGHT W(t)	(1) FR.70 LEVER k	(1) MOMENT k×W	(2) FR.82.5 LEVER k	(2) MOMENT k×W	(3) FR.95 LEVER k	(3) MOMENT k×W	(4) FR.107.5 LEVER k	(4) MOMENT k×W	(5) FR.120 LEVER k	(5) MOMENT k×W	(6) FR.132.5 LEVER k	(6) MOMENT k×W	(7) FR.145 LEVER k	(7) MOMENT k×W
1	FORE PEAK	WB		108.36		97.74		87.11		76.49		65.86		55.24		44.61	
2	NO.1 CARGO HOLD P&S		3,507	94.52	327,975	82.90	290,730	72.27	253,451	61.65	216,207	51.02	178,927	40.40	141,683	29.77	104,402
3	NO.1 TOPSIDE P&S	WB/GRAIN		93.72		83.10		72.47		61.85		51.22		40.60		29.97	
4	NO.1 D.B. P&S	WB		91.58		82.96		72.33		61.71		51.08		40.46		29.83	
5	NO.2 CARGO HOLD	WB/GRAIN	3,724	74.39	277,028	63.77	237,479	53.14	197,843	42.52	158,344	31.89	118,713	21.27	79,209	10.64	39,623
6	NO.2 TOPSIDE CTR.			74.35		63.73		53.10		42.48		31.85		21.23		10.60	
7	NO.2 D.B. CTR.	WS		73.94		63.32		52.69		42.07		31.44		20.82		10.19	
8	NO.2 D.B. P&S	WB		73.90		62.28		52.65		42.03		31.41		20.78		10.15	
9	NO.3 CARGO HOLD		4,067	53.47	217,462	42.85	174,271	32.22	131,039	21.60	87,847	10.97	44,613	2.83	11,510		
10	NO.3 TOPSIDE P&S	WB/GRAIN		53.12		42.50		31.87		21.25		10.62		2.65	567		
11	NO.3 D.B. CTR.	FO	244	53.12	11,368	42.50	9,045	31.87	6,820	21.25	4,558	10.62	2,273	2.65			
12	NO.3 D.B. P&S	WB		53.16		42.54		31.91		21.29		10.66		2.67			
13	NO.4 CARGO HOLD		5,283	32.25	170,377	21.63	114,271	11.00	58,113	2.84	15,004						
14	NO.4 TOPSIDE & WING P&S	WB/GRAIN		31.87		21.25		10.62		2.65							
15	NO.4 D.B. CTR.	FO/WB	259	31.87	8,234	21.25	5,504	10.62	2,755	2.65	686						
16	NO.4/5 D.B. P&S	WB	4,162	11.00	45,782	2.84	11,821	5.35		1.34							
17	NO.5 CARGO HOLD			21.33		12.02		5.35	657								
18	NO.5 TOPSIDE P&S	WB/GRAIN		11.00		2.84		2.65									
19	NO.5 D.B. CTR.	FO/WB	247	10.63	2,626	2.66		2.65									
20	NO.6 CARGO HOLD		4,402	10.63		2.66											
21	NO.6 TOPSIDE P&S	WB/GRAIN	197														
22	NO.6 D.B. CTR.		353														
23	NO.6 D.B. P&S	FO/WB	136														
24	NO.7 D.B. P&S	DO	60														
25	UPPER D.O. TANK P&S		60														
26	L.O./DRAIN TANK		65														
27	DRINKING WATER TANK P&S		57														
28	F.W. TANK P&S																
29	APT PEAK	WB															
30	LIGHT SHIP & CONSTANT WEIGHT		6,962		205160		167110		132960		103050		77060		55320		37490
31	DISPLACEMENT Δ (SUM OF LINE 1-30)		33,725														
32	WEIGHT MOMENT (SUM OF LINE 1-30)	(m-t)			1,266,032		1,010,938		783,027		585,686		421,632		288,284		181,516
33	BUOYANCY MOMENT CORRESPONDING TO Δb	MBb			1,325,820		1,068,720		839,540		638,300		465,000		319,590		202,100
34	MULTIPLIER FOR (Δ-Δb) CORRECTION	Cd			37.08		29.47		23.62		18.02		13.19		9.13		5.82
35	(Δ-Δb) CORRECTION	Cd x (Δ-Δb)			-10,197		-8,242		-6,496		-4,956		-3,627		-2,511		-1,600
36	MULTIPLIER FOR TRIM CORRECTION	Ct			-30,657		-26,769		-22,896		-19,002		-14,707		-10,870		-7,489
37	TRIM CORRECTION	Ct x TRIM			-24,526		-21,415		-18,317		-15,202		-11,766		-8,696		-5,991
38	BUOYANCY MOMENT (LINE 33+35+37)	(m-t)			1,291,097		1,039,083		814,727		618,142		449,607		308,383		194,508
39	BENDING MOMENT (LINE 32 - LINE 38)	(m-t)			-25,065		-28,125		-31,700		-32,456		-27,974		-20,004		-12,993
40	ALLOWABLE BENDING MOMENT	(m-t)			±60660		±60660		±60660		±60660		±60660		±60660		±60660
					(41%)		(46%)		(52%)		(54%)		(46%)		(33%)		(21%)

NOTE: LINE 20 - 29 AND 31 ARE PROVIDED TO CHECK THE DISPLACEMENT.

BUOYANCY MOMENT DATA (MBb, Cd AND Ct ARE TO BE TAKEN APPROPRIATELY TO THE BASIC DISPLACEMENT Δb)

BASIC DISPLACEMENT Δb (t)	CHECKING POSITION (1) MBb	(1) Cd	(1) Ct	(2) MBb	(2) Cd	(2) Ct	(3) MBb	(3) Cd	(3) Ct	(4) MBb	(4) Cd	(4) Ct	(5) MBb	(5) Cd	(5) Ct	(6) MBb	(6) Cd	(6) Ct	(7) MBb	(7) Cd	(7) Ct
34000	1325820	37.08	-30657	1068720	29.97	-26769	839540	23.62	-22896	638300	18.02	-19002	465000	13.19	-14707	319590	9.13	-10870	202100	5.82	-7489
31000	1213940	37.45	-29688	978340	30.24	-25956	768360	23.81	-22226	584000	18.16	-18463	425260	13.27	-14286	292130	9.16	-10552	184620	5.83	-7263
28000	1101040	37.92	-28748	887190	30.61	-25181	696620	24.09	-21601	529330	18.41	-17972	385130	13.41	-13913	264590	9.25	-10282	167130	5.87	-7080
25000	986750	38.36	-27990	794930	30.96	-24562	624010	24.36	-21108	474000	18.56	-17589	344910	13.55	-13628	236720	9.34	-10081	149430	5.93	-6948
22000	870820	38.76	-27483	701360	31.29	-24160	550390	24.62	-20709	417920	18.76	-17360	303970	13.70	-13469	208490	9.45	-9979	131510	6.02	-6893
19000	754040	39.11	-27041	607100	31.57	-23807	476220	24.84	-20525	361420	18.95	-17158	262890	13.83	-13326	180030	9.54	-9888	113340	6.07	-6842
16000	636400	39.39	-26666	512140	31.80	-23506	401500	25.02	-20291	304480	19.07	-16982	221100	13.93	-13201	151340	9.61	-9806	95200	6.12	-6795

Ship/shore safety checklist and guidelines[65]

Introduction

The IMO Recommendations on the Safe Transport, Handling and Storage of Dangerous Substances in Port Areas contain the requirement that:

The master of a ship and the berth operator should, before liquid bulk dangerous substances are pumped into or out of any ship or into a shore installation:

1.   agree in writing on the handling procedures including the maximum loading or unloading rates;

2.   complete and sign the appropriate safety check list, showing the main safety precautions to be taken before and during such handling operations; and

3.   agree in writing on the action to be taken in the event of an emergency during handling operations.

Annexed to the Recommendations is the safety checklist reproduced on pages 165 to 167 covering the arrangements and conditions under which the loading and discharging of bulk liquid dangerous cargoes and associated operations such as bunkering, ballasting or tank cleaning may be carried out safely. The following guidelines have been produced to assist berth operators and ships' masters in their joint use of the checklist.

The Mutual Safety Examination

A tanker presenting itself to a loading or discharging terminal needs to check its own preparations and its fitness for the safety of the intended cargo operation. Additionally, the master of a ship has a responsibility to assure himself that the terminal operator has likewise made proper preparations for the safe operation of his terminal.

Equally the terminal needs to check its own preparations and to be assured that the tanker has carried out its checks and has made appropriate arrangements.

The Checklist, by its questions and its requirements for exchange of written arrangements for certain procedures, is a minimum basis for the essential considerations which should be included in such a mutual examination.

Some of the Checklist's questions are directed to considerations for which the ship has prime responsibility, others apply to both ship and terminal. It is not suggested that every item should be the subject of personal checking by both representatives conducting the examination.

All items lying within the responsibility of the tanker should be personally checked by the tanker's representative and similarly all items of the terminal's responsibility personally checked by the terminal representative. In carrying out their full responsibilities however, both representatives, by questioning the other, by sighting of records and, where felt appropriate, by joint visual inspection should assure themselves that the standards of safety on both sides of the operation are fully acceptable.

The joint declaration should not be signed until such mutual assurance is achieved.

Thus all applicable questions should result in an affirmative mark in the boxes provided. If a difference of opinion arises on the adequacy of any arrangements made or conditions found, the operation should not be started until measures taken are jointly accepted.

A negative answer to the questions coded "P" does not necessarily mean that the intended operation cannot be carried out. In such cases, however, permission to proceed should be obtained from the designated port officer.

Where an item is agreed to be not applicable to the ship, to the terminal or to the operation envisaged a note to that affect should be entered in the "Remarks" column.

While the Checklist is based upon cargo handling operations, it is recommended that the same mutual examination, using the Checklist as appropriate, be carried out when a tanker presents itself at a berth for tank cleaning after carriage of substances covered by these Guidelines.

Deviations

The conditions under which the operation takes place may change during the process. The changes may be such that safety can no longer be regarded as guaranteed. The party noticing or causing the unsafe condition is under an obligation to take all necessary actions, which may include stopping the operation, to re-establish safe conditions. The presence of the unsafe condition should be reported to the other party where necessary, co-operation with the other party should be sought.

Tank Cleaning Activities

The questions on tank cleaning, including "crude oil washing", are included in the list in order to inform the terminal and the port authorities of the ship's intentions regarding these activities.

Ship's Name _____

Berth _____ Port _____

Date of Arrival _____ Time of Arrival _____

INSTRUCTIONS FOR COMPLETION

The safety of operations requires that all questions should be answered affirmatively ☑. If an affirmative answer is not possible, the reason should be given and agreement reached upon appropriate precautions to be taken between the ship and the terminal. Where any question is not considered to be applicable a note to that effect should be inserted in the remarks column.

☐—the presence of this symbol in the columns 'ship' and 'terminal' indicates that checks shall be carried out, by the party concerned.

The presence of the letters **A** and **P** in the column 'Code' indicates the following:
A—the mentioned procedures and agreements shall be in writing and signed by both parties.
P—in the case of a negative answer the operation shall not be carried out without the permission of the Port Authority.

PART A

Bulk liquids—general

		Ship	Terminal	Code	Remarks
A1	Is the ship securely moored?	☐	☐		
A2	Are emergency towing wires correctly positioned?	☐	☐		
A3	Is there safe access between ship and shore?	☐	☐		
A4	Is the ship ready to move under its own power?	☐		**P**	
A5	Is there an effective deck watch in attendance on board and adequate supervision on the terminal and on the ship?	☐	☐		
A6	Is the agreed ship/shore communication system operative?	☐	☐	**A**	
A7	Have the procedures for cargo, bunker and ballast handling been agreed?	☐	☐	**A**	
A8	Has the emergency shut down procedure been agreed?	☐	☐	**A**	
A9	Are fire hoses and fire-fighting equipment on board and ashore positioned and ready for immediate use?	☐	☐		
A10	Are cargo and bunker hoses/arms in good condition and properly rigged and, where appropriate, certificates checked?	☐	☐		
A11	Are scuppers effectively plugged and drip trays in position, both on board and ashore?	☐	☐		
A12	Are unused cargo and bunker connections including the stern discharge line, if fitted, blanked?	☐	☐		
A13	Are sea and overboard discharge valves, when not in use, closed and lashed?	☐	☐		
A14	Are all cargo and bunker tank lids closed?	☐	☐		
A15	Is the agreed tank venting system being used?	☐	☐	**A**	
A16	Are hand torches of an approved type?	☐	☐		
A17	Are portable VHF/UHF transceivers of an approved type?	☐	☐		

PART A—continued	Ship	Terminal	Code	Remarks
Bulk liquids—general				
A18 Are the ship's main radio transmitter aerials earthed and radars switched off?	☐			
A19 Are electric cables to portable electrical equipment disconnected from power?	☐	☐		
A20 Are all external doors and ports in the amidships accommodation closed?	☐	☐		
A21 Are all external doors and ports in the after accommodation leading onto or overlooking the tank deck closed?	☐	☐		
A22 Are air conditioning intakes which may permit the entry of cargo vapours closed?	☐	☐		
A23 Are window-type air conditioning units disconnected?	☐	☐		
A24 Are smoking requirements being observed?	☐	☐		
A25 Are the requirements for the use of galley and other cooking appliances being observed?	☐	☐		
A26 Are naked light requirements being observed?	☐	☐		
A27 Is there provision for an emergency escape possibility?	☐	☐		
A28 Are sufficient personnel on board and ashore to deal with an emergency?	☐	☐		
A29 Are adequate insulating means in place in the ship/shore connection?	☐	☐		
A30 Have measures been taken to ensure sufficient pumproom ventilation?	☐			

PART B	Ship	Terminal	Code	Remarks
Additional checks—bulk liquid chemicals				
B1 Is information available giving the necessary data for the safe handling of the cargo including, where applicable, a manufacturerer's inhibition certificate?	☐	☐		
B2 Is sufficient and suitable protective equipment and protective clothing ready for immediate use?	☐	☐		
B3 Are counter measures against accidental personal contact with the cargo agreed?	☐	☐		
B4 Is the cargo handling rate compatible with the automatic shut down system if in use?	☐	☐	A	
B5 Are cargo systems' gauges and alarms correctly set and in good order?	☐	☐		
B6 Are portable vapour detection instruments readily available for the products to be handled?	☐	☐		
B7 Has information on fire-fighting media and procedures been exchanged?	☐	☐		

PART B—*continued* *Additional checks—bulk liquid chemicals*	Ship	Terminal	Code	Remarks
B8　Are transfer hoses of suitable material resistant to the action of the cargoes?	☐	☐		
B9　Is cargo handling being performed with the permanent installed pipeline systems?	☐	☐	P	

PART C *Additional checks—bulk liquefied gases*	Ship	Terminal	Code	Remarks
C1　Is information available giving the necessary data for the safe handling of the cargo including, where applicable, a manufacturer's inhibition certificate?	☐	☐		
C2　Is the water spray system ready for use?	☐	☐		
C3　Is sufficient and suitable protective equipment (including self-contained breathing apparatus) and protective clothing ready for immediate use?	☐	☐		
C4　Are void spaces properly inerted where required?	☐			
C5　Are all remote control valves in working order?	☐	☐		
C6　Are cargo tank safety relief valves lined up to the ship's venting system and are bypasses closed?	☐			
C7　Are the required cargo pumps and compressors in good order, and have the maximum working pressures been agreed between ship and shore?	☐	☐	A	
C8　Is reliquefaction or boil off control equipment in good order?	☐			
C9　Is gas detection equipment set for the cargo, calibrated and in good order?	☐	☐		
C10　Are cargo system gauges and alarms correctly set and in good order?	☐	☐		
C11　Are emergency shut down systems working properly?	☐			
C12　Does shore know the closing rate of ship's automatic valves? Does ship have similar details of shore system?	☐	☐	A	
C13　Has information been exchanged between ship and shore on minimum working temperatures of the cargo systems?	☐	☐	A	

	Ship	Shore
Are tank cleaning operations planned during the ship's stay alongside the shore installation?	Yes/No*	
If so, have the port authority and terminal been informed?	Yes/No*	Yes/No*

Delete yes or No as appropriate

GUIDELINES FOR COMPLETING
THE SHIP/SHORE SAFETY CHECKLIST

1 **Is the ship securely moored?**

In answering this question, due regard should be given to the need for adequate fendering arrangements.

Ships should remain adequately secured in their moorings. Alongside piers or quays ranging of the ship should be prevented by keeping all mooring lines taut; attention should be given to the movement of the ship caused by currents or tides and the operation in progress.

Wire ropes and fibre ropes should not be used together in the same direction (i.e. breasts, springs, head or stern) because of the difference in their elastic properties.

Once moored, ships fitted with automatic tension winches should not use such winches in the automatic mode.

Means should be provided to enable quick and safe release of the ship in case of an emergency.

The method used for the emergency release operation should be agreed, taking into account the possible risks involved.

Anchors not in use should be properly secured.

2 **Are emergency towing wires correctly positioned?**

Emergency towing wires should be positioned both on the off-shore bow and quarter of the ship. At a buoy mooring, towing wires should be positioned on the side opposite to the hose string.

The eyes of these wires should be maintained about the waterline and regularly checked and adjusted if necessary during the operations. They should be properly made fast on the ship's bollards, while having sufficient slack on deck.

Means should be provided to prevent the slack from accidentally running into the water. These means should be so arranged that they can easily be broken by a tug boat's crew.

3 **Is there safe access between ship and shore?**

The access should be positioned as far away from the manifolds as practicable.

The means of access to the ship should be safe and may consist of an appropriate gangway or accommodation ladder with a properly secured safety net fitted beneath it.

Particular attention to safe access should be given where the difference in level between the point of access on the vessel and the jetty or quay is large or likely to become large.

When terminal access facilities are not available and a ship's gangway is used, there should be an adequate landing area on the berth so as to provide the gangway with a sufficient clear run of space and so maintain safe and convenient access to the ship at all states of tide and changes in the ship's freeboard.

Near the access ashore suitable life-saving equipment should be available. A lifebuoy should be available on board the ship near the gangway or accommodation ladder.

The access should be safely and properly illuminated during darkness.

Persons who have no legitimate business on board, or who do not have the master's permission, should be refused access to the ship.

The terminal should control access to the jetty or berth in agreement with the ship.

4   Is the ship ready to move under its own power?

The ship should be able to move under its own power at short notice, unless permission to immobilise the ship has been granted by the harbourmaster and the terminal manager. Certain conditions may have to be met for permission to be granted.

5   Is there an effective deck watch in attendance on board and adequate supervision on the terminal and on the ship?

The operation should be under constant control both on ship and shore.

Supervision should be aimed at preventing the development of hazardous situations; if, however, such a situation arises the controlling personnel should have adequate means available to take corrective action.

The controlling personnel on ship and shore should maintain an effective communication with their respective supervisors.

All personnel connected with the operation should be familiar with the dangers of the substances handled.

6   Is the agreed ship/shore communication system operative?

Communication should be maintained in the most efficient way between the responsible officer on duty on the ship and the responsible person ashore.

When telephones are used, the telephone both on board and ashore should be continuously manned by a person who can immediately contact his respective supervisor. Additionally, the supervisor should have the possibility to override all calls. When RT/VHF systems are used the units should preferably be portable and carried by the supervisor or a person who can get in touch with his respective supervisor immediately. Where fixed systems are used the guidelines for telephones should apply.

The selected system of communication together with the necessary information on telephone numbers and/or channels to be used should be recorded on the appropriate form. This form should be signed by both ship and shore representatives.

The telephone and portable RT/VHF systems should comply with the appropriate safety requirements.

7   Have the procedures for cargo, bunker and ballast handling been agreed?

The procedures for the intended operation should be pre-planned. They should be discussed and agreed upon by the ship and shore representatives prior to the start of the operations. The agreed arrangements should be recorded on a form and contain at least the information shown in the annex to these guidelines. The form should be signed by both representatives. Any change in the agreed procedure that could affect the operation should be discussed by both parties and agreed upon. After agreement has been reached by both parties substantial changes should be laid down in writing as soon as possible and in sufficient time before the change in procedure takes place. In any case the change should be laid down in writing within the working period of those supervisors on board and ashore in whose working period agreement on the change was reached. The operations should be suspended and all deck and vent openings closed on the approach of an electrical storm.

The properties of the substances handled, the equipment of ship and shore installation, the ability of the ship's crew and the shore personnel to execute the necessary operations and to sufficiently control the operations are factors which should be taken into account when ascertaining the possibility of handling a number of substances concurrently.

The manifold area both on board and ashore should be safely and properly illuminated during darkness.

The initial and maximum loading rates, topping off rates and normal stopping times should be agreed, having regard to:

—the nature of the cargo to be handled;
—the arrangement and capacity of the ship's cargo lines and gas venting systems;
—the maximum allowable pressure and flow rate in the ship/shore hoses and loading arms;
—precautions to avoid accumulation of static electricity;
—any other flow control limitations.
A note to this effect should be entered on the form referred to above.
If the static electricity properties of the substance handled and the situation in the tank so require, no conducting object should be inserted into that tank during loading and during a period of at least 30 minutes after the cessation of loading.

8   Has the emergency shut down procedure been agreed?

An emergency shut down procedure should be agreed between ship and shore and recorded on an appropriate form.

The agreement should designate in which cases the operations have to be stopped immediately.

Due regard should be given to the possible introduction of dangers associated with the emergency shut down procedure.

9   Are fire hoses and fire fighting equipment on board and ashore positioned and ready for immediate use?

Fire fighting equipment both on board and ashore should be correctly positioned and ready for immediate use.

Adequate units of fixed or portable equipment should be stationed to cover the ship's cargo deck and on the jetty. The ship and shore fire main systems should be pressurised, or be capable of being pressurised at short notice.

Both ship and shore should ensure that their fire main systems can be connected in a quick and easy way utilising if necessary the international ship/shore connection.

10   Are cargo and bunker hoses/arms in good condition and properly rigged and, where appropriate, certificates checked?

Cargo hoses and metal arms should be in a good condition and should be properly fitted and rigged so as to prevent strain and stress beyond design limitations. All flange connections should be fully bolted.

Other types of connections should be properly secured. It should be ensured that the hoses or metal arms are constructed of a material suitable for the substance to be handled taking into account its temperature and the maximum operating pressure.

Cargo hoses should be identifiable with regard to their suitability for the intended operation.

11   Are scuppers effectively plugged and drip trays in position, both on board and ashore?

Where applicable all scuppers on board and drainholes ashore should be properly plugged during the operations. Accumulation of water should be drained off periodically.

Both ship and jetty should ideally be provided with fixed drip trays; in their absence portable drip trays may be used.

All drip trays should be emptied in an appropriate manner whenever necessary but always after completion of the specific operation.

Where corrosive liquids or refrigerated gases are being handled, the scuppers may be kept open, provided that an ample supply of water is available at all times in the vicinity of the manifolds.

12   Are unused cargo and bunker connections including the stern discharge line, if fitted, blanked?

Unused cargo and bunker line connections should be closed and blanked. Blank flanges should be fully bolted and other types of fittings, if used, properly secured.

13   Are sea and overboard discharge valves, when not in use, closed and lashed?

Experience shows the importance of this item in pollution avoidance on ships where cargo lines and ballast systems are interconnected.

The security of the valves in question should be checked visually.

14   Are all cargo and bunker tank lids closed?

Apart from the openings in use for tank venting (see question 15) all openings to cargo tanks should be closed gastight.

Ullaging and sampling points may be opened for the short periods necessary for ullaging and sampling.

Closed ullaging and sampling systems should be used where required by international, national and local regulations and agreements.

15   Is the agreed tank venting system being used?

Agreeing should be reached by both parties, as to the venting system for the operation, taking into account the nature of the cargo and international, national and local regulations and agreements.

There are three basic systems for venting tanks:
1. Open to atmosphere via open ullage ports, protected by suitable flame screens.
2. Fixed venting systems which includes inert gas systems.
3. To shore through other vapour handling systems.

16   Are hand torches of an approved type?
and,
17   Are portable VHF/UHF transceivers of an approved type?

Battery operated hand torches and VHF radio-telephone sets should be of a safe type which is approved by a competent authority. Ship/shore telephones should comply with the requirements for explosion-proof construction except when placed in a safe space in the accommodation.

VHF radio-telephone sets may operate in the internationally agreed wave bands only.

The above-mentioned equipment should be well maintained and damaged units, though capable of operation, should not be used.

18   Are the ship's main radio transmitter aerials earthed and radars switched off?

The ship's main radio transmitter should not be used during the ship's stay in port, except for receiving purposes. The main transmitting aerials must be disconnected and earthed.

The ship's radar installation should not be used unless the master, in consultation with the terminal manager, has established the conditions under which the installation may be used safely.

19   Are electric cables to portable electrical equipment disconnected from power?

The use of portable electrical equipment on wandering leads is prohibited in hazardous zones.

The supply cables should be disconnected and preferably removed from the hazardous zone.

Telephone cables in use in the ship/shore communication system should preferably be routed outside the hazardous zone. Wherever this is not feasible, the cable should be so positioned and protected that no danger arises from its use.

20   Are all external doors and ports in the amidships accommodation closed?
and,
21   Are all external doors and ports in the after accommodation leading onto or overlooking the tank deck closed?

External doors, windows and portholes in the amidships accommodation should be closed during the operations.

In the after accommodation external doors, windows and portholes facing or near the cargo zone should be closed during operations. These doors should be clearly marked, but at no time should they be locked.

22   Are air conditioning intakes which may permit the entry of cargo vapours closed?
and,
23   Are window-type air conditioning units disconnected?

Air conditioning units which are located wholly within the accommodation and which do not draw in air from the outside may remain in operation.

Window-type air conditioners should be disconnected from their power supply.

24   Are smoking requirements being observed?

Smoking on board the ship may only take place in places specified by the master in consultation with the terminal manager or his representative.

No smoking is allowed on the jetty and the adjacent area except in buildings and places specified by the terminal manager in consultation with the master.

Places which are directly accessible from the outside should not be designated as places where smoking is permitted. Buildings, places and rooms designated as places where smoking is permitted should be clearly marked as such.

25   Are the requirements for the use of galley and other cooking appliances being observed?

Open fire may be used in galleys whose construction, location and ventilation system provides protection against entry of flammable gases.

In cases where the galley does not comply with the above, open fire may be used provided the master, in consultation with the terminal manager, has ensured that precautions have been taken against the entry or build up of flammable gases.

On ships fitted with stern discharge lines no open fire in galley-furnaces and cooking appliances is allowed when these lines are used, unless the construction of the ship's accommodation allows for the safe use of open fire.

26   Are naked light requirements being observed?

Naked light or open fire comprises the following: fire, spark formation, naked light and any surface with a temperature that is equal to or higher than the minimum ignition temperature of the products handled in the operations.

The use of open fire on board the ship—other than covered in questions 24 and 25—and within a distance of 25m of the ship is prohibited, unless all applicable regulations have been met and subject to agreement by the port authority, terminal manager and the master.

27   Is there provision for an emergency escape possibility?

In addition to the means of access referred to in question 3, a safe and quick emergency escape should be available both on board and ashore.

On board the ship it may consist of a lifeboat ready for immediate use, preferably at the after end of the ship.

28   Are sufficient personnel on board and ashore to deal with an emergency?

At all times during the ship's stay at the terminal, a sufficient number of personnel should be present on board the ship and in the shore installation to deal with an emergency.

29   Are adequate insulating means in place in the ship/shore connection?

Unless measures are taken to break the continuous electrical path between ship and shore pipework provided by the ship/shore hoses or metallic arms, stray electric currents, mainly from corrosion protection systems, can cause electric sparks at the flange faces when hoses are being connected and disconnected.

The passage of these currents is prevented by an insulating flange inserted at each jetty manifold outlet or incorporated in the construction of metallic arms.

Alternatively, the electrical discontinuity may be provided by the inclusion of one length of electrically discontinuous hose in each hose string.

It should be ascertained that the means of electrical discontinuity is in place and in good condition and that it is not being by-passed by contact with external metal.

30   Have measures been taken to ensure sufficient pumproom ventilation?

Ship's pumprooms should be mechanically ventilated and the ventilation should be kept running throughout the operation. Ventilation should be aimed at maintaining a safe atmosphere throughout the pumproom.

This appendix is reproduced by permission of ICS/OCIMF from *ISGOTT Guide*.

Tanker information exchange checklist

Before cargo operations commence, the following information should be exchanged between the ship and the shore.[65]

☐ Cargo and ballast distribution on arrival.

☐ Quantity, density and temperature of each grade to be handled.

☐ Characteristics of the cargo which may require attention—for example flashpoint, true vapour pressure, sour crude or water content.

☐ Ship's tanks to be filled or emptied, and the sequence in which they are to be loaded or discharged. The sequence of various grades.

☐ Shore tanks to be emptied or filled.

☐ Manifold connections, including reducers, and lines to be used by the ship/shore. (If several grades are to be handled concurrently, then grade name boards should be available to be placed at each connection.)

☐ Limitations on the movement of hoses or hard-arms (operating envelope).

☐ Initial cargo transfer (pumping) rate for each grade.

☐ Maximum cargo transfer (pumping) rate for each grade.

☐ Topping off rates, and the notice required for completing each grade.

☐ Maximum manifold pressures for each grade.

☐ Precautions to avoid the accumulation of static electricity.

☐ The venting system to be used. (Taking into account the loading rate, the atmospheric conditions and the true vapour pressure of the cargo.)

☐ Sequence and timing of (de)ballasting operations, and tank cleaning, and any restrictions these may have on the cargo operations.

☐ The expected duration of pumping each grade, and time of completion.

☐ Ship and shore tank changeover procedure.

☐ Methods for avoiding contamination of the cargo and/or ballast—e.g., valve separation, dedicated lines, loading over the top, etc.

☐ Pipeline clearing for loading/discharging, and methods for separating grades, to avoid contamination (e.g., flushing lines, line pigs, etc.).

☐ Other operations which may affect flow/ pumping rates.

☐ Crude oil washing (COW), or other tank cleaning operations.

☐ Normal and emergency communications.

☐ Emergency shutdown procedures.

☐ Other operations taking place, including those in chapter 14.

☐ Names of people in charge of operations ashore/on board.

Signed: Time/Date:

Anti-pollution checklist

- ☐ Has the ship/shore checklist been completed?—see appendix XIV.
- ☐ Has the cargo operations plan agreed with the terminal?—see 9.6.
- ☐ Are all personnel familiar with the oil spill contingency plan?
- ☐ Is the spill containment equipment checked and readily available?
- ☐ Is the pipeline system lined up as per the Chief Officer's orders:
  - ☐ Manifold? ☐ Deck valves? ☐ Pumproom?
- ☐ Are all deck scupper plugs in place?
- ☐ Have arrangements been made to keep the main deck free of water?
- ☐ Has the cargo manifold been drained before removing the blanks?
- ☐ Are all unused cargo and bunker connections blanked and fully bolted?
- ☐ Are pressure gauges in place, and any cocks/drains securely closed?
- ☐ Are the relevant valves in the drop lines closed (for discharge), or open (for loading)?
- ☐ Are all sea and overboard valves connected to the cargo system confirmed closed and lashed/sealed/locked/immobilised?
- ☐ Are engineroom and pumproom bilge discharge valves confirmed closed and lashed/sealed/immobilised?
- ☐ Have all hoses and connections been checked?
- ☐ Are drip cans or trays in place?
- ☐ Is there a multiple valve separation between cargo system and the sea?
- ☐ Have the procedures for cargo/bunker/ballast handling been agreed?
- ☐ Are the methods for routine and emergency communication between the ship and the terminal fully understood and agreed by all parties?
- ☐ Have all emergency procedures been discussed and understood?
- ☐ And emergency stops tested ?
- ☐ Are the segregated ballast tanks free from contamination ?
- ☐ Is there sufficient planned space in the last tank for draining the shore lines/hoses/arms ?
- ☐ Will the manifolds be properly supervised throughout the operation ?
- ☐ Are sufficient personnel available, with defined and tested methods of communication with the Officer of the Watch ?
- ☐ Will physical checks be maintained on the ullages of all tanks ?
- ☐ Have all valve indicators been checked ?
- ☐ Are cargo pumps to be started before opening the manifold/sea valves?

Signed: Time/Date:

Appendix XVII
COW checklist

☐ The COW/discharge operation discussed with the terminal supervisors.

☐ Ship/shore communications procedures established and tested.

☐ Conditions for aborting COW defined and agreed with the terminal.

☐ All tanks have positive inert gas pressure, and a system in place to monitor continuously this pressure.

☐ A system in place to monitor tank oxygen content, and maintain this level below 8%.

☐ Fixed and portable oxygen analyzers functioning correctly.

☐ The manifold, deck and pumproom correctly lined up.

☐ A responsible person stationed on deck at the tank being washed.

☐ A crew member assigned to check deck lines for leaks.

☐ COW machines set for the required washing pattern.

☐ A system in place to check the COW machines frequently for correct operation.

☐ A system in place to verify the wash pressure regularly.

☐ Float gauges wound up.

☐ A system in place to closely monitor the level in the slop tanks.

☐ Communications checked between the COW team and cargo control room.

☐ A notice displayed at the gangway to indicate that COW is taking place.

Signed: Time/Date:

Appendix XVIII
Preparations for departure checklist

☐ Cargo work completed.
☐ Ballast completed, valves secured.
☐ Ship's services completed.
☐ Engines available.
☐ Shore authorities informed.
☐ Bridge gear tested, and the separate checklist completed.
☐ Communications tested.
☐ All crew on board.
☐ Cargo secured.
☐ Excess dunnage and lashing gear stowed away or secured.
☐ Stores, spares and all ship's equipment stowed away.
☐ Hatches, tank lids, ullage ports, sounding caps and accesses secured.
☐ Tankers: Ullage gauges wound up, and locked in stowage position.
☐ Tankers: Pressure-vacuum (PV) valve set to the sea-going condition.
☐ Cargo-handling equipment housed.
☐ Departure draft and density read and recorded.
☐ Draft survey, or other cargo calculations and paperwork completed.
☐ Official paperwork completed, clearance obtained.
☐ Weather report obtained.
☐ All shore personnel disembarked.
☐ Drugs/stowaway search completed.
☐ Mooring winches powered up and tested.
☐ Accommodation ladder prepared, ready to lift and stow.
☐ Officers and crew called for stations.
☐ Master informed that these checks have been completed successfully.
☐ Departure check logged.
☐ Pilot(s) on board, names recorded.
☐ Tugs in attendance, names recorded.

Signed: Time/Date:

Bridge gear checklist

☐ Propeller and rudder sighted clear.
☐ No.1 steering motor.
☐ No.2 steering motor.
☐ No.1 control system.
☐ No.2 control system.
☐ Autopilot.
☐ Emergency steering.
☐ Steering gear power failure alarm.
☐ Control system power failure alarm.
☐ Rudder angle indicator.
☐ Verify actual rudder movement (in steering gear compartment).
☐ Visual inspection of steering gear.
☐ Communication bridge—steering gear compartment.
☐ Emergency power supply.
☐ Bridge and engine room clocks synchronised.
☐ Engine telegraph.
☐ Engine movement recorder.
☐ Bridge recording equipment, time set and checked.
☐ Engines tested on air, ahead / astern.
☐ Engines tested on fuel, ahead / astern.
☐ Bridge control of engines, ahead / astern.
☐ RPM indicator.
☐ Manoeuvring air pressure.
☐ Gyro, and all repeaters.
☐ No.1 radar.
☐ No.2 radar.
☐ Arpa.
☐ Echo-sounder.
☐ Satnav.
☐ Other electronic navigation systems (e.g., Loran, Decca).
☐ Log.
☐ Course recorder.
☐ Binoculars.
☐ Azimuth mirrors.
☐ Sextants.
☐ Aldis lamp, and battery.
☐ VHF.
☐ Walkie-talkies, including spare batteries charged.
☐ Emergency communications to fore/aft/engineroom.
☐ Internal communications / crewcall / telephones.
☐ Window wipers / Clear-view screens.
☐ Sun visors.
☐ Primary navigation lights.
☐ Secondary navigation lights.
☐ Emergency navigation lights.
☐ Whistle forward / aft.
☐ Emergency whistle.
☐ Flags / shapes / lights.
☐ Passage plan.
☐ Charts for next passage.
☐ Charts corrected to NTM_____ and local area notice _____.
☐ Latest navigation warnings.
☐ Latest weather report / fax.
☐ Tidal and current information
☐ Pilot card / manoeuvring information sheet.
☐ Power on deck fore / aft.
☐ Pilot boarding / disembarkation.
　☐ Ladder.
　☐ Light.
　☐ Lifebuoy.
　☐ Heaving line.
☐ Checks logged.
☐ Inform Master that these checks have been completed successfully.

Signed: Time/Date:

The development of maritime commercial practice

Robert Tallack is a master mariner and a Fellow of The Nautical Institute. He has served on a variety of general cargo, passenger and refrigerated vessels, as well as frigates and minesweepers. He read for a degree in maritime commerce at the University of Wales in the early 70s after which he worked as a shipbroker for several years. He had a special interest in sale and purchase and newbuilding projects, subjects on which he lectured for the Seatrade 'Anatomy of Shipping' courses. As a general manager with Maersk, he was responsible for a mixed fleet of bulk carriers, tankers and offshore support vessels before moving to manage a freight ferry and terminal operation in the Irish Sea. This was followed by two years establishing a joint venture in eastern Europe.

Mr Tallack is Director of Developments for the National Sea Training Trust and a senior consultant with Trinitas Services Limited, where he has a special interest in ship operations and management, particularly in connection with the insurance industry.

'Transport is civilisation:'
Rudyard Kipling

THE purpose of this Nautical Briefing is to remind us of how our role in the business of international trade has grown, changed and developed and to raise the profile of this aspect of our responsibilities so that they are not altogether lost in an (albeit necessary) sea of safety regulations and operational procedures.

In the words of the 1993 Annual Institute of London Underwriters' Report:

> Everywhere you look in shipping, there is increasing regulation . . . while it is debatable whether more regulation is necessarily the key to safety, it is a fact that much of the regulation we see today applies to matters which, in any case, the prudent operator should have acted on before being forced to do so.

The tradition of shipmaster is an ancient and honourable one. Perhaps, in the UK at least, the 'Navy' in Merchant Navy, an honorific title bestowed in recent times in recognition of the bravery of our forebears, and the technological and structural changes of the past 30 years, have focused firmly and properly on the skills of navigating our vessels efficiently and safely.

Our true roots, however, lie in the other half of our title. Sometimes as sailing master, often as owner or part owner, frequently as merchant and trader, the shipmaster's role has, from time immemorial, been linked intimately with the business which is our raison d'être, maritime trade.

Although wireless communication changed forever the way in which trade is conducted, the shipmaster still retains important legal obligations, both towards the cargo owners—the merchants—as well as a professional duty towards his owners—and their shareholders—to manage their investment efficiently. We never have been, and in the opinion of The Nautical Institute, never should be 'just drivers'.

The new Nautical Institute book, *Commercial Management for the Shipmaster*, sponsored by the UK P&I Club and due to be published in April 1996, concentrates on our mercantile duties as shipmasters in what more accurately should be seen as the mercantile marine.

Before the flood

In approximately 2500 BC an unsuspecting prospective shipowner received a verbal letter of intent for a **contract of affreightment** or **COA**. The COA was quite specific with regard to the cargo to be carried, although the **laycan** (the lay days and cancelling date) and details of the **intended voyage** were a little unclear. Nevertheless, so compelling was the prospective **charter** that the owner built a vessel specifically to charterer's design.

When the vessel was completed, the owner gave firm **notice of readiness** seven days before the **cancelling date**.

Initially, the general public was very sceptical about the radical new design, especially as it was being constructed many leagues from the sea. However, as details of the proposed voyage leaked out, increasing numbers of the public clamoured for the right to book a passage on the vessel and load some of their own cargo.

The owner consulted with his charterer who enquired whether the owner had advertised the prospective voyage, in which case, the vessel could have been classed as a **common carrier** and been obliged to accept cargo and passengers against the payment of a reasonable freight rate.

Fortunately, apart from a few injudicious words one evening at a local tavern, the owner had kept the **fixture P&C** (private and confidential) and so was able to engage in the charter as a **private carrier** without obligation to offer passage or space to the general public.

Stores and cargo were loaded with a careful **tally** being kept by the ship's three mates (who were all sons of the shipowner's own mate: two of them later took up farming and one came to a sticky end, but that is a different story.)

After carefully reading the small print in the **charter party**, the owner decided to sail as master. He also took his wife with him as did the rest of the crew, who happened again to be his sons, thereby exhibiting an enlightened approach to personnel management and a shrewd grasp of how to keep crew costs down.

Once the voyage had commenced, the master realised that, although the specification of both ship and cargo were very comprehensive, the charter party said little about the intended length of the voyage nor did it clearly specify the **discharge port or ports**. This made navigation difficult and remains to this day the master's excuse as to why he ran aground.

It took three separate messages (one raven and two doves) to the charterer before a reputedly **safe port** was nominated for discharge and the cargo was carefully tallied ashore.

Grateful to have completed such a hazardous and harrowing voyage, it was some time before the master realised that he had released the cargo without having been presented with an original receipt for the cargo and proof of who owned the cargo.

As this **bill of lading** also set out the conditions under which he was carrying the cargo, he was never paid any **freight**. It was all a bit confusing, as he was never quite sure whether he should rely primarily on the **charter party** or on the **bill of lading**.

There is no doubt that today the master could have been referred to various legal judgements which supported his action—or not.

In one way, Noah was lucky; he at least knew where arbitration would take place.

The role of trade

Most of us have been brought up with our eyes and minds focused on ships and the cargoes they carry. We can, perhaps, be forgiven for considering ourselves centre stage in the international transportation of goods. But sea voyages are not an end in themselves and are generally undertaken for one of the following reasons:

● Exploration leading to new trading opportunities as well as movements of passengers and emigrants;

● Conquest, as often as not, in defence of or in extension of, land and trade, and requiring logistical support;

● The transportation of foodstuffs, raw materials and trade goods and, in modern times, assembly parts;

● The exploitation of the resources of the oceans—a process which, as resources are increasingly recognised as finite, has lead to a fundamental challenge of the age-old principle of freedom of the seas.

In large measure, the raison d'être for the shipmaster is international trade. Trade itself predates agriculture: tribes would travel far to barter, say, flint knives for good reed baskets.

Evidence of maritime trade has been found in Egypt as far back as 5000 BC by which time there was evidence that their seafarers had already harnessed the propulsive power of the wind. As well as Noah and his early version of a livestock carrier, loggers were also in vogue with a scribe crediting the Pharaoh Snefru with 'bringing of 40 ships filled with cedar logs' from the Lebanon to Egypt at around 2650 BC. Around 1000 BC Psalmists were referring to:

'Others [who] went out on the sea in ships; they were merchants on the mighty waters'

Psalm 107.23

Very early evidence has been found of Indian trade with Babylon using the Red Sea ports; and there is no doubt that India traded eastward and linked with the China Sea trade around the Malay Peninsula.

During his reign from 321-291 BC, Emperor Chandragupta Maurya created a Board of Admiralty and devoted the first chapter of the Arthastra of Kautilya, his treatise in Hindu polity, to shipping. Shipping was opening up the world and it was the shipmaster on the merchant trading vessel who was at the forefront.

The volume of trade was, admittedly, small at first but in AD 45, during the reign of Claudius, the pilot Hippalus discovered the potential of the monsoons and, according to the Roman historian Strabo, the thirty-odd vessels which traded with India each year soon could be numbered in hundreds. Considerable quantities of Roman coins dating from AD 68 have been found in the

Malabar Islands indicating the extent of travel and are believed to be associated with Jews fleeing from the Roman empire.

The first recognisable maritime nation in the Mediterranean was Phoenicia; and by 600 BC their shipmasters had extended Phoenician trading boundaries past Gibraltar (later to be known as the Pillars of Hercules and believed for many hundreds of years to be the end of the known world) and 1,000 km down the Atlantic coast of north Africa. Among the commodities the Phoenicians traded was a valuable purple dye made from a certain sea shell. Over 2,000 years later, in 1892, another trader in sea shells, Marcus Samuel, commissioned the first ship of what was to become one of the world's foremost tanker fleets—and named her *Murex* after that valuable sea shell.

As the Greek civilization took over from the Phoenicians Demosthenes, a maritime lawyer of his day, was already noting that 'Neither ship nor shipowner nor merchant can put to sea without the assistance of the lenders' (to finance the voyage) with the vessel being pledged as security.

Partial records exist of two lenders providing two merchants with 3,000 silver drachmas to finance a trading voyage. The written agreement provided that they would 'employ a 20 oared vessel of which Eucidius is the owner and master' and load 3,000 amphoras of wine on two local islands. Specific sailing directions permitted them to pass the Bosphoros into the Pontus Euxinus (Black Sea) and 'sell the wine at Histria (now a landlocked port but then close to the mouth of the Danube) or Tomis (now Constanza), and to load a return cargo of grain'.

Ancient Athens was dependent upon imports for nearly two thirds of its grain and the fertile Danube plain was already a major exporter of grain (an early example of seasonal trade for bulk carriers). On arrival back in Athens, the cargo was held as security by the lenders until it was sold and the charge of 22.5 per cent settled. In a similar way, the owner/master also held a claim until his lump sum freight was settled.

Greek amphoras can be seen to this day in Constanza, in the park above the harbour. Local folklore relates that one of the archaeologists tasted the honey sweet semi-solid found sealed in one of the amphoras. Some hours later, and after a couple of glasses of water on a hot afternoon, he was found by his colleagues, happily drunk. (What happened to the rest of the honey wine is not recorded but it is likely that it had once helped to finance a return cargo of grain.)

Towards maritime commercial practice

Foremost amongst the ancient Greek shipping and trading communities was the Island of Rhodes. Firm believers in the freedom of the seas for all, the seafarers and merchants of Rhodes were already establishing the beginnings of a maritime commercial practice which is still recognisable today. One of their greatest contributions was the concept of providing for a common contribution (general average) to be made if goods were jettisoned to lighten the vessel for the common good.

Although still influencing the way in which we trade today, Rhodian Law only survives in written form through the digest prepared for the Roman Emperor Justinian. An extract reads:

'Lege Rhodia cavetur ut si levandae navis gratia jactus mercium factus est, omnium contibutione sarciatur quod pro omnibus datum est'

De Lege Rhodia de Jactu

'The Rhodian law decrees that if in order to lighten a ship merchandise has been thrown overboard, that which has been given for all should be replaced by the contribution of all'

That the sea was free for all was an inherent principle which has stretched through the centuries. Even in all powerful Rome, Emperor Antonius would rule:

'Let it be judged by the Rhodian Law which deals with nautical matters, so far as it is not directly contrary to our own law.

'For I am the lord of the whole world but the law is the lord of the sea.'

The Roman Empire saw a great expansion of maritime trade, pushing up into northern Europe. Part of the shipping activity was to support far-flung legions but much was engaged in trade and then, as now, grain played a major role. By AD 100, Rome was importing 150,000 tonnes of grain a year.

Surprisingly, in such a well ordered empire, Roman maritime law was not codified and thus, like Rhodian law, it has not survived in detail. It is known that it covered the five broad areas of:

mare: the public use of the sea as, in common with the Rhodian principle, free for all. This is very different from the Roman approach to travel on land within their area of dominance and it is an important principle which has been defended, in concept if not entirely in practice, until the oceans as a source of resources rather than just a medium of travel coloured national thinking.

navis: covering the legal ownership and operation of the vessel.

merx: cargo, its carriage, delivery and the payment of freight.

obligations: responsibilities of the owner, merchant and shipmaster as well as those making maritime loans.

actions: the settlement of disputes.

Roman law recognised the need for finance and saw the further formalisation of the provision of maritime credit. Loans for trading ventures were made against the security of the vessel and were only repaid if the voyage were successful. In AD 554 Justinian I established standard, risk related premiums of 6 per cent, 8 per cent and 12 per cent.

However, not everything was well ordered and controlled. Petronius Arbiter, Governor of Bithynia (who seems to have lent his name to a venerable body of men) made the immortal statement:

> '*We trained hard, but it seemed that every time we were beginning to form up in teams we would be reorganised. I was to learn later in life that we tend to meet any new situation by reorganising and a wonderful method it can be for creating an illusion of progress while producing confusion, inefficiency and demoralisation.*'

Today he might suggest that we tend to meet any new situation by producing a convention or reorganising the operations manual. He committed suicide in AD 65.

The fall of the Roman Empire and the unsettled period of the Dark Ages obscured developments in maritime trade, with delivery as likely to be made against the point of a sword as against production of a bill of lading.

The legal advice: 'Never kill a man from whom you can recover damages' heralded the return to a more ordered society which established itself in Europe after the Crusades, and two discernable trading blocks were to influence maritime trade and the development of maritime commercial practice.

Mediterranean regulations

In the Mediterranean, the northern Italian city states, and principally Venice and Genoa, established well regulated ways of conducting maritime trade. Vessels, owned by one or more dedicated shipowners would advertise them for trade (much as a common carrier), with the ship's name and proposed destination carved on a board and carried round the town on a lance. Merchants would appoint a supercargo to travel with their goods and vessels were inspected for seaworthiness prior to sailing with the inspector frequently carving a mark on the planking to indicate how deep he thought it safe to load the vessel—some 500 years before Mr Plimsoll regularised the practice.

Protectionist laws were promulgated to ensure cargoes were carried in locally owned vessels. At its height, Venice boasted 3,000 vessels and 28,000 seamen out of a total population of 200,000 while Amalfi, then a thriving seaport near Naples, claimed to have invented the mariner's compass.

A charterparty of 1263 for a voyage between Porto Pisano and Bugea shows interesting similarities with modern commercial practice. It required the shipowner to 'provide a vessel in good condition and furnished with tackle and equipment as specified, together with a crew of 36 skillful seamen (including the master, clerk and supercargo) and six servants'. The master and mariners were to be properly armed and, together with the stevedores, were required to take an oath to observe the terms of the contract. Lightering at his own expense against payment of the customary freight, the owner undertook to sail within 10 days of contract and to deliver the cargo to the receivers in Bugea in the same condition 'as signed for'.

Hanseatic League

Outside the Mediterranean, to the north and east of a Thames/Rhine dividing line, the Hanseatic League of more than 60 cities, including Lubeck, Hamburg and Bremen, dominated maritime trade and transportation in a different way.

Here, there was a much closer relationship between cargo and vessel, merchant and mariner. Vessels were generally smaller, voyages shorter and ownership, or part ownership of several vessels in partnership, more common. Cargo also tended to move in smaller parcels spread between more vessels.

One of the premier trading cities, whose name remains with us today, was Visby on the Island of Gotland. During the 12th century Visby was reported to have 12,000 active merchants and as many vessels—at least until the town was sacked by the Danes in 1361. The basis of marine insurance, the principle of spreading the risk, became interwoven into the very fabric of trade.

Laws and conventions were promulgated to control differing aspects of maritime trade and transportation and generally took their name from an important trading city in that particular trading area. The wine trade from Bordeaux (then an English province) was regulated by the Judgements (or Rolls) of Oleron, a small island off La Rochelle where Richard I is reputed to have paused on his return from the Crusades. Promulgated in the latter part of the 12th Century, they required, among other things, the master to consult his crew before sailing, a recognition of the hazardous nature of the Bay of Biscay and western approaches to the Channel. Some of the provisions of the Judgements of Oleron were incorporated into the 'Ancient Maritime Code of Visby', produced half a century before the Danes paid their courtesy call.

In the Mediterranean, Barcelona had become a powerful trading centre and, in 1258, published, in Catalan, the Consulate del Mare or Barcelona Ordinances. Running to 300 chapters, and including the provision that the crew should be provided with saltmeat, bread, vegetables, oil, wine and water, they were still influencing maritime commercial practice nearly 500 years later. In 1705 they were translated into Dutch. In England, Rhodian Law and the Judgements of Oleron were combined under the rule of Edward II in the Black Book of the Admiralty.

Discovery of America

The discovery of "the other side of the Atlantic" in 1492 and of a route into the Pacific in 1520 marked the beginning of the end of the Italian city republics and the rise of Spanish and Portuguese maritime power.

The massive importation of American gold and silver into Europe through Spain and, to a lesser extent, Portugal, resulted in two significant events which helped to change the face of maritime trade and exploration right across the globe.

One was a period of severe inflation, that lasted for about 150 years from the mid 16th century and which contributed to the end of the Italian city republics and their dominance of trade. The other was the emergence of Dutch and British sea power; the latter through growing confidence after the defeat of the Spanish Armada in 1588 and the former following the weakening of Spanish control of Le Pays Bas.

Although the Dutch did not formally secure their independence until the signing of the Treaty of Westphalia in 1648, by 1610 they recorded a fleet of 16,000 vessels totalling one million tons and manned by 160,000 seafarers. The spirit of the age is encapsulated in the quotation:

'Whosoever commands the sea commands trade, whosoever commands the trade of the world commands the riches of the world and, consequently, the world itself':

Sir Walter Raleigh ca. 1610

Together, and often in fierce competition, these two countries sailed east round Cape Agulhas in part commercial, part military conquest; the British to India and the Dutch to the East Indies. In 1601 and 1602 the English and Dutch India Companies were incorporated and grew to generate a third trade and transportation structure which, by the second half of 17th Century, had eclipsed the Hanseatic League, the power of the Italian city states and Spain.

The steady weakening of Italian influence and control in the Mediterranean resulted in another phenomenon which is all too prevalent in certain parts of the world today.

Pirates, operating out of Algeria, seized 466 vessels between 1609 and 1615. In the course of a short period in 1625, 27 British ships were seized or sunk; and 1,000 seamen killed or captured.

The India companies grew in strength and their growing wealth led to increasing political power. The Dutch, in particular, knew not only how to trade but also how to protect and expand trade through the use of their fleet.

Despite 40 years of war with Spain, Amsterdam's importance as a financial centre grew. The Battle of the Downs in 1639, when Admiral Tromp soundly defeated the Spanish fleet, made Holland dominant in northern waters.

English protectionism

England wanted to secure its monopoly over the riches of India, so it resorted to straightforward protectionism with the first Navigation Act of 1646. In 1651 Cromwell strengthened these acts, requiring cargoes trading to and from English territories to be carried in ships, built and owned in England; with a British master and three-quarters of the crew British.

This attempt to monopolise trade resulted in the first Anglo-Dutch war between two dynamic and expanding nations that had so much in common.

A little more than 10 years later, in 1666, England—now under Charles I—and Holland were at war again.

Despite early successes, the Dutch fleet was eventually defeated; and this led to the weakening of Amsterdam's position as a leading financial centre in favour of London.

Just as it is today, information was at a premium and of great commercial value.

In the second part of the 17th century Edward Lloyd's coffee house was providing a meeting place for merchants, financiers and shipmasters who needed to know the latest news about ships and their cargoes.

In time, this led to a market-place for marine insurance. Lloyd's of London, Lloyd's Register, *Lloyd's List* and Lloyd's Shipping Intelligence all owe their existence to this unique coffee-shop.

The English penchant for restricting free trade emerged again in 1720. In exchange for a little immediate financial support (£300,000), the king granted a statutory monopoly to Royal Exchange Assurance and London Assurance as the only companies authorised for the conduct of maritime insurance business. Fortunately for underwriters at Lloyd's Coffee House, they were operating as individuals rather than companies.

As the century progressed shipowners, dissatisfied with the cost and scope of hull insurance, began to form regional hull insurance clubs. These were unincorporated associations or cooperatives of shipowners who came together to share hull risks on a mutual basis, each being both an insured party and an insurer of others. In the field of law and contract things were also changing and it can be argued that the start of the modern period of maritime commerce and legislation originated in France. Here the radical thinking, which eventually led to the French Revolution, is typified by Colbert's attempt to draft a general code to regulate trade, published in 1673 as 'Les Ordonnances du Commerce' and followed by 'Les Ordonnances de la Marine'.

Trading acumen

Meanwhile, the transfer of maritime finance to London strengthened England's monopoly position and reduced competition. Vessels became larger and embarked upon lengthy voyages with the shipmaster and 'company man' on board directing the trading.

As an incentive, the master would be allocated a certain hold capacity for his own trade—one record shows an allocation of 10.75 per cent of burden or 86 tons in an 800 tonner. Thus the shipmaster, who was paid £10 per month (twice as much as the mate and four times as much as a sailor), would expect to retire after four or five voyages with £20-30,000 in the bank from legitimate trading alone. He would then probably join others in investing in a part share of one or more vessels.

During the 18th century, with monopoly-protected freight rates on an East Indiaman climbing to £25 per ton, profits of 350 per cent or more would be expected on a two year voyage. Much of this depended upon the trading acumen of the shipmaster as well as on his ability to navigate and manage his vessel. A major part of the voyage's success also depended upon the mate for, while the master was about his trading business, it was the mate who ran the ship: organising the lighters, controlling the stevedores and stowing often strange and unusual cargoes for long voyages and, of course, signing for the condition, quantity and quality of the cargo on the mate's receipt.

Cargoes were varied. In 1790 *The Spy* sailed for Africa with a cargo which included brandy, swords, muskets, clothes, iron bars, brass wear and cooking pots. These were traded for slaves who were sold for up to £44 in the West Indies. This profit in turn was used to purchase cargoes of tobacco, molasses, sugar and rum for the return voyage to England and a vast profit.

Unwittingly, these wretched slaves were the reason for a radical change in ship design and, as a result, trading practice and patterns.

Slavery made unlawful

In 1807, the British Parliament passed an act making trading in slaves unlawful and this resulted in profound technological and trading changes. The merchant fleet of the United States of America had been growing steadily and profitably (a return voyage with pepper from Sumatra in the 1780s was recorded as yielding a 700 per cent profit) and also encompassed the profitable West African slave trade. With the outlawing of slavery by the British government, it became necessary to design and build vessels which could outrun British frigates. Thus the impetus was given to the development of the fast American schooners and clippers, capable of sustaining 17-18 knots in the trade winds, and a long period of international maritime competition between Britain and America.

Among the many changes of the early part of the 19th century which contributed to the changing face of trade was the slow decline of the British and Dutch monopolies. The East India Company lost its monopoly in 1814, and the China monopoly ended in 1834 but it was not until April 1849 that the British Navigation Acts were finally repealed.

In their final years they had produced many counter-productive practices, with coffee brought to Amsterdam in a Dutch-flag vessel and then transhipped to a British flag vessel before being taken to a South African port where it was discharged and reloaded before finally being delivered to the London market at a consequently high price.

Despite the increase of trade, documents could still be simple and straightforward, as is evidenced by a complete charter party dated 26 July 1813 and containing only 300 words. Despite its commendable brevity, it still contains the salient information necessary to evidence the agreement and prosecute the voyage.

The charterer and owner are identified, together with the vessel, her cargo capacity and where she is lying. A statement relating to her seaworthiness and 'fitness for purpose' is made and laycan and loadport defined, together with a statement covering 'safe ports'.

The appointment of agents and the cargo to be loaded '. . . a full and complete cargo of tallow, and other goods but not less than 490 casks of tallows'. Freight rate, demurrage, discharge and delivery of the cargo against presentation of bills are all addressed together with Acts of God and other exceptions; all in the equivalent of one typed page of A4. Is our professionalism such that we could efficiently undertake a voyage charter today on similar information?

Fast clippers

The end of the Napoleonic wars in 1815 released 1,000 vessels on to the market, with Britain owning some 2.5 million gross tons of what was to prove not very competitive tonnage. While the fast clippers and schooners were challenging the 'Indiamen', which could trace their development back to the old Spanish galleons of the early 16th century, a new technology was appearing. In 1818 the *Savannah* made the first steam auxiliary crossing of the Atlantic, two years after the Black Ball Line had established the first regular trans-Atlantic liner service.

The advent of liner services marked a fundamental change in the way in which maritime trade and maritime transportation were related. The specialist ship owner grew in prominence, frequently devoid of any direct trading interests or any specific connection with the cargoes which the vessels were carrying.

In 1824 the insurance monopoly in favour of the Royal Exchange Assurance and London Assurance was removed. Great competition had a salutary effect on the rates, terms of cover and service offered on the commercial market and by Lloyd's underwriters. However it is interesting to note that the Lloyd's SG policy form survived and remained in existence until 1983.

The mutual hull clubs became less necessary and went into decline. A few still exist today but their share of the market is not large.

Government mail contracts and increasing bilateral trade agreements aided the development of the liner companies, which held sway until containerisation changed their traditional structure in the 1970s. Looking back, we see a familiar scene: increased competition and freer trade dropped trans-Atlantic freight rates from £7-8 per ton to £3.5-£4.0 per ton over a two year period in the 1850s giving more competitive nations the opportunity to increase their share of trade.

As sail and steam struggled for supremacy, the 19th century, fuelled by the spread of the industrial revolution, saw an unprecedented growth in world trade. Maritime trade, valued at US$1.5 billion at the turn of the century, had reached US$4.0 billion by the 1850s and was to reach US$24.0 billion by 1900—during the same period, world population was to have grown only threefold by comparison.

Gold-rush fever

A new phenomenon was about to occur: the mass movement of people. In 1848 gold was discovered in California and in 1851 it was discovered in Australia. The resultant gold rush drew in prospectors from all parts of the globe and they travelled by sea. Between 1850 and 1860, the population of Australia grew from 400,000 to over 1,100,000 and in America the rush of prospectors became a steady river of emigrants from Europe. By 1880, half a million were arriving in the United States every year, placing new demands on shipping—and offering new opportunities.

By the time gold fever hit the world, Great Britain and the United States of America owned 5.7 and 5.3 million tons of shipping respectively. But there was a difference. The British sailing fleet was still typified by the relatively slow 'Indiaman' of 1,500 tons with a crew of 125. Massachusett's shipbuilders, with access to a good supply of plentiful timber and open minds, had designed a 450 tonner that could be sailed by a crew of 18. Although lifting less than half as much cargo, they averaged twice the speed and, in terms of ton-miles transportation capability, represented a significant increase in world shipping capacity.

Costs and competition

Around this time, a 500 ton steamer, which cost £9,000 to build on the Tyne would cost only £4,270 in Prussia, £4,500 in Norway, £5,500 in Sweden, £7,000 in Holland and £7,250 in America. Annual operating costs were £2,623 in the UK, £2,110 in the USA and only £1,329 in Sweden and Prussia. Competition was fierce but technology and a steady supply of steam coal was to come to the aid of British industry and British shipping. Britain supplied the world with its coal and its shipping fleets with their bunkers. Coal exports expanded from 3.2 million tons in 1850 to 29 million tons by 1890, with 8.1 million tons consumed as ships' bunkers, to 64 million tons in 1907 with 21 million tons used as bunkers.

Despite all the economic activity, supply (ships—and especially ton mile capability after the Suez Canal opened on 17 November 1869) exceeded demand and freight rates were weak. To counter this, many of the liner companies established conferences, offering regular sailings at scheduled times and publishing common freight rates, undertaking to sail their ships whether full loaded or not.

Liner trades, with 'company' offices or agents well established in their various ports of call resulted in another change in commercial practise. Merchants travelled with their vessels less and less, leaving the master 'under God', fully responsible for the safe and economic prosecution of the voyage and for the 'ship, with all her ordinance, tackle, apparel & etc' and, especially, 'Goods and Merchandises'.

Despite these changes, the shipmaster remained, and still remains today, the arbiter of quality and quantity when he signs the bill of lading.

It is arguable how much the divergence of merchant, owner and operation was responsible for the industry's poor safety record during this period but technological development was not synonymous with increasing safety. Rather the opposite; as in many of the factories spawned by the industrial revolution, life was cheap.

The resulting coffin ships, together with the mass movement of immigrants during the second part of the century, had a direct effect on the formation of maritime legislation and maritime insurance, stimulated to a great extent by a coal merchant who became a Member of Parliament in 1868.

Samuel Plimsoll's book *Coffin Ships* and his subsequent 'un-Victorian' outburst against entrenched indifference in the House of Commons, led directly to a Royal Commission on Unseaworthy Ships in 1874. This resulted in a Bill in 1876 giving power to the British Board of Trade to survey vessels and affix the now famous Plimsoll Line. Not too different from the practice in Venice in the 13th century.

Victorian values

A strange mixture of indifference and philanthropy typified much of Victorian England. Lord Campbell's Act of 1846 made it much easier for injured crew members to seek compensation from their employers; and especially to seek compensation for the dependants of crew members who were killed.

The possibility of claims from the flood of passengers and immigrants travelling to the Americas and Australia also concentrated the shipowner's mind. They became increasingly aware of the limits of the insurance cover they had in respect of collisions with other ships and their liabilities to third parties.

As a direct result the first protection association was formed in 1855, based on the principle of mutual insurance started on a regional basis, by the hull clubs a century earlier.

The risk of liability for loss of, or damage to, cargo carried on board the insured vessel added the insured ship to the cover in 1874. Nevertheless, the duty of the shipmaster 'to carefully carry' is in no way reduced. Just as the shipper remains the prime customer, so the dedication and professionalism of master and crew remains paramount.

Sometimes it is tempting to draw parallels. The essentially technical problems of crew and cargo claims from overloaded ships, and the increase in collisions in an expanding fleet that put strains on training and the supply of competent seafarers, initially found a solution through increased insurance.

Are there parallels today in the imposition of high premiums and increasing regulation as a solution to the lack of sufficient properly trained masters, officers and ratings?

One other major technological and commercial development was to influence world trade and maritime transportation.

Naft had been known in Arabia for thousands of years and accounted for the eternal flames of Egypt, Persia, Greece and Rome. It was not until 1854, when the Rock Oil Company drilled its first well in Titsville, Pennsylvannia, that commercial exploitation really commenced. The American well was followed by drilling in southern Russia; in 1877 the first tankship sailed in the Caspian Sea; and the first ocean tanker was delivered in 1886.

According to Lloyd's Register, by 1911 there were 280 vessels carrying bulk oil in the service of an industry which was to generate new commercial and legal challenges. Nevertheless, even in this totally new demand for maritime transportation, the bill of lading, the mate's care and attention and the master's signature and authority remained central factors.

Black Gold, in challenging King Coal, had another effect on shipping and life at sea. When ss *Mauritania* was converted to oil and her many boiler fires eliminated, so were the jobs of 270 of her 300 engine room firemen.

Trading rules

The rapid expansion and increasing internationalisation of trade and commerce during this period, together with sharpening competition, was putting pressure on the legal system under which trade and maritime transportation were conducted.

Although, as we have seen, maritime law and practice largely evolved from the same Rhodian roots, it had become increasingly intertwined with the domestic law of the various trading nations. This was particularly so in Britain where maritime law was mixing with common law precedent. The 80 or so years from the middle of the 18th century saw intense international endeavour, and at times procrastination and self-interest, as nations tried to find a common and effective structure for world trade.

As two centuries earlier, it was a radical and free thinking French lawyer, Monsieur de Courcy, who, as much as anyone else, started the move towards codification and uniformity with the publication in 1863 of his treatise 'Reformes Internationales du Droit Maritime'.

The baton was taken up by a Belgian government minister, August Beernaert, through the Institut de Droit International in Ghent. In 1873 he promoted the first International Maritime Conference (Comité Maritime Internationale) which was convened in The Hague. The long history of meetings, reflecting the subjects that were exercising the minds of shipowners, merchants and their insurers, is illustrated in Figure 1, which summarises half a century of primarily private maritime law formation (private concentrating on contract law as opposed to public which incoporates the freedom of the seas and which the discovery of offshore oil was to effect).

The agendas for the Hague conferences were proving to be over-ambitious and the first attempt to produce an all-encompassing maritime code which would cover the whole world, in the words of

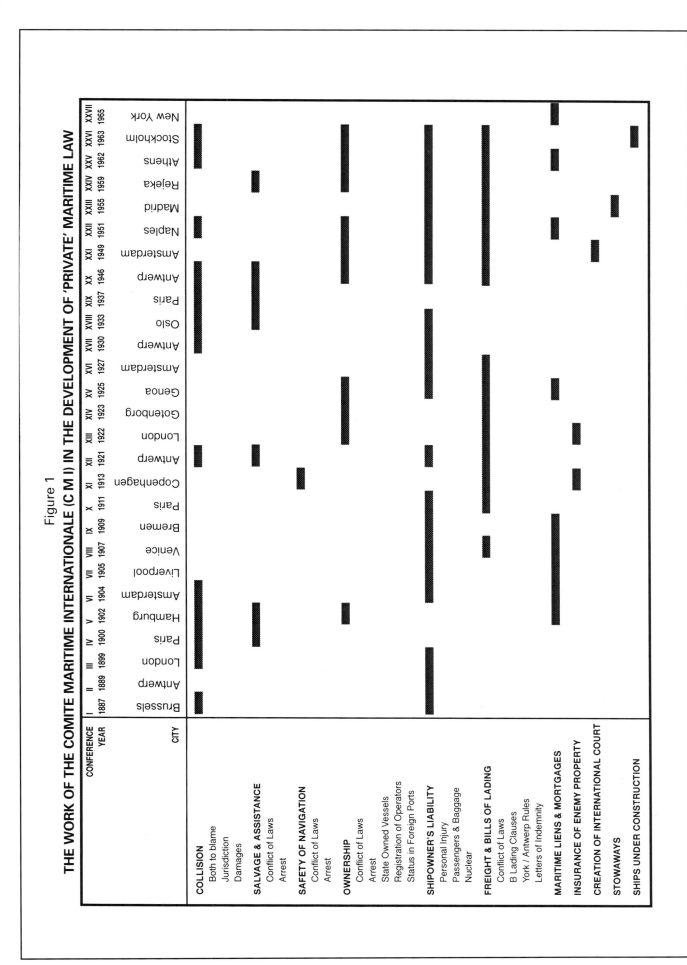

Figure 1

THE WORK OF THE COMITE MARITIME INTERNATIONALE (C M I) IN THE DEVELOPMENT OF 'PRIVATE' MARITIME LAW

Lilar and Van den Bosch of the Comité Maritime Internationale 'overran the goal through an excess of generosity and, consequently, an absence of realism [and ended] without any concrete result.'

One result was that the recently 'United' States of America became involved and, in 1889 held an International Maritime Conference in Washington DC lasting two and a half months. The list of agenda items provides an interesting snapshot of what was concerning the maritime world, at least at governmental level:

1: Collision Rules
2: Seaworthiness
3: Draught of Loaded Vessels
4: Uniform Regulation for the Design & Making of Vessels
5: Saving of Life and Property—Shipwreck
6: Necessary qualifications for Officers and Seamen
7: Lanes for Steamers and Frequented Routes
8: Night Signals for Communicating Information
9: Storm Warnings
10: Reporting, Marking and Removing Wrecks
11: Notices of Dangers to Navigation
12: Uniform System of Buoys and Beacons
13: Establishing a Permanent International Maritime Commission.

As can be seen from the subjects contained in the proceedings of the CMI (Figure 1), the shipowner's right to limit his liability ranked high on the agenda. The balance was tipping against the shipper and it is hardly surprising that, as a major exporting nation, it was the United States, with the Harter Act of 1893, that first established the legal obligation of the shipowner to provide a seaworthy vessel and exercise due diligence in the prosecution of the voyage before he could limit his liability.

However, it was not until 1921 that the International Law Association adopted what we now know as the Hague Rules.

Hague Rules

The unique concept of general average was, and continued to be one of the most powerful concepts in maritime law and commercial practice; perhaps because it recognises—as we may sometimes be in danger of ignoring—the perils of a 'maritime adventure'. In 1857, the National Association for the Promulgation of Social Sciences in London inaugurated a study of the ancient principal of general average and commenced the long route towards the York-Antwerp Rules.

In 1860, an appeal to the Association from a meeting in Glasgow of, among others, Lloyd's and the Liverpool Association of Underwriters, resulted in a proposal for a draft bill to define general average accompanied by eleven rules covering its implementation, generally referred to as the Glasgow Resolution. International debate took place in London in 1862 and eleven 'York Rules' were agreed at the third International General Average Conference held in York in September 1864.

Procrastination and prevarication then set in. But in Antwerp in August 1887, the rules were thoroughly reviewed and repromulgated, despite Lloyd's rather peeved suggestion that abolition of GA might be the best road to uniformity. After a practical test of some 10 years, it was the Association of Average Adjusters who were next to take up the baton and push for formal adoption.

The two central standards of maritime law and practice, general average and the right to limit liability and the conditions under which this could be done, finally came together in 1924 when common definitions of the two main strands of maritime commercial law, general average and the shipowner's responsibility to exercise due diligence and consequent ability to limit liability, were finally agreed.

It was following conferences of the International Law Association in London and Stockholm, that the York-Antwerp Rules were finally agreed. (The International Law Association (ILA), the successor to the Association for the Reform and Codification of the Law of Nations was founded in 1873.) At the same time the Hague-Visby Rules were agreed. (Visby was tacked on after a historic visit to the famous island by conference hosts in Gothenborg in 1923.)

Public maritime law, relating mainly to the freedom of the sea, a principle also rooted in pre-Rhodian practice and championed by Grotius in his work 'Mare Librum', published in 1609; and private maritime law, the law of commerce, had for many years developed in relative isolation. In 1937 an event took place which was to bring the two strands of maritime law into closer focus. The Pure and Superior Oil Company built a large platform in 15 feet of water off the coast of Louisiana; drilled and found oil.

Internationally, there was a new era and the USA changed almost overnight its conservative 'total freedom of all the seas' approach. The use of the seas as a resource base as well as a means of transport had arrived and was to bring with it exclusive economic zones and the seemingly eternal debates of the United Nations Law of the Seas Conferences (UNCLOS). This factor, reinforced by the realisation that fish stocks were not an infinite resource, together with the separate but closely related modern phenomenon of marine pollution (and especially the shipowner's desire to limit his liability) have brought the two aspects of maritime law closer together. Today, there is a much greater liaison between the ILA, for example, and the International Maritime Organization (IMO), the guardian, through its United Nations roots, of much of the public law of the sea.

Over a period of 6,000 years we have traced some of the major factors influencing international trade and maritime transportation and shown the central role played by the shipmaster and, in an important supporting role, the mate. In more modern times we have seen how the maritime heritage of Venice and the northern Italian city states has been taken up by that most successful of modern trading nations, Greece, where the relationship between owner and master remains strong, enduring—and commercial.

Similarly, we have seen how the partnership trading structure of the Hanseatic League has left a strong, competitive shipping industry in Scandinavia, again based on the realisation that master, crew and owner all have an important role to play in meeting the demands of the shipowner's essential customer, those who generate international trade. We have also seen the large Anglo-Dutch trading monopolies give way to liner trades, containers and through transportation.

Although the shipmaster, and even the owner, is no longer so involved in trading decisions affecting the cargo, the shipmaster's role is still central and the common focus for shipper, receiver and charterer. It is the view of The Nautical Institute, that we ignore this role at our peril, even in the face of the increasing avalanche of technical and safety regulations, and the all too frequent failure of the modern shipowner to realise the potential of the properly trained and motivated master and mate.

This briefing so far has been aimed at setting the scene for a description of how international trade is undertaken today, as it is from this activity that the demand for maritime transport and, consequently for our professional services, arises.

International trade today

Although hedged by trade barriers, bilateral trade agreements and trading blocks (such as the European Community) and, theoretically at least, liberalised through international agreements such as the General Agreement on Tariffs and Trade (GATT), international trade at its most basic involves the flow of goods from a seller to a buyer in accordance with the terms of a contract of sale. Much of this trade is carried by ships and thus the maritime link is an integral part of any sale contract. Through its role as document of title, the bill of lading and, consequently, the shipmaster, play a key role in the process of delivery and payment as well as carriage and care.

Every international trade transaction starts with a buyer and a seller and a contract of sale. Once the price and specification is agreed, the two parties must consider two other crucial aspects: how to get the goods from seller to buyer and how and when the payment is going to pass from buyer to seller. These issues immediately bring other parties into the transaction.

Every international trade transaction requires:
● an agreed product or service,
● a sales contract,
● shipping and delivery details,
● terms of payment,
● documentation,
● insurance cover,
and to this list could be added:
● a means of triggering payment for the goods (and, indirectly linked to that, the payment of freight); together with
● a means of transferring title, and therefore the risk, in the goods.

There are three different times at which payment can be made:
1: In advance: this can be in whole or in part and requires a high degree of trust by the buyer in the seller. One of its uses is to assist the seller finance the production of the goods
2: At the time of shipment: immediately involving the vessel in the transaction; and
3: After shipment or on receipt: invariably effected through some kind of credit.

We shall look first at the various methods of settling international trade transactions through the procedures controlling one of the most common methods of payment, the documentary credit. These procedures are established by the International Chamber of Commerce (ICC) and the following descriptions and definitions, are based on the Uniform Custom and Practice for Documentary Credits (UPC 500) and, where applicable, Incoterms 1990, a set of uniform rules codifying the interpretation of trade terms.

However sophisticated the procedures surrounding a trade transaction, payment against documents for imports en route (ie payment by documentary credit) cannot give protection against the risk of fraud, especially when the seller is not well known. The strong advice for both parties is to know who you are trading with and, if uncertain, to get a recognised bank guarantee.

There are 13 Incoterms 1990 controlling the transfer of risk from seller to buyer, designed so that this can be effected at a convenient place where the goods can be inspected and condition and quantity verified. They are explained in more detail in the forthcoming book *Commercial*

EXW	Ex Works	(named place)
FAC	Free Carrier	(named place)
FAS	Free Alongside Ship	(named port of shipment)
FOB	Free on Board	(named port of shipment)
CFR	Cost and Freight (C&F)	(named port of destination)
CIF	Cost, Insurance & Freight	(named port of destination)
CPT	Carriage Paid to	(named place of destination)
CIP	Carriage & Insurance paid to	(named place of destination)
DAF	Delivery at Frontier	(named place)
DES	Delivery Ex Ship	(named port of destination)
DEQ	Delivery Ex Quay (duty paid)	(named port of destination)
DDU	Delivery Duty Unpaid	(named port of destination)
DDP	Delivery Duty Paid	(named port of destination)

Management for the Shipmaster but are: Once the terms of trade have been decided, the exact means of payment must be selected.

Cash in advance is straightforward, cheap and, as has been stated, requires a high degree of trust. **Open account** describes an arrangement whereby the goods are manufactured and delivered before payment is required; and obviously a particularly high degree of trust is required by the seller.

Collection describes an arrangement whereby the goods are shipped and a **bill of exchange** (draft) is drawn by the seller on the buyer and documentary evidence (of which the bill of lading is a key ingredient) is sent to the seller's bank in order to effect collection through the buyer's confirming bank.

The logical extension of this is the **documentary credit** or letter of undertaking. This is issued by a bank for the account of a buyer (the applicant)—or for its own account—and is an undertaking to pay the beneficiary the value of the draft, provided that the terms of the documentary credit are complied with. The documentary credit can satisfy the seller's desire for cash and the buyer's desire for credit; it serves the interests of both parties independently and offers a unique and universally used method of achieving a commercially acceptable undertaking by providing for payment to be made against complying documents that represent the goods, and making possible the transfer of title to those goods without contemporaneous physical transfer of the goods being necessary.

It will immediately be obvious that payment (and consequent transfer of ownership, ie title and risk) by way of a documentary credit, introduces the financial institutions and converts the originally simple, one-contract transaction into a distinct, triangular contractual arrangement:
- First—the sale contract between buyer and seller;
- Second—the 'application and security agreement' or the 'reimbursing agreement' between the buyer (the applicant) and the issuer (the issuing bank); and
- Third—the documentary credit between the issuing bank and the beneficiary.

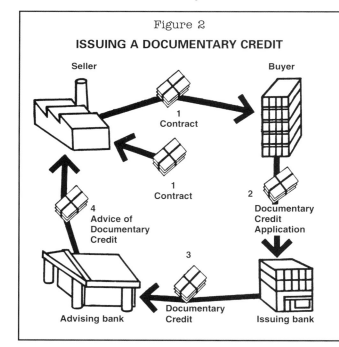

Figure 2

ISSUING A DOCUMENTARY CREDIT

1. The buyer and the seller conclude a sales contract providing for payment by documentary credit
2. The buyer instructs his bank (the issuing bank) to issue a credit in the favour of the seller (beneficiary)
3. The issuing bank asks another bank, usually in the country of the seller to advise and perhaps also to add its confirmation to the documentary credit
4. The advising or confirming bank informs the seller that the credit has been issued.

The documentary credit may also be confirmed by another (confirming) bank and it is important to understand that each contract is independent of the other:

'Credits, by their nature are separate transactions from the sales or other contract(s) on which they may be based, and banks are in no way concerned with or bound by such contract(s), even if any reference whatsoever to such contract(s) is included in the credit. Consequently, the undertaking of a bank to pay, accept and pay draft(s) or negotiate and/or fulfil any other obligation under the credit is not subject to claims or defences by the applicant resulting from his relationship with the issuing bank or beneficiary'

and

'A beneficiary can in no case avail himself of the contractual relationships existing between the banks or between the applicant and the issuing bank.'

UPC 500 sub-Articles 3a & b.

Process of documentary credit

There are many advantages which flow from the use of documentary credits of which the foremost can be seen to be the provision of a confirmed method of payment. However the process involves many more institutions (and their costs) than in the originally simple contract between buyer and seller; and as the frequent non-availability of bills of lading in the port of delivery proves, documentary credits generate a paper chase of their own.

A particular advantage of credits documentary or otherwise, to commodity traders and others who buy and sell goods is that they can enable an onsale to take place before the buyer's bank has to effect payment under the credit. If the trader structures his transaction correctly, his buyer will pay him before the trader's bank settles under the credit, thereby leaving the trader with a positive cashflow.

A cargo of crude oil from the Gulf may be traded several times in this way en route to North America, Europe or the Far East. Behind each of these complementary but totally separate transactions is, at its simplest, a banking structure similar to the one depicted in Figure 2. Each set of transactions requires original documentation in order to effect payment, and central to this documentation, is the bill of lading in the dual roles of document of title and proof of quantity and quality.

Although a documentary credit represents the payment end of a single sale contract, each link in the chain—buyer (or applicant) to issuing bank, issuing bank to advising (or confirming) bank and advising bank to seller (or beneficiary)—is a separate and distinct contract. Thus, if incorrect documentation is presented to the issuing bank by the advising bank, the issuing bank's recourse is to the advising bank, not to the seller. Since the documentary credits department of a large, international bank will be handling thousands of transactions daily, they will rely totally on the validity of the documents presented to them, and will have no knowledge of or, for that matter, interest in the physical movement of that cargo.

This goes a long way to explain why banks will generally only accept a clean bill of lading, that is, a bill of lading that normally stipulates that the goods were 'in apparent good order and condition' when accepted.

Since, as is inherent in their very name, documentary credits are executed by the presentation of the specified documents, including inevitably, the bill(s) of lading, it is hardly surprising that these same bills of lading are frequently unavailable at the port of discharge.

Figure 2 reproduces a standard application for an irrevocable documentary credit and there are a number of points to note from the 'shipping' end of the transaction.

For a start, a documentary credit is time-related and stipulates an expiry date. Secondly it describes the goods to be shipped and this description, which should tally with the description on the bill of lading, will certainly contain no reference to defects in quality, quantity or even packaging. Thirdly, the application stipulates the documents that must be presented; and it is against these documents alone that the credit is transacted.

There is a wide range of documentary credits, from irrevocable to transferable and revolving which all follow the same basic principles. The 'Red Clause' documentary credit, so-called because it was originally written in red ink is an interesting variation. Here funds can be made available before shipment and this can be useful where traders or dealers require a form of pre-financing.

An example might be where a grain exporter is purchasing parcels of grain to form an economical Panamax cargo. HIs eventual buyer may allow him partial advance payment to settle with his supplier and reserve silo space in the port of loading. Whatever method of credit is used, the same basic principles apply and settlement follows the procedure illustrated in Figure 3.

The customers' objectives

The use of terms of settlement as well as the type of sale contract, reflects the objectives of our customers, the buyers, sellers and traders who generate the demand for maritime transport. At one end of the spectrum is the regular movement of goods from established seller to established buyer that typifies the user of liner services and, increasingly today, containers. Here, the decision as to whether the sale contract will be EXW (ex-works) or DDP (delivered duty-paid) at the other end of the spectrum, will depend upon the relative strength of buyer and seller.

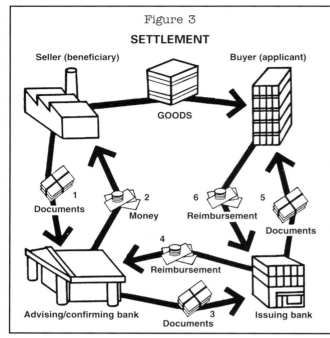

Figure 3
SETTLEMENT

1. The seller sends the documents evidencing the shipment to the bank where credit is available (the nominated bank)
2. After checking that the documents meet the credit requirements, the bank makes payment
3. This bank then sends the documents to the issuing bank
4. The issuing bank, after checking that the documents meet the credit requirements, makes reimbursements in the pre-agreed manner
5. The issuing bank then sends the documents to the buyer
6. Reimbursement is obtained in the pre-agreed manner.

A manufacturer of finished goods may well wish to enhance his sales service by taking responsibility for arranging freight (transportation) and documentation and deliver his product to his buyer's warehouse or retail outlet. On the other side of his business, when he is sourcing assembly parts, he may well wish to retain maximum flexibility and purchase ex-works, FAC (free carrier), or FAS (free alongside ship) from a number of sources. In such cases, he will require a relatively large and sophisticated shipping department and will control and own the goods throughout the sea passage, if not the whole, transportation phase.

This will lead towards his using a liner bill of lading, or even a non-negotiable sea waybill. In these instances the use of the document is concentrated on its role of evidence of a contract of carriage and of quality and quantity rather than on the bill of lading's role in transferring title. The way in which containers enable the whole transport chain to be regarded as one overall operation, involving sea, road and/or rail has led to the natural, though not necessarily uncomplicated, extension of the liner bill of lading/sea waybill into the through bill or universal bill of lading.

While liner bills of lading, defined as ocean or marine bills of lading under UPC 500, form the basis for regular shipments of the 'common carrier' kind, traded commodities tend to travel on chartered vessels and charter party bills of lading are used.

When the movement of oil, and especially crude oil, was largely controlled from well to refinery and beyond by the 'Seven Sisters', the original oil majors that also owned, or chartered most means of transportation, the role of the bill of lading was of relatively low significance. As they moved back from their dominant role, the independent tanker owners increased their role in transportation, operating under voyage rather than time charters.

As the oil industry fragmented more, and political instability in the oil producing nations produced increased price volatility, so the trader/speculator moved into a more central role as the users of sea transport. For many independent traders, living and profiting on their ability to predict the movements of the market, credit was essential. With cargoes being sold five, six or more times a voyage, the bill of lading, linked to a documentary credit, became increasingly important and increasingly more delayed within the banking system.

The requirement for shipmasters to deliver, frequently at transhipment terminals in favour of little known receivers, put severe pressure on the carrier and his P&I Club. Letters of indemnity, with or without bank guarantees, became a common occurrence; and shipmasters were put under intense pressure to sign clean bills of lading which would pass, trouble-free, through the banking system.

It is logical, if payment is to be made against the passing of a document rather than the physical transfer of the goods themselves, that the buyer should be able to rely implicitly upon the details shown on the document. Herein lies the rub for the carrier, for, through the doctrine of estoppel, he is legally barred from denying the accuracy of any detail which he has acknowledged on the bill of lading. If any carrier, or his 'servant' ie the master, knowingly shows incorrect details on the bill of lading in order for it to comply with letter of credit details, he joins the shipper in becoming party to a fraud on the consignee.

Since a confirming bank can and must rely only on the documents presented, and ensure that they comply with the documents stipulated in the application for credit, it is easy to see how a forged bill of lading can enter and pass through the system. Many companies are now making a much greater effort to control the distribution of, and access to, blank bills of lading and to track them through a discrete numbering system.

Dry market commodities

In the dry bulk market, commodity traders often tend to specialise in a product, or range of products such as coffee, cocoa and sugar, rice, beans and pulses or, the biggest market of all, grain. They will take future positions, guessing the level of next season's production levels. They will buy ahead and put 'on the book' produce that is not yet sown, let alone grown, to a value far greater than the company's net asset value. Much of this exposure may be hedged or sold on the futures market (sold 'off the books') in a risk management exercise. Nevertheless, it would not be unusual for a company capitalised at US$300 million to have an overnight exposure of US$2 billion.

Part of their 'book' they will deliver physically, either sold on the market or to meet future contract commitments, and this will bring marine transport into their risk equation. In many cases, they will be delivering essential foodstuffs, for example sugar, to poorer nations or receivers with less than triple A credit ratings. Credit arrangements will need to be put in place and, if payment is by a national or regional bank, corresponding confirming banks in one of the international financial centres will be required, adding yet another link to the chain.

Shipping costs can add 10 per cent and frequently more to the trader's costs and so he will keep a close and constant eye on the freight market, possibly hedging his future shipping needs on Biffex, the Baltic International Freight Futures Exchange, or by taking a percentage of his requirement on time charter.

The majority, however, will be secured 'as and when' on the spot market. This means there is a tendency for traders to think of ships as taxis, expected to be available when required but ignored otherwise. It is, perhaps, this attitude which precludes a true premium being paid for quality.

The first concern common to traders is that the chartered vessel will not make her laycan, leaving him paying a fortune in storage costs or demurrage on rail cars. Young traders are frequently taught that shipowners tend to be economical with the truth regarding the exact position of their vessels. Once the vessel is fixed, the trader wants to ensure that his buyer has his letter of credit in place before bills of lading are signed. At the port of loading, the trader may well receive the cargo 'in warehouse' or 'in silo' or even free on board and have the same feeling of apprehension that the shipmaster feels; that is that the agents, surveyors, stevedores and authorities 'are not on his team'.

High on the trader's priority list, especially if he is shipping foodstuffs, will be the cleanliness of the holds and the level of the master's knowledge of how to stow and carry that cargo. If he is an experienced trader, he will make available to the shipowner details of the cargo and how he wants it to be carried. In a competitive market, the owner's chartering brokers may well feel that to enquire too overtly about the method of carriage will weaken their negotiating position. With the vertically integrated shipowner giving way to the more remote ship manager/crew manager relationship, masters and mates are liable to find themselves changing trades and cargoes with far more frequency. They should, however, not forget that advice is available through the P&I Clubs as well as in the IMDG Regulations, other IMO publications and in a variety of text and reference books.

The break up of the integrated shipping company can also produce an environment where it is difficult for a master to ask for advice on surveying, accepting, stowing and carrying a particular cargo, or on the custom of the trade in that particular port. Carrying timber and bauxite in the North Atlantic does not prepare one well for decisions on the fumigation and acceptance of a two-parcel cargo of rice in a South East Asian port—especially if the mate is a tanker man and the second and third mate last sailed on offshore supply vessels.

In this environment, it is understandably difficult to build up an in depth knowledge of every particular cargo type, a factor which has been reflected in the incidence of cargo claims over the last decade or so. Masters, owners and charterers/traders could all benefit by a more open approach to the carriage and care of cargoes.

By the time the master is ready to commence loading, the trader will have ensured that his receiver has a valid letter of credit in place. This, as we have seen, will invariably stipulate a requirement for clean bills of lading. While it is frequently impossible to make any assessment as to quantity until loading is completed and the draught survey carried out, an assessment on quality and, if relevant, packaging often can and should be made at the earliest opportunity possible.

The master, or the mate as his representative, should participate actively in the cargo survey if at all possible. It is, after all, the best way to learn. In many cases the local cargo surveyors will have a much closer relationship with the shipper than the trader. If in doubt, ask the local P&I Club representative to recommend or appoint a cargo surveyor. The cost is not generally high compared with the risk and in some cases it is reasonable for the trader to share or carry this cost.

On other occasions, the receivers will have their cargo surveyor in attendance. It is essential that the master identifies the various parties involved and recognises their ultimate interests as soon as possible.

The mate's responsibilities during loading are to ensure that he and his fellow officers take a lively, constant and intelligent interest in the loading and the stow. Despite the undoubted pressures exerted by terminals it is, after all, your ship and you are acting as servants of the charterer and as bailee on behalf of the cargo owner.

Be aware how the cargo is being weighed (and make a record), keep up to date with the tally—or organise one if you feel it necessary—and constantly check the quality of cargo and packaging. Check with the charter-party or the charterer's loading instructions: if it is, for example, a bagged cargo, ensure all involved know the type and quality of bag stipulated, the number of spare bags to be provided and at what level part damaged bags become unacceptable.

The trader's real requirement is early and accurate advice about actual or impending problems or discrepancies so that he can take prompt action within the loading lay-days. The objective is to load a cargo that fairly matches the description on the bill of lading so that the master need have no qualms about signing bills 'clean'. To do this, the mate's receipts should either be clean themselves or show the corrective action that has resulted from the mate making an endorsement.

This means that mate's receipts should be kept up to date and reviewed daily at the very least. If there is a golden rule it is that if the master, or any of his officers, become aware of any factor which could justifiably prevent the master from signing clean bills of lading, the charterer/trader is to be advised immediately, and if necessary, loading should be stopped.

Turning from our customers' interests to our own, the reason for all this activity is to earn freight, the wherewithal from which, either directly or indirectly, the master and crew are paid. Even if the vessel is on time charter, where the payment is or should be automatic, the charterer will be depending upon the payment of freight.

Usually, freight is paid 'upon completion of delivery' and is calculated on the basis of that delivered cargo. This, understandably, is enough to make any shipowner nervous. It is exceedingly difficult to establish a lien or claim for unpaid freight on a cargo of crude oil that has disappeared through the ship's manifold in the direction of a heavily (if not necessarily well) guarded tank farm half a mile away.

This raises the question as to whom the master should deliver the cargo and when. Apart from the universally known stricture that the master must only release the cargo to the first person to present a properly endorsed original bill of lading, the law and text books—and indeed operations manuals—are generally light on assisting the master in the practicalities of carrying out this duty. If, as so often happens, the bill of lading is caught up in the banking system, the obligation to authorise the release of the cargo moves to the shipowner, his position being guaranteed by a letter of indemnity from the shipper/charterer, frequently backed by a bank guarantee.

The shipowner's position

The shipowner's position is, however, very exposed. If the cargo is wrongly delivered without a bill of lading, the owner's P&I insurance is invalid and the owner could be liable for the entire value of the cargo, plus consequential damages, to the rightful intended recipient.

The master must therefore take every reasonable precaution that the cargo is being delivered to the correct receiver, including questioning the agent; a most careful and documented enquiry as to local custom and practice. Help can also be sought from the P&I club correspondent to ascertain the best course of action.

Although the Bill of Lading Act of 1855 established the shipowner's right to sue the receiver for freight on the basis of the bill of lading contract, as mentioned, the owner's lien on the cargo is a possessory lien and lapses, both legally and practically, on discharge.

These, then are some of the practical reasons why the shipmaster and his officers should be as aware of, and involved in, the commercial aspects of the operation of their vessel as they are in the technicalities of navigation, maintenance, crew management and safety.

Another reason is because we are professionals, with a proud history stretching back to the earliest days of civilisation. To repeat the words of Rudyard Kipling, 'transport is civilisation'. Without the merchant shipmaster there would have been little transportation and, by implication, little civilisation.

Acknowledgements: The use of the Guildhall University, Institute of Chartered Shipbrokers and Nautical Institute libraries, as well as the British Library, has been invaluable. In addition to the International Chamber of Commerce and P&O's *Merchant's Guide*, sources have included *General Average and the York Antwerp Rules* by Lowndes and Rudolf; *A Short History of the World's*

Shipping by C. Ernest-Foyle; *Maritime Transport* by Edgar Gold; *The Origin and Development of the Law of the Sea* by R.P. Anand, *Maritime Affairs, a World Handbook* by H.W. Degenhardt; as well as sources from the UK P&I Club.

Cargo residues on deck which are washed overboard by rain or overflowing ballast may give rise to claims for pollution. See chapter 15.2.
Photograph: courtesy of Brookes, Bell & Co.

Some useful conversion factors

Length.

1 INCH (in) = 2.5400 CENTIMETRES (cm.)   1 cm. = 0.3937 in.
1 FOOT (ft) = 0.3048 METRES (m.)   1 m. = 3.2808 ft.
1 FATHOM = 1.8288 METRES.
1 NAUTICAL MILE = 1853.225 METRES.

Area.

1 SQUARE INCH (in^2) = 6.4516 SQUARE CM. (cm^2)   1 cm^2 = 0.1550 in^2
1 SQUARE FOOT (ft^2) = 0.09293 SQUARE METRES. (m^2)   1 m^2 = 10.7639 ft^2

Volume.

1 CUBIC INCH (in^3) = 16.3871 CUBIC CENTIMETRES. (cm^3)   1 cm^3 = 0.0610 in^3
1 CUBIC FOOT (ft^3) = 0.02832 CUBIC METRES. (m^3)   1 m^3 = 35.3146 ft^3

	IMP.GALLON	USA GALLON	CUBIC FEET
1 GALLON (IMPERIAL)	x 1	x 1.2	x 0.1604
1 GALLON (USA)	x 0.8333	x 1	x 0.1337
1 CUBIC FOOT	x 6.2344	x 7.48	x 1
1 LITRE	x 0.22	0.2642	x 0.0353 *
1 TON FRESH WATER	x 224	x 269	x 35.84
1 TON SALT WATER	x 218.536	x 262.418	x 35

Grain.

	IMP.BUSHEL	USA BUSHEL	CUBIC FEET
1 BUSHEL (IMPERIAL)	x 1	x 1.0315	x 1.2837
1 BUSHEL (USA)	x 0.9694	x 1	x 1.2445
1 CUBIC FOOT	x 0.789	x 0.8035	x 1

Weight.

	LONG TON	SHORT TON	METRIC TONNE
LONG TON (Imperial)	x 1	x 1.12	x 1.01605
SHORT TON (USA)	x 0.89286	x 1	x 0.90718
METRIC TONNE	x 0.98421	x 1.10231	x 1

1 LB. = 0.45359 KG.   1 KG. = 2.20462 LB.

Stowage.

1 ft^3/ton = 0.02787 m^3/tonne.   1 m^3/tonne = 35.8816 ft^3/ton.
1 ton/ft^3 = 35.8816 tonne/m^3.   1 tonne/m^3 = 0.02787 ton/ft^3.
1 ft^3/ton = 0.16 Gallons (Imp.) per ton.

1 KNOT   = 0.5144 METRES PER SECOND.
MCT-1inch = 0.1219 MCT-1cm.   MTC-1cm. = 8.2017 MTC-1inch.
TPI   = 0.40 TPC   TPC   = 2.5 TPI